To   Peter,

Benedict's Brother

Happy Birthday,

with much

Tina Wauke

Tricia Walker

Benedict's Brother

COPPICE
PUBLISHING

Published by Coppice Publishing (York)
17 Hunters Way, Dringhouses, York, YO24 1JL

www.coppicepublishing.com

First published in Great Britain
by Coppice Publishing (York) 2007

ISBN 978-0-9555199-0-1

Edited by Sarah Smelik
Designed by Ned Hoste of 2h Design
Back cover photograph of Tricia Walker
by www.davidxgreen.com

Printed by CLE Print, St. Ives, Cambridge

The publisher and author would like to thank Arts Council
England for their support for the promotion of this book

Benedict's Brother first reached a reading audience in instalments as a blog in August 2006. Some reaction to the Blog

"Beautiful." viveka, USA

"Thank you for one of the best books I've read in ages." steph, UK

"Your uncle's diary moved me to tears. I could see it all. Thank you for telling us this story." smudge, UK

"Your story is lovely. It's sacred yet human, humbling but heartwarming and Mae Li is just ... wonderful." betheserpent, UK

"My lunchtime reading. Can't wait for the next instalment." steph, UK

"Fantastic. Really enjoying it."
jo, UK

"Can't wait to find out what happens next."
legal gal, UK

"I love it."
malaysian queen, USA

"Written from the heart.
Thanks for sharing it all with us."
yin teing, Malaysia

"What an adventure.
Keep those episodes coming."
viveka, USA

"Very moving. It's great."
nicola, UK

"Compelling reading."
annie, UK

"Loved this."
uglymug, UK

"Please don't let those bad ass
Bewd-hists get to you."
simon, Canada

"It's great. Thanks very much for my
on going entertainment."
bella, UK

"I'm hooked already, can't wait
for the next instalment."
bobbie, UK

"Looking forward to the next instalment even
though you don't sound keen on the Bee Gees!"
peejayvee, UK

Benedict's Brother is dedicated to

Margaret Basso
(25.7.63 – 5.9.94)
and
Joshua Raynar
(3.1.89 – 8.3.07)

And to Uncle Ernos everywhere.

August,
York, UK

Today, my great uncle left me one hundred and thirty-nine thousand pounds. I've no idea what to do with it.

Also today, I heard from the solicitor asking if I'd arrange to see him. Something about a letter.

 August,
York, UK

My uncle wants me to scatter his ashes. In Thailand.

"At Kanchanaburi, Miss Taylor," said our family solicitor, Mr Hollingsworth. We were sat in his office. A comfortable armchair for me, an old, well worn leather desk chair for him. There was one of those expensive-looking rectangular reading lamps on his leather covered desk, the ones with the dark green glass shades, and together with the soft, orange wall lights tucked away above the row upon row of leather bound books, it cast a sombre, low glow over the proceedings.

Mr Hollingsworth wore a smart pinstriped suit, had friendly grey hair and a kind, humble face but he peered at me earnestly from behind the reading lamp over his silver, half-moon spectacles. And he called me 'Miss'.

"It's where they built the railway, Miss Taylor," he informed me in subdued, deferential tones. "The one your uncle worked on. The Death Railway? The Bridge On The River Kwai?"

I couldn't say anything. I'd heard tales of a fit, strong, healthy Erno but I'd never met that Erno. Uncle Erno was a

postman. I never heard anything about what had actually gone on while he was away during the war and The Bridge Over The River Kwai was a film I'd never seen. I explained this to Mr Hollingsworth.

"On," was all he said, with quiet authority, taking off his silver half-moons.

"I beg your pardon?"

"On," he repeated pedantically and then, suddenly, he became very self-conscious. "It's the Bridge On The River Kwai. You said 'over'. It's a minor point." He replaced his spectacles and waved what he said away as if it hadn't really been important when clearly it had. He obviously knew more about the subject than me.

"The film was inaccurate too," he added, talking to himself as much as to me.

Then he blinked, smiled kindly and looked straight at me, the light from the lamp catching his saddened brown eyes. He moved on.

"Your uncle has left provision to fund your trip in his will," he continued, half-moons back in place. "Travel information and details are in the letter. He specifically asked that you scatter his ashes in person and he suggests that you get there soon after the monsoon later this year. Also I believe he's left provision for you to visit your brother. He's not left a copy of the letter with us but requested that I convey all that I'm relating to you at this meeting."

So much, so fast, I could hardly take it in.

"Why?" I asked.

"I think I explained, about the railway."

"I don't mean why Thailand, I mean why me? It's a lot of money."

"I honestly couldn't say. We witness all kinds of requests at

these times. And he didn't have any family of his own." Our solicitor looked at his desk and began checking through his papers, moving the meeting on again.

Uncle Erno had indeed left provision. He'd left a ticket, cash, details on what jabs to have, maps, weather advice and mosquito coils. He'd left a note stuck to his old army penknife saying it would be useful, even for a woman, and he'd dug out a photograph of himself with some army friends standing at the River Kwai during a reunion ten years ago. Old, weather-beaten, smiley men standing stiffly for the group memento. Behind them was a low, not very impressive metal bridge, curved sections of black ironwork set against a backdrop of lush forest.

There was also a short letter from Uncle Erno, in his frail laboured handwriting:

My dearest Niece,
Do this for me, please. Remember me as you scatter my ashes from the bridge. Remember me to your brother, remember my Angel, Muriel, and remember those the world forgot.
My golden child.
Your loving,

Uncle Erno.

It's strange reading a letter from someone who has died. You're reminded of how they talk, their voice, the way they hesitate before any word beginning with 'T', and you're reminded that they are no longer around and they never will be.

He'd often called me his golden child. I have brown hair

now but was blonde at birth. He and Aunty Muriel hadn't had children and when Mum had named me Benedict, Uncle Erno apparently hadn't approved.

"That's a boy's name," he'd reminded her sharply, in his quirky, half-Yorkshire, half-Lancashire accent. "She can't have a boy's name. I'm put out. I'm very put out."

Twenty-eight years later, I'm still proud that Mum hung on in there. She hadn't known it was a boy's name. She'd just liked it and now, even if I'm the only female in the world called Benedict, it's a girl's name too.

I miss Uncle Erno. And I miss Mum. Dreadfully.

I cried when I read the letter in the solicitor's office, quietly and full of the love I felt winging its way to me from wherever Erno had gone. Mr Hollingsworth was as discreet as ever while I read, leaning back in his comfortable chair, waiting for me to finish. He must have realised that I'd forgotten he was even there and self-consciously nudged a box of expensive, three-ply, solicitor office tissues towards me.

"It's a beautiful place you're going to," he said warmly, the soft lines of his face creasing as he changed from his studied, slightly officious tone of earlier. "Beautiful sunsets, lovely people. You'll be fine, if you decide to go that is."

"You've been?" I asked shakily.

He nodded and looked away, not able to meet my eye and he removed his half-moon spectacles again. The detached, professional lawyer seemed to have momentarily left the room and a saddened little boy had taken his place.

"My father died building that railway," he struggled to tell me. "His grave is there."

I paused for a moment to let the information settle.

"He knew Uncle Erno? I asked tentatively, wiping my eyes.

"They were in the same regiment." He nodded, took a deep, brave breath and turned back towards me before continuing, leaning forward to rest his elbows on the desk as he did. "Your uncle was with my father when he died," he said. "He made sure his body received a proper burial and he traced my mother after he got back to England to tell her."

We were both silent for a few, still moments. I didn't know what to say.

"I never met my father," Mr Hollingsworth continued. "I was born while we were at war and he never came home. Your uncle's arrival was how my mother knew that my father had learnt about the birth of his son before he died."

Silence again. Awkward pauses. I still didn't know what to say.

Mr Hollingsworth gave a swift shake of his head, took a deep breath, carefully replaced the spectacles and said in a clear deliberate voice, "I am sorry, Miss Taylor, I've let myself digress," and he began tidying his desk. "Please be assured that if I can help in any way, I'd be more than delighted."

I thanked him and slowly took my cue to say goodbye. On my way to the door I made up my mind. I would go to Thailand and I would carry out Uncle Erno's wishes. It was the least I could do.

Might buy myself some half-moons too.

I am seriously thinking of buying a motorbike with some of the money. Nothing flash, just a smart Harley look-a-likey bike. When I ride it I'll think of my brother when we were younger, him tearing away on an old 1970s Honda Superdream, dreaming of a real Harley, dreaming of Highway One from Los Angeles to San Francisco and cruising over the Golden Gate Bridge.

"One day," he'd said to me, "I'll do it, one day."

Yeah, yeah. More like Highway to Hell via the Golden Lion Inn or better still, upside down in a ditch.

Later that day, listening to music at home, I felt scared, excited and a little bit sad because Uncle Erno has died. I hear Nina Simone sing the words:

You don't know what it's like to love somebody the way I love you.

Why is it that one of the most beautiful songs in the world has to be written by the Bee Gees?

 September,
Manchester Airport, UK

After a summer of anticipation and a lot of rain I'm about to leave for Bangkok. My house and everything is sorted. Molly The Cat is being looked after by Ruth and Michaela. I'm going to miss Molly snuggling up to my ankles when I get in from work, sitting on my lap while I watch Coronation Street and purring comfortingly into my ear as I fall asleep. I wonder if they have cats in Thailand? Bound to. Of course they'll have cats, Benedict. Everywhere's got cats.

I was a bit worried about leaving the house empty but, as soon as he heard I was going away, Captain Archie next door offered to keep an eye on it. He'll love it. A retired army officer with a mission. He'll probably look after it better than me and he's already worked out a strict regime of curtain drawing, light switching, post retrieval and plant watering. He nearly bored me to tears with the detail of it all, but I am grateful to him.

The young couple on the other side probably won't even notice I'm gone. They'll be too busy shagging as usual.

At work they were fine about me taking time off. I work

on the river boats ferrying visitors up and down the main vein of our great, historic city. I'm the deputy manager. It was no great shakes me leaving at this time of the year. Most of the tourists have left York by now and there's enough crew to look after things until the season is finally over. I'll miss all this when I'm away. I love stealing a late afternoon ride up and down the River Ouse, especially on a sunny day, gliding softly under the arches of the old bridges, past all the medieval buildings and slowly out of the city towards the Archbishop's Palace.

I'll miss the river and I'll miss Joe.

Joe's a Viking. Well, he's not really; he just looks like one. Six foot seven of thirty-five year-old, blond haired beef cake with a shorn head and stubbly beard. He's worked all his life on the river, lives on it in fact, in his houseboat two miles downstream, and he holds the proud record of being the only boat skipper in the country to have been prosecuted for speeding. The speed limit on a Yorkshire river is five knots, which is barely faster than walking, but the Viking in Joe simply wanted to rampage a bit too often and a police officer on a push bike booked him.

There's not a lot Joe doesn't know about the river although he doesn't let on. He keeps it all hidden under his beard. It took a while to get to know him or even to like him but it was worth it. I don't think he spoke to me for the first two weeks, just made fun of the rope knots I was trying to tie.

"You'll need to use a clove hitch," he said, expressionless, as I was tying the rope round a cleat.

"A cleavage?" I repeated, like a lamb to the slaughter. I was on my two week induction, getting a feel for handling the boats.

"Aye, that's it. You'll need to use a cleavage." And he kept

the joke going at my expense for over a month until finally one of the other crew put me out of my misery. I tied off hundreds of tourists with my cleavage during that month.

I fell in the river at the end of my induction. Not a good thing. I jumped from our enormous hundred and seventy passenger carrying cruiser as it was coming in, lost my footing on the wet landing stage and slipped backwards into the water between the quay and the incoming boat. Joe, thank God, was waiting on the quayside and quickly grabbed me as I began to struggle, petrified of being trapped by the metal hull of the unstoppable, massive boat. In a second he'd pulled me up and out of the way, saving my life as the boat came crashing into the fragile landing stage, obliterating the place where I had been and freaking out hundreds of tourists looking on. All Joe said as he held me, wet and shaking, was,

"You daft bugger."

Saving my life kind of broke the ice between Joe and me and he's been my friend ever since.

"Me dad taught me to spot a kingfisher's tunnel," he confided in me once, explaining why he'd often stop the boat mid-cruise because he'd spotted a kingfisher on the riverbank.

The passengers never had a clue what was going on when Joe's boat came to an unannounced halt mid-river and were more interested in seeing a view of York Minster than chasing a small, brilliant bird up and down the sandy banks. But, despite many disgruntled customers, it was always worth seeing the kingfisher. Always special. A stolen moment given to us by Joe.

I'll miss the daft bugger while I'm away.

Right now I'm feeling anxious and frightened at the

thought of being alone and lonely. Last night I cried so much I nearly threw up. It's not really like me. I cried too as my friends Michaela, Ruth, Stella, Angie and Becca waved goodbye to me on the platform at York station, and I sobbed quietly into my plastic cup of Fresh Leaf Tea on the train. I played California Dreaming by the Mamas and Papas to cheer me up.

I'm OK now as I write this, sitting alone in the departure lounge with my flash new Sony notebook, waiting for my flight to be called.

Thoughts of Mum have paid a visit over the last few days. Standing at her hospital bedside when I was seven, no one told me what was going on. I didn't know what cancer was but I knew it took her away from me.

Thoughts of Dad visited too. Five years ago he died in a car crash and I remember how Michaela recently mentioned therapy to me, that she thought it might do me good to talk. I told her to fuck off and she kindly has never mentioned it again. People die. It's nothing new, nothing I can't handle. It's just what happens.

And I've been thinking of you Antony, my brother. You went backpacking to Thailand a year after Dad died. You never came back Antony and I have never forgiven you. Tomorrow I will be meeting you at Ubon airport, an hour's internal flight from Bangkok. I know I will want to hit you.

There's so much to think about when you're planning a trip and I'm planning to be away for at least two or three months – inoculations, clothing, how to be contacted in an emergency, do I have to pay council tax? The biggest headache was sorting out the bank. Someone needed my power of attorney in case for some reason I need more money or bills need paying. It's not half as simple as I

thought it was going to be. In the end I gave my power of attorney to my attorney. He said he wanted to help. Michael Hollingsworth, son of Arthur, friend of Erno.

For the trip I bought some new sandals and I'm still wearing them in. They're rubbing a bit while I'm sitting here and my bare ankles are cold as the evening air is beginning to nip. I had my hair cropped shorter than usual so I probably won't need it cutting too often while I'm away, and I've put on jeans and a fleece to travel in. I thought that they'd keep me warm enough for Manchester but I'd not be too hot for Bangkok. In the end I wish I'd brought an extra layer. Manchester's never that warm, especially in September.

I'm sure that everyone can see my nerves, waiting here for my ten past ten flight with my rucksack and sitting on the bag I'd brought specially for the wooden box I picked up from Mr Hollingsworth's office. The wooden box, cleared by Customs, that contains Uncle Erno's ashes.

They are heavier than I'd imagined and he'd been such a frail man.

I know I'll see my friends again in a couple of months but I still can't believe that this is actually happening, that I'm actually about to leave for Bangkok. I like York, I like my life and I'm not sure I'm ready to fly halfway round the world to God knows where, to find God knows what. Logic tells me to treat it like a long holiday, enjoy it and not to worry because everything will be OK.

Logic doesn't account for a strange knowing voice that tells me my world as I know it is about to fall apart.

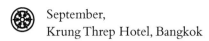 September,
Krung Threp Hotel, Bangkok

I'm here. Lying on my hotel bed in Bangkok. Eight-thirty in the evening Thailand time, one-thirty in the afternoon UK. It's hot and sticky and I'm in a bit of a daze. The flight was fine and I'd had an intriguing chat with a scrawny little man sat next to me who travels the world promoting British education. He told me he crossed about three major time zones each trip and said he never had a clue what the time was, just set his watch to wherever he was going and slept when his body told him to.

Speaking of which, it strikes me as odd that we can be so choosy about who we share our beds with at home but think nothing about sleeping the whole night through, arm to arm with a complete stranger, just because we are on an aeroplane. There'd be more space between us in my double bed.

I'd listened to the inflight radio for a while. It was crap. There's only so much Celine Dion you can take. I managed to sleep for five hours in between watching two Wallace and Gromit films and it meant I arrived alert and fresh, making finding the hotel all the more easy. I felt good. Not scared like I'd imagined I would, just wary about not talking to any of the touts and keeping my belongings with me.

Bangkok Airport had felt smaller than Manchester. The new airport hadn't yet opened. Here, the walls were nearer, the colours were darker and the terminal was lit by dull, dismal orange bulbs that only partially lit the way to the next dull, dismal orange bulb. The noise was different and it took me a while before I realised that it was the sound of another language, a soft, singing language spoken by smiling people.

I noticed too that it was now night time as I dragged my rucksack along the floor to try and scuff it up a bit and make it not look so new.

As I was hauling my things to the taxi rank, I noticed a dark haired American sounding woman. She was with a group of travellers, excited and chatting to each other, and as they passed, she looked over at me. Her gaze lingered a little bit too long and was followed by a mutual smile that told me that though I may be miles away from home in a strange land, I still belonged.

Bangkok was very busy. It's a loud, built-up, smoggy mass of streets, endless flyovers, shanty type houses that look as if they'd collapse in a stiff breeze and incredible, hulking, futuristic skyscrapers. The place is almost permanently clogged with frantic, screeching traffic but about every halfmile or so there's an enormous and incongruous beautiful golden temple thrown in for good measure. The temperature is only manageable with air-conditioning. The heat hits like a brick wall the moment you step outside.

Once we'd landed in Bangkok and were queuing at customs, something occurred to me. Security was very tight and this was Thailand, the country where you get thrown into prison for thirty years for even smelling of drugs, and where the authorities are renowned for their harsh treatment of suspects, let alone convicts. And here was I about to try and enter their country with a whole boxful of unidentified powder. What on earth did I think I was playing at? I hadn't even bothered to check if I was breaking any Thai law. If I was stopped, which by then I was convinced I would be, how long would it take to explain that the suspicious powder was actually my Uncle Erno?

I saw a dirty cell looming, me peeing in a bucket in the

corner and definitely no air-conditioning.

The unsmiling customs officer in his tight fitting, slender hipped, navy blue uniform, glanced up sternly from my passport and ushered me through with a flick of his head. I've had a similar feeling every time I've walked through customs. Knowledge of my own innocence but an unshakable certainty that I looked as guilty as hell, even if all I was taking through was a cheap bottle of Ouzo. Unlike at Athens International or Gatwick, at Bangkok Airport slight uneasiness quickly turns to fear.

Having said all that, the customs officer couldn't have given a toss. I was through.

So here it is. Thailand. The Land of the Smile, as the poster says. I've arrived. I fly tomorrow to Ubon. I'm relieved that the heat, the jetlag, the shock of the new and my excitement has kept me from feeling scared or lonely.

And anyway, I'm too bloody knackered to care.

 Wat Pah Chatanan,
N.E. Thailand

My life has been invaded by insects.

What a contrast to smelly old Bangkok. To my utter relief, Antony was waiting for me at Ubon airport. It's a minuscule place, all grey tiles and polished floors, and I could see him as I came through the exit gate and down the escalator. A distant figure looking up at me through the gathering crowd of relatives waiting to greet their nearest and dearest. I surprised myself by crying as the steps carried me down. So much locked-in emotion. I'd been waiting for this moment for four years. I'd wanted it for four years and now it was finally here. I suppose tears were wholly appropriate.

There had been no other westerners on the flight from Bangkok to Ubon, and I was acutely aware that nearly every eye in the airport had followed me from the plane and was now watching my brother and I in intrigued silence. Ubon is a fairly remote town in the rural region of North East Thailand known as The Isaan. The region nestles alongside the mighty Mekong River which forms the border with neighbouring Laos and its mysterious lost plains.

As I went up to hug Antony, a natural gesture after years of not seeing someone you love, he prevented me by stepping back and I was left in an empty space with my arms outstretched. He remained where he was and bowed at me as rejection thumped me in the heart, making my legs weaken. I swallowed hard and coughed, knowing that we were being watched. I felt part of myself crumble inside as my pride evaporated into a void. I hated Antony at that moment and, as predicted, almost slapped him.

My brother is a Buddhist monk. He wears a browny orange robe, shaves his head, shaves his eyebrows and lives on food given to him each day by the local people. He has no money, is celibate and is not allowed to touch women, not even his sister, the only living member of his family who has travelled halfway round the world to be there and who has not seen him for four years.

My brother was accompanied by another monk, also a white westerner, who I later found out was called Amaro. He was a tall, solid, vibrant young man with a kind, suntanned face and bold temples where you could see the strong flow of blood pumping away. He wore his robe proudly, the large folds of it hugging his neck and he had an air about him that almost said, "Hey, look what I'm wearing!"

Amaro smiled at me as I glanced over, a warm, I-know-

how-you-must-be-feeling kind of a smile and I immediately felt a tiny bit better for being welcomed by a stranger.

"How was the flight?" my brother asked.

After a deliberate stern silence I told him coldly that it had been fine.

He looked fairly well, my brother, as far as I can tell for someone without hair or eyebrows. But he was very thin which I put down to the very basic lifestyle he led. We talked about I-can't-remember-what as a minibus took us to the monastery. A minibus we shared with eight strangers. Antony and I were nervous with each other and all I could see of him as we trundled through the darkness on a rough, rocky road was his monk's robe, a browny orange dress. I felt very uncomfortable, not sure what I'd do next that might offend, when what I really wanted was just to be alone with Antony and get my brother back, even if that did mean me shouting at him for a week. I wanted everything to go away, especially that monk's robe which he seemed to be hiding behind, keeping him from me, but my jetlagged haze kept me mute and all I could do was absorb. I had no reaction available. I was losing the energy to even feel like hitting him, let alone actually do it.

We arrived at Wat Pah Chatanan, the forest monastery, in the dark. It was surrounded by trees which I could hear rustling in the light breeze and the nearly full moon was high up above, it's magical silver light filtering through the canopy. Antony and Amaro carried my bags to my kuti, my cute kuti, the small wooden hut that was to be my home for the first few days. The monks each live their own kuti. I'd be moving into the guest villa soon, but it was currently in use.

My kuti was very welcoming but far removed from my terraced house in York and from the neat air conditioned

hotel room I'd slept in the previous night. Someone though had clearly spent time making this dark wooden hut special. There were soft candles already burning in the corner underneath a low, shuttered window, and there were fresh lotus flowers and orchids in a glass standing on small, highly polished teak stool. Someone had also made up a mattress on the floor for me and found some checked blankets and a neat, newly ironed pillow case for a small, lovingly placed pillow. I knew from the letters Antony had sent over the last couple of years that a mattress and a pillow were a rare comfort in the forest. Whoever had made the room up had also created a makeshift shrine in the corner with a small bronze Buddha standing guard over the kuti, looking out for its guest. It was all very different from home, but it was my room. Someone had created it for me and I liked it already.

I was exhausted from jetlag by this time and knew I needed to sleep. I wanted to take time to digest my new surroundings but my eyes wouldn't stay open and as soon as the boys put my bags down, I knew I was about ready to collapse.

"I hope you find it comfortable," Antony said, and we looked at each other awkwardly. This was such a strange feeling. I was here in the jungle in Thailand with my brother who I hadn't seen for ages, my closest living relative, and I didn't know what to do. I so desperately wanted to hug him and be hugged. I wanted to know that he still cared, I needed him to show it in some way but these Buddhist rules seemed to be keeping him from me. Come on Antony! I thought to myself. I've been travelling alone for two days, I'm in a strange place the other side of the world and I need some sort of comfort.

I dropped my eyes to the floor and stared mutely at my

feet as I realised it wasn't going to be my big brother who provided that comfort tonight.

Amaro, who was still chaperoning us, saw what was going on and quietly told Antony to give me a hug.

"Go on," he coaxed in playful conspiracy and I was surprised at hearing a sing-song Australian accent. I'd arrogantly expected him to be English. Waving Antony forward he added reassuringly, "No one's looking."

Having been given permission, Antony nervously and apologetically at first stepped closer and, finally, we shared a hug. It was only then, as I held this virtual stranger with a shiny, shaved head and felt his bony body shaking, that I realised he needed to be hugged far more than me.

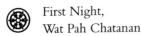 First Night,
Wat Pah Chatanan

Everything here is so strange but I like my kuti. At least it's somewhere of my own, somewhere to lie down and be myself. It's dark now, pitch black and I'm alone apart from the glow of my notebook. There are no lights outside to see my way down the path to the bathroom. The windows contain no glass, they're just mosquito screens made from thin metal mesh and I can feel and hear the breeze outside as it rustles through the trees and into my kuti. It's so quiet. No traffic and no people but there is noise. Noise of the strange insects which I don't recognise.

Something has just started scratching outside my window, shuffling through the fallen leaves. It's unnerving me. There's no real lock on the door and for all I know it could be someone wandering into the monastery looking for rich foreigners to kidnap. On this first night here, in my tired,

jetlagged state, my reason has all but vanished and I'm so unused to this new environment that I can't place the source of the scratching and scrunching. My heart is beating louder than the jungle as I'm huddled in the corner of my kuti with Uncle Erno's Swiss army penknife at the ready. I'm really scared.

 First Morning,
Wat Pah Chatanan

The rustling I heard last night eventually moved into the distance and I was left alone with the creepy-crawlies that invaded my room, and that I'd been convinced would eat me alive by morning or give me some tropical disease which would kill me. I frantically searched for my stick of maximum strength insect repellant and drew a big fat line with it on the tiles around the edge of my mattress. No bugger was getting across that! I slapped some more onto every inch of my flesh, knowing full well that the stuff was so strong that by the time it'd finished eating my skin there'd be nothing left for any insect to be interested in anyway.

The rush of fear induced adrenaline finally subsided and instead began to tire me. I lay down to sleep, slightly reassured by my fortress of insect-repellent. I hugged a blue neckerchief I'd brought with me and wept quietly, the tears washing anxiety away. Things weren't working out like I thought and I was thousands of miles away from home.

At one point, I dared to open my eyes and looked out into the darkened room, only to find a giant spider hanging inches from my face. It survived about three seconds. It was him or me and I had shoes.

By that time I was beginning to wonder if I'd ever get to

sleep, I was so convinced that sleep would mean my defence was down and the insects would mount a full-scale invasion. I knew I would have to stay awake until my body took over and forced me to sleep, like the guy on the plane had told me. To pass the time I listened to Oasis.

Where were you while we were getting high?

Down the pub getting pissed probably.

I cried the final tears of jetlag on that first long night in a strange Buddhist monastery, as I fell asleep to the final strings of Champagne Supernova caught beneath a landslide, disappearing into the night.

Despite the insects, which wouldn't have woken me even if they'd worn hobnailed boots, I slept so well that my alarm clock didn't wake me either and, hence, I was late. Antony had told me that he and the other monks get up at three-thirty in the morning, and after various duties, have their main meal at eight o'clock in the morning. It was now six forty-five, and I'd arranged to meet Antony in the kitchen at seven. He'd told me where it was. I rushed and no doubt looked as if I'd only just woken up as I approached the kitchen along the pathways that led to the heart of the monastery. My new world was opening out in front of me. Antony was sitting waiting in the kitchen, his orange robe standing out vividly against the backdrop of lush, deep green undergrowth.

"Good morning," he smiled. "I would have come to collect you but I'm not allowed into the women's quarters unescorted. Here it's OK though."

I managed a smile.

The kitchen was an area with no walls, only thin wooden pillars holding a polished wooden roof in place. There was a tiled floor, some rush mats and an area sectioned off with a

couple of primitive gas stoves and two water taps. It was completely open to the forest and we weren't alone. Over in the corner a small grey haired women squatted, preparing fruit, and some men quietly watched over the stove. There were trays of food on the floor behind us and people milled about busily arranging salads, fruit, rice and all the time smiling over at us as they went about their routine.

A middle-aged, thin man with straight black hair, who was wearing half-mast black cotton trousers and a pale blue shirt, came over with his head to the floor and put his hands together in front of his face, knelt down and gently bowed towards my brother. Then he stood and bowed from the waist towards me. He had a wiry, hardened face that looked as if he'd seen unhappy times but had braved them out and I could see a very faint scar on his left cheek as if a knife had once kissed it.

"Hello, Miss," he said. "You Thanavaro's sister, yes? He very happy you come to Wat Pah Chatanan. He talk about you, make room with flowers."

And I nodded at him in acknowledgment. So, it had been Antony who had prepared my kuti so lovingly.

"I am Christopher," the man continued in a strangely formal English. "I am very pleased to make your acquaintance. I tell your brother I look after you, cook Thai noodles in afternoon. Anything you need Miss, Christopher do."

I barely had time to thank him before he had bowed again and dashed away to find his sandals before disappearing through the trees. My brother was still smiling.

"Christopher's Malaysian," he told me. "He used to be a soldier but decided to join us last year. He's been very excited about you coming."

I smiled back. What about you, I wondered. Have you been excited too?

Then Antony added, self-consciously, "I know this must all be very strange for you."

Too right, mate.

In the morning light I now had a chance to look at my brother properly. Antony, my good looking, handsome, big brother. Have you ever imagined what someone you're close to looks like, not just without hair but without eyebrows too? Why would you? It's quite a shock, believe me. While the person is talking to you, your eyes keep wandering to the baldness and the tiny bits of stubble that have begun to edge their way through the skin. The person takes on a slightly alien, odd-bod quality, that made me think this was really a wind-up. A shaved head is difficult enough to adjust to for one used to seeing a thick head of familial brown curls, but it's the lack of eyebrows that really threw me. Without eyebrows a face loses its frame, it's reference point, and it becomes really difficult to recognise someone. Features become featureless without eyebrows. To tell you the truth, it also looks painful, like it hurt when the razor was scraped over the brow, violently removing what really ought not to be removed, scraping away an identity.

And it wasn't just the eyebrows that I struggled with. There was the dress too. Sorry, I mean robe. It's a robe, Benedict. Your big biker brother is not wearing a dress. He's wearing a robe which is far more macho, not that there's a problem either way and to tell you the truth it's quite a nice colour but even so, it is still an adjustment seeing your brother in a dress for the first time. Wearing a robe seems to be a bit of an art. It is one long piece of cloth, wrapped round his body, over one shoulder and then swung round in a tight

twist which is left hanging down his back, falling to his elbow and which he keeps adjusting. I also noticed that his feet were bare and I realised for the first time that I was the only one in the kitchen wearing shoes.

Buddhists take their shoes off when they enter a room.

"Don't worry about it," reassured Antony. "You'll soon get used to all the rules. The hard bit is remembering where you left them. Always leave a room by the same door that you came in and you won't lose track of your shoes."

Antony had a mole on the right hand side of his face, just above the cheek bone. When he smiled or got excited, the mole moved upwards and when he got nervous, the muscles in the side of his face would twitch slightly making the mole pulsate. It had always been a soft, endearing feature on a kind, supple face and it sat well against his soft, thick, brown hair. Now, post ordination, it was a dot on a blank canvas reminding me of the Antony I used to know, in there somewhere, saved from the savage strokes of the Buddhist razor.

The mole was still now. Antony wasn't smiling and I knew that he wasn't nervous either. He was calm and at home in this strange, alien place.

There was a lot of activity going on around us by this time. Industrious women in sarongs fetched and carried trays of food and industrious men in sarongs, helped out in the distance. Through the trees, other monks began to emerge silently from the forest one by one, orange robes moving silently through the green leaves, making their way to a building I could just make out through the plants and vines ahead of us.

"That's the main Sala through there," Antony pointed out, glancing over to his right. "It's where we eat and meditate

when the whole community gets together. At eight o'clock we'll go through there to have the meal. That's what everyone's preparing now."

The formerly quiet monastery was now coming to life and Antony began to get up and rearrange his robes. I was to go through to the Sala with him and one of the lay people would show me what to do and where to go. Once the meal was over and Antony had finished his duties, he'd meet me back here and we could chat and maybe go for a walk. He'd have to bring another monk to escort him but that would be OK wouldn't it?

Couldn't really argue.

Antony left and I watched as he turned his back on me, tugging his robe in place, walking barefoot up the path and disappearing into the Sala up ahead. After a few minutes, I made my own way up the same path.

How my life has changed in the space of a few brief days. I hadn't known what to expect when I left England. I knew it would be different but even the few letters I'd received from Antony hadn't got anywhere near conveying what this place was like. I felt lost, like I ought to know how to behave but no one was really telling me. Someone should have given me lessons, a crash course in Buddhist forest monastery etiquette.

The Sala was a large, peaceful, high-ceilinged room with shutters down one side and open to the forest on the other. There was a hushed atmosphere here. Whispered words but no conversation. It had a beautiful, polished, deep brown wooden floor and the room radiated an unavoidable sense of peace. To one end there was a shrine, adorned with stunning displays of colourful flowers and an array of yet more greenery. In the centre was the Buddha statue. He sat

serenely, watching the world unfold beneath him without ever moving his eyes but I knew he could see it all. He was calm, he was profoundly beautiful, and he exuded an inner wisdom and strength for which I could only yearn. Made of polished bronze, I was utterly captivated by the all-seeing eyes of this inanimate statue as it looked at me, searching my inner core and touching a place in me that I'd not yet dared to visit.

Those eyes, watching over me.

I slowly made my way over to where the other lay people were kneeling. They were silent, both men and women, young and old, in colourful sarongs and shirts, others in plainer clothes or with a white shawl wrapped round their shoulders. They were all barefoot and I was struck by the suppleness of their limbs as what looked like a sixty-year-old woman squatted effortlessly on the floor like a two-year-old child. A few people used a round cushion to prop themselves upon as they knelt on the floor but most seemed happy to rest unaided.

The monks were all on one side of the Sala on a raised ledge. Each sat in the lotus position with a large bowl set out in front of them, a glass, a jug of water and, intriguingly, a roll of kitchen paper. Some had their eyes closed, some were talking quietly to their neighbour and some were settling into place. They were a mixture of westerners and a few Thais. It was still very strange to see all these bald, featureless heads. They were almost indistinguishable from each other and I had to get used to recognising individual monks using different references than those I was used to. Their weight, the shape of their head, their height.

Antony was there. I recognised his posture first, the slightly stoopy way he leant forward as he sat and the way he

shuffled around to get comfortable. He fidgeted with his robe a lot and the way he did it was Antony all over but there was no denying that he looked more at home in the orange dress than in anything else I'd ever seen him wear.

The other monks looked relaxed as they shuffled and settled. Some of the western monks were still very white, their skin not yet exposed to the sun and they looked strange in their robes. Seeing the white skin of some of the monks made me look at my own pale complexion. God, I looked unhealthy. I'd chosen to wear a dark blue T-shirt covering my shoulders which Antony had suggested, and a pair of thin jeans, which I was quickly discovering got very dusty from kneeling on the floor. Skimpy clothes were out as they weren't seen as suitable, and short of wearing one of the traditional, plain dark sarongs and white shirts or shawls that the lay people were wearing, I'd opted for what I had on.

Not only did I feel pale and unhealthy I also felt very big. A big fat white foreigner amongst all these petite, slim, agile Thais. I'm not fat at home, I'm pretty slim in fact, but here in Wat Pah Chatanan, I was beginning to feel enormous.

The white haired lady from the kitchen rustled over to me as I stood wondering what to do next. I wasn't sure where to go and she whispered something to me in Thai. She was beaming at me and we both knew that neither of us understood a word but still she chatted away and waved me through the kneeling people towards the back of the room. She took my arm and we knelt down together. Then she, like everyone who entered the Sala, bowed three times towards the Buddha, respectfully, sincerely and with such agility that I knew I would struggle to emulate her. I was at least half her age. Her bow was graceful, completely to the floor and once she'd finished, she turned slightly and bowed

three times to the Abbot who was sat at the head of the row of monks, close to Buddha.

She leant over to me, again holding my arm gently, and said something, pointing to the monks as she did. I looked over. She was pointing at Antony and then at me and repeating whatever it was she was saying. Pointing again at him, then to me and repeating it again.

"Yes," I nodded, "my brother," putting my hand to my chest in a gesture of ownership. "My brother," I repeated, nodding and smiling back as wide as she smiled at me.

"Tan Thanavaro," she said, pointing. "Tan Thanavaro."

"Thanavaro," I repeated, still grinning for England.

For all I knew she could have been trying to tell me that she thought Antony was the worst monk she'd ever clapped eyes on but somehow I doubted it. She had too much joy in a face which possessed far too many smile lines. While we knelt she pointed at my feet. I looked down, trying to understand what she meant and then, she pointed at her feet and the feet of her friends around her. I still couldn't understand what she meant, so she kept on pointing at my feet, her feet, her friends' feet. Then she pointed at the Buddha and again at my feet. She started shaking her head and frowning.

I knew I was doing something wrong but I wasn't at all clear what it was. I'd taken my shoes off so it couldn't be that.

I looked over for help at Antony who had been watching the whole thing and who was gently laughing with his neighbour, a young Thai monk. He gestured for me to come over.

"They're facing the wrong way," he told me, smiling affectionately. "Your feet. They mustn't point at the Buddha. But don't worry Benedict, it's no big deal."

The white haired lady smiled at me as I returned to my spot and she gave a little chuckle as I sat down and tucked my feet away. I was sure I'd offend someone big time soon.

She stayed by my side, holding my arm throughout the chanting that followed and only let go to put her two, small hands together and bow again with the rest of the sixty or so lay people who were attending the morning meal. I was touched by the display of respect and puzzled by the strange rituals that were unfolding before me. Most bizarre of all was seeing people repeatedly go up to my brother to say something, and, like Christopher had done, bow down in front of him. My brother, being bowed at.

I vowed that I would never do it. I couldn't. Not to my own brother.

Food had been brought from the kitchen and was being placed onto what looked like skateboards and wheeled gently down the line from monk to monk. The monk helped himself to a portion of whatever the bowls contained, a twenty minute, slow process which ended when all the trays had been passed down the line and lowered to the floor by a waiting lay person. The skateboards were then wheeled down another line of people, kneeling on the floor. These were mainly westerners who seemed to be novices, and who clearly hadn't yet made it to the dizzy heights of the elevated ledge where the monks sat. Only orange robes seemed to be allowed to eat up there. There was some more chanting and then all the lay people left the Sala while the monks tucked into their meal.

Antony looked up and caught my eye at that point and smiled. A wide, happy smile that told me he was glad I was there.

Bon Appetito, Bro. My odd-bod, bald Brother.

I'd wandered into my first morning in the forest monastery lost and wary. By the same afternoon, the kindness and warmth of the lay people who had befriended me so readily had left me feeling safe and loved in a world so removed from my life in York, that I could easily forget it ever existed and forget why I'd actually come to Thailand at all.

And still those Buddha eyes watched over me.

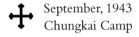 September, 1943
Chungkai Camp

The heat is almost unbearable. I lie secretly writing this journal on scraps of stolen paper, dripping with sweat, with a thirst I know shall not be quenched and with an ache in my soul I know shall not be relieved.

I received a letter from Muriel today. My beloved Muriel, who knows not whether I live or die. It was written in the spring of last year, believing our regiment to be in Singapore still. I wept when I read it. The pain of reading her words, of hearing the hope in her voice edged with unspoken fear, wrenches at my being. Far easier not to be reminded of her, to learn to adapt to my fate and not dare to hope for redemption.

Muriel talks of home, of visiting the Rialto to see pictures of our ship's departure, of going to church, of taking the ferry over to see her sister, of things so mundane that I can barely begin to imagine a life like that again. I yearn for the mundane, for a jar of stout, to listen to Tommy Handley on the radio. I cannot begin to describe how important these small events are nor the essential part they played in a gloriously mundane life before Singapore.

Reading Muriel's letter saps my strength. Far better not to

be reminded. To hear from Blighty is such sweet sorrow. A confusion of joy at reading the words of my loved one, knowing her hand has touched this paper and that her sweet breath has lingered on it, and a deep wound as sharp as a hot knife in my belly as I am forced back to my reality. Her image wrenched from me and emptiness left in its place.

How will we survive this place? This beautiful, treacherous place.

 September,
Wat Pah Chatanan

I thought of Uncle Erno today. I can't imagine him here. The Uncle Erno I knew was a frail, thin, white haired old man who loved his routine, who always sat in the same place on his old, soft, squashed green sofa making the armrests shiny from wear. The Uncle Erno I knew never went abroad. He was a pie-and-tinned-peas sort of old man, a half-pint-of-ale-in-a-glass-with-a-handle sort of old man who always sat on the same bar stool, same time, same place. He would have hated this hot, sticky weather and the warm sticky rice. I really couldn't imagine him here at all.

I'm settling into life at Chatanan a bit more now. I met Antony after the meal the other day and we went for a walk round the edge of the monastery. As ever, a monk accompanied us. This time it was Tikaro, a young, American monk with a holy-looking face that made him resemble a bald-headed Jesus in John Lennon glasses. Whenever Tikaro smiled, which wasn't often the first morning I met him, he revealed two bright teeth which stuck out rather too far. Shy, slightly goofy, short sighted Jesus. He rarely spoke and simply nodded when I said "Hello" to him.

They both still look very odd in their robes and shaved heads and it didn't make talking to them easy. I found it hard not to be distracted because I kept looking at their stubbly heads and eyebrows. They just look weird, very weird. I noticed that Tikaro's hair seemed to grow faster than Antony's and he was taking on the first stages of a hedgehog head. I wasn't sure if hedgehogs had eyebrows but those were looking pretty prickly too.

It gets very hot towards midday here, once the morning moisture has been frazzled by the sun. The air is dry and the sun unrelenting as it scorches down. As we walked, Antony's head quickly began to burn so I dug some sun lotion out of my bag and handed it to him.

"You can't hand it to me directly," he said, a little too abruptly.

"I beg your pardon?" I said, a little too intolerantly.

The honeymoon of politeness was over and I knew he could sense me beginning to bristle. I could sense that he was wanting to say what he had to say calmly but was anticipating my response, which he knew of old would not be calm. He knew me as only siblings know each other and I sighed impatiently, true to form, increasingly irritated by these seemingly needless rules.

Meanwhile, I could feel the shy Tikaro's eyes flitting between me and Antony, monitoring and evaluating.

"It's the rules we have," explained Antony, twitching his lips nervously. "A monk can't take something out of your hand. It has to be offered formally."

The rice fields next to us rustled and shifted like uncomfortable passers-by witnessing a growing row.

"I am offering it to you," I insisted pedantically.

"I know," he said, the muscles in his cheek beginning to

twitch and his mole getting agitated. "But you can't hand it to me. It has to be done formally. You have to place it on something and then I can pick it up." He was nervous, I could tell, and I, uncharitably, enjoyed watching it.

He crouched awkwardly and used a clean handkerchief as an offering cloth, spreading it out on the dusty road. I placed the bright yellow and white tube of sunscreen on it without saying a word and stood up, folded my arms and watched, knowing I was intimidating him.

After both of them had covered their bare, reddened scalps with Boots Factor 15, the tube was placed carefully on the ground again, a cue for me to pick it up.

Antony tried to look calm and at ease with it all but failed. His lips still twitched and his mole joined in.

"You don't have to be so apologetic about it," I told him bitterly as we continued our walk.

"I'm not," he said and then added in contradiction, "Apologetic about what?"

And now his brow began to furrow. Believe me, a furrowed brow looks mighty peculiar without the eyebrows.

"All this," I said. "The rules, the clothes, the bald head. You."

He paused thoughtfully. "I know it all seems strange, Benedict, but this is my life now and there are reasons for all the rules."

"I've said, you don't have to apologise."

"I'm not apologising!" He finally shouted at me, provoked enough to raise his voice and his arms in insistence. Then, letting his arms drop, he slapped them down against his thighs.

"I'm not apologising for it," he repeated insistently but more quietly.

Antony sighed loudly and Tikaro flinched. I don't think a monk losing his temper is the done thing here, and I think he was finding this brother-sister show a little difficult but was far too gracious to say anything. We carried on walking.

"I'm so pleased you've come," said Antony, completely changing the subject, a tactic he often used to avoid confrontation. I rolled my eyes. At least some things had stayed the same.

"Especially now," he continued. "You must have meant a lot to Uncle Erno."

"We all meant a lot to him."

Dad used to make us write to Uncle Erno when we were younger and we never got out of the habit. It was a family thing. We all wrote to each other. It was what you did. What I really wanted to say to Antony was that I'd missed him. I'd missed my brother like hell. I'd loved getting his letters but I didn't say it because it didn't seem the right moment. My anger at Antony grew.

Tikaro stayed a few steps behind us, politely silent throughout the walk. I got the sense that he was a little freaked out. Too many hearts on sleeves for one day.

"Why didn't you come back for Uncle Erno's funeral?" I asked, deliberately broaching a particular hotbed of fury. I knew that Antony knew that I was building up to blow and he knew I knew he knew. Pity the poor American.

"I couldn't get back," he said. "It wasn't felt appropriate for the monastery to fund the trip."

"I beg your pardon? It was Uncle Erno! Family funerals matter more when there's not any family left!"

"It wasn't my decision," he said softly, resolved to my reaction.

"It never bloody is!" And I whacked a tall piece of grass,

frustrated that responsibility always seemed to be passed on to someone else.

Rules, bloody rules.

I sighed and stopped walking. It was hard to articulate what I was thinking. I waited for a few moments and then became flustered by my inability to say anything, knowing that Antony was looking straight at me, waiting, and that Tikaro was stood a few metres away, acting deaf but no doubt feeling mortified. This particular chaperone had drawn the short straw this morning.

"What did you mean by that, Benedict?"

I looked at him, straight in the face, his stupid bald head gleaming in the sunshine, his cheerful orange dress being swayed by a gentle, Isaan breeze and his beautiful big brother face looking as familiar to me as the day he built the red train track in our front room when I was three and he was four.

"I don't know!" I shouted. "OK? I don't bloody know what I meant!" And I stomped off up the track without a clue where I was heading, having never been there before.

I didn't know at the time what I'd meant by it but I do now. No one ever did anything on purpose. It was never their fault, never their decision, things just happened. Mum. Dad. Antony. It all just happened and there was never anyone to blame, nowhere to aim everything that was burning up inside me. I couldn't put into words there and then just how angry I was that Antony had left me like everyone else and, when he had an opportunity to come back, he seemed happy to blame someone else for not doing so.

Antony and Tikaro followed me as I stomped my way through the dry Thai countryside, leaving a healthy gap between us for a few minutes until I'd calmed down.

We were walking past open rice fields which up here in

The Isaan were desperately short of water. The fields were golden and dry, stretching out across the plain with a complex system of walkways connecting them which provided a route through to the other villages. There was only one tarmac road in this area, about a kilometre to the west of the monastery gates. The villages were linked by dusty tracks, winding their way through mile upon mile of rice fields, a flat expanse of golden waves, gently bristling in the breeze and stretching out forever. There were few trees except for the cluster that formed the small forest in which Wat Pah Chatanan sat. Unlike my mood, it was sublimely calm as we continued and only the sound of a few birds and the occasional whispering insect interrupted the quiet.

The Isaan's beauty humbled me.

My anger at Antony was left unresolved as we continued to circle the monastery grounds and I was told more of its history by Antony and Tikaro. Wat Pah Chatanan was established nearly thirty years ago as a place where western monks could come and practice in the Theravada Buddhist tradition. It was created by Ajahn Chah, a respected abbot who had already set up a forest monastery close to Chatanan. He ordained western monks for the first time and his school of teaching was now one of the most highly respected in Thailand.

My brother had stumbled across a small temple practising the Ajahn Chah's teaching on an island in southern Thailand while he was backpacking. The infamous Ko Pha Ngan, island of the hippy drop-out, haven of the drug-seeking, spaced-out, all-night, full-moon-raver, is where my brother found the path that changed his life. He stayed for a few months at a temple tucked away high in the forest, liked it and eventually ordained as a full 'Bhikku'. That was three and

half years ago and now he thought he'd be a monk for the rest of his life.

"I don't have to," he explained. "I can leave without any disgrace whenever I want. Most Thai men come into a monastery at some time in their lives. They'll come for a three month retreat or ordain for a year. Even the King has been a monk. It's very different from the Judeo-Christian tradition."

"You don't say," I ventured sarcastically but Antony chose to ignore me. I wasn't sure if he was uncomfortable with his new faith and all its rules and formalities, or whether he was just uncomfortable with me.

In the fields beside us some people were working. They were harvesting the rice, painstakingly picking it by hand, sheaf by sheaf. The sun was searing above and they were wrapped from head to foot to protect themselves from the rays and the dust. Their arms, legs and faces were swathed in layers of cloth and their faces were hidden under yellow straw hats and behind woollen balaclavas. A more uncomfortable way of spending a day I could not imagine. They watched in silence as we passed and only broke off from their methodical hacking to respectfully bow to my brother and Tikaro.

Further down the track, as we began to curve round the edge of the forest, we came across one of the water buffalo which the farmers keep to haul their loads and cultivate the fields. It was as magnificent in its ugliness as it was in its size. A great big, hulking, black mass of solid flesh staring at us as if to query why on earth we should be there. I'm sure it would have arched an eyebrow if it had one. The buffalo was rooted to its spot, a rope tied round its thick neck and it had enormous, sweeping, scary horns. This was definitely water

buffalo territory and we were there by permission only.

"Chill," said Tikaro, the first word he had uttered all morning. "They're used to us humans an' they only charge if they're feelin' threatened."

He talked in a slow, deceptively reassuring southern drawl full of home spun logic and I was utterly taken in by his apparent expert knowledge of the behavioural characteristics of this massive beast in front of us. I was confident he knew what he was talking about. I was fooled. We heard the shouts of the Thais working in the fields behind us and swung round to be faced by a second buffalo, this one clearly feeling very threatened because it was in full charge.

At us.

And those scary horns were aimed straight at me.

We all began running, robes flying, decorum flying and the hitherto chilled and silent Tikaro emitting a shriek loud enough to wake the dead from three lifetimes ago. He raced down the pathway ahead as we all heard the buffalo closing the gap behind us. We could see its rope tied to a post set deep in the ground ahead of us and we had about fifty metres before it would pull tight and yank the buffalo to a halt. That was the theory. Sadly, in practice, the path decided to turn a sharp right angle through the paddy field and took us no further away from the lurching, snorting, thundering bulk that was now beginning to gain ground on us, chasing us through the irrigated fields.

There was only one thing for it and Antony and I followed the shrieking American as he leapt into the shallow, muddy water. He was fast this guy and when this was all over he wasn't going to believe the Olympian feat he had accomplished. He charged through the water ahead of us as

we heard the enormous splash of the buffalo following.

Tikaro dared to look round, sheer terror in his once holy face coupled with utter panic that served as high energy food for Antony and me. We ran faster through the unrelenting mud and water. Surely the rope must stop by now? I pleaded to whoever was listening. Please? God? Buddha? The Universe? Allah? Don't let this happen now! And of all the stupid things to come into my head, I thought how unfair it would be if I was to die now not having had a chance to go shopping for fakes in Bangkok.

Tears began to well in my eyes as I felt the strength begin to drain from my legs and saw Antony gain ground ahead of me, wet robes whipping against the breeze.

"You're leaving me again," I heard my brain tell me. "You bastard, you're leaving me again when I've come all this way to see you. You ungrateful, robe clad bastard!"

As I ran, the sting of salt burned down my cheek.

My fury and fear spurred me on and then, through the blur of my tears, I saw that Tikaro had collapsed to the floor, his dishevelled robes soaked in brown muddy water and Antony too had stopped running. I finally caught up with them, running a few feet further for good measure. We all looked back in silence, chests craving the air, taking great gulps as we watched the buffalo which was still running. Its rope had pulled tight and forced it to make a large arc through the field. It snorted as it lunged awkwardly through the water, destroying a week's crop as it went. The farmer shouted at it, waving his arms and sending it back towards the path. It may have scared the shit out of us but as far as he was concerned, the buffalo knew which side its bread was buttered and, remarkably, it quietened.

The farmer said nothing to us but looked over and gently

bowed.

"The poor guy," said Tikaro panting, his glasses splashed with muddy water. "His buffalo nearly killed two monks an' a monk's sister. That would keep his karma in overdraft for twenty lifetimes, minimum."

And we laughed with sweet relief. I pointed out to my two companions that now I knew why their robes were that browny shade of orange.

"It's the same colour as the mud."

"Well, it is now," said Antony, and we laughed stupidly until our chests hurt and we each fell back into the muddy water.

When we picked ourselves up and started to head back to the monastery, our clothes drying rapidly in the heat, I reminded Antony that this wasn't the first time he'd ended up upside down in a ditch.

"Your Honda Superdream?" I told him, reminding him of the time he came off his motorbike.

He laughed endearingly, my brother again, and glanced furtively at Tikaro, his dark eyes twinkling with glee. Then he began to grin like a naughty school boy. He whispered something to the American.

"We've got something to show you when we get back," they boasted like children, and Tikaro's two front teeth gleamed as he grinned away.

"It's not strictly against the rules to keep a motorbike," explained Antony as we headed up the track. "There's a monk in Thailand who gave up everything to be ordained – his wife, his mistresses, his vast wealth, his rich lifestyle, you name it. He gave it all up to be a monk and therefore had to follow the precepts. He had to be celibate and he couldn't drink."

I could hear our father now in Antony's voice, holding court, telling stories while our imaginations were captured. My heart leapt at the memory.

"He gave all this up to become a monk," he continued, "but couldn't bear to be parted from the loves of his life, his Harley-Davidsons."

Tikaro at this point was nodding and grinning like a demented holy rabbit.

"It's true," he blurted out. Our earlier episode with the buffalo had obviously destroyed any continued need for shyness on his part. "There ain't no rule saying a monk can't ride no motorbike. Can't own it, but he can ride it!"

Meanwhile, Antony had started grinning like a teenage boy who'd just scored for Manchester United.

"Y'see," drawled Tikaro, enjoying his moment. "There weren't no Harley-D's when the Buddha was around so there ain't no rules about it. We can't ride no elephant because that was the transport of the kings and monks shouldn't travel in such style, but a motorbike?"

With that, Antony opened the doors of a small shed we'd reached, so tucked away in the undergrowth that you'd barely know it was there. In the darkness, chrome glistening from the sunlight that pierced through the gaps in the wooden walls was the secret behind these two boys' smiles.

"Is this what I think it is?" I asked, disbelieving.

"It sure is," said Tikaro, beaming. "A genuine 1938 Harley-Da-vid-son Soft-tail Knuckle-head. Ain't she beautiful? Perfect like the day she was born."

It was an enormous, wire spoked, single seated dream of a Harley. Its wide teardrop tank had been lovingly polished. The well-worn leather saddle had been soaped and waxed and sat on giant, shiny coiled springs. The chunky, hallmark

V-twin engine gleamed at the heart of this delightful machine and the ancient chrome footplates stood out boldly to the side. At the front there was a large, proud, shining headlamp and the handlebars spread like giant antlers from the head of this truly wonderful, manmade beast. The grey, solid paintwork was immaculate and the big, fat, pumped up tyres were just waiting.

"The man owned sixteen," explained Antony as he circled the bike, trailing a finger lovingly across the tank. "All different, all Harleys and he gave them all to the lay people of the monasteries. This one came from a temple about fifty miles from here. Christopher brought it with him."

I caught Antony's eye as we each recognised the old, familiar joy of anticipation. The American looked at us both and grinned, even wider, even more teeth. All of us knew what was coming next.

Antony was the first on the bike, robes billowing, engine growling like an oil-fired symphony. The bike went like a dream, a rattling dream but a rattlingly good one and the countryside reverberated to an old, familiar sound that we'd each learned to love.

Shake, rattle and roll, chocolate and Mozart. The sound of a Harley.

"Why God invented metal," Tikaro quoted in a love-struck daze as we watched James Dean in an orange robe sail through the dust, waiting for our turn to ride the dream machine.

It was as sublime as it was surreal. An hour spent with Buddhist monks cruising illicitly through golden dust and dirt on a sunny morning in the hazy north-eastern tip of Thailand.

✟ October, 1943
Chungkai Camp

And what of the year since my Angel put pen to paper? Has no word got through since then? Have the Nips not told anyone we are here? Goddamn them and Goddamn this war. I am not a soldier. I was never born to this and now I find I am a leader of men far braver than I shall ever expect to be.

Many of the other chaps have received letters and each shrank away into a quiet corner to read in peace, alone with their memories and with the inevitable grief which we each feel every time we think of home. I could have wept for those who did not receive mail.

Muriel asks how we are. God forbid that she should ever know. How can I possibly convey to my dearest what it is like to be here? How could I do that to her, my sweet Angel? I can't describe to her the hell in which I find myself, or how far life has fallen since the day I waved goodbye to her two years ago, sailing away proudly, ready to fight for King and country. We all thought it would be over so quickly. Now I'm not sure I will ever see her pretty, smiling face again. I want to believe it to be true, I really do, but part of me knows that fate will defy hope and so I dare not begin even to hope. I cannot face having that taken from me also.

I have jaundice and a few septic spots but each appear to be clearing. I am thankful for small mercies since I have nothing more. The monsoon lasted a long time in these parts, far longer than we expected. It brought with it disease and death on a scale beyond imagining. One never knows how the Nips are going to react. I thought we'd get used to them and them to us but no, they remain a breed apart and

reach sadistic depths I could not have believed possible. I know they keep letters for weeks before giving them to us. We see them being delivered and they make us wait and wait, grinding our souls to pieces. They only give the letters to us eventually because it is decreed that they must.

Today Arthur learnt he has a son, born after we left. He is happy at the news, though his pain is also visible. Like him, we know not if he will see his new son but we are afraid to say what is in our thoughts. But a son! My word, what a blessing. I hope I too will one day have a son and that he is spared the hell of war.

The Nips still refuse to provide the basic medicines to cope with the malaria which has swept through the camp, and they still refuse to allow us to build better latrines. No latrines but they deliver the mail.

The rains have flooded the camp and we have had to wade knee-deep in the overflow of excrement. For weeks we slept amongst stagnant water which contained the remnants of our own sewage as the rain continued its downpour, the dampness hanging in our lungs, with the weary falling into sickness and the sick dying. And still, the Nips worked us, day and night. No work, no food.

Dysentery and fever are rife. The Nips have taken our clothes, our boots, all our belongings and we fall like swatted flies. If we don't bow to the Nips they beat us and if we try to protect ourselves from the blows, a group of them beats us and we end up in the camp hospital. They stub cigarettes out on us and our flesh grows septic in the heat and damp. Our food consists of a pathetic amount of rice and occasional leaves and if we faint from hunger we are punished. Left to stand for hours in the blistering sun or, of late, left for days in a bamboo cage, drenched in the monsoon rain which beats

down on our weary bodies day and night, left without food or water and regularly thumped in the body with the rifle butt of a passing Nip. This life is breaking me.

I can't tell you all this, Muriel. I can't shatter your belief in the ultimate goodness of man. I can't shatter your belief in God. My own belief has not been shattered. Shattered is not the correct word. My own belief has been slowly and painfully peeled away like a sunburnt skin being picked piece by piece from a screaming man until, finally, only the raw unprotected flesh remains and the man is left at the mercy of every grain of salt, every sting of a whip, every infection and every injustice a living soul could possibly encounter.

Some of the lads go to a service each Sunday in the camp. I am jealous of their faith, knowing my religion is lost. Forgive me, Muriel, for speaking like this but faith has left me. The inhuman sights I have witnessed, the barbarism we have endured and the relentless stench of death in the air cannot be overseen by any God that I have known. No God I have known could inflict this. No higher plan made by a benevolent being could have included this. Here lives only chaos. Bleak, tortuous, sickening chaos.

 October,
Wat Pah Chatanan

I've been here nearly a month now. I like it here and it's great to see Antony, if a little odd, but I'm homesick. It's been hard enough adjusting to Thailand, but being thrown into a monastery as well has been a lot to get used to all at once. I don't think Antony realises that and I imagine he's forgotten what life back in England is like. Not much happens here. It's

not a 'doing' place, it's a 'being' place and that takes a while to adjust to.

I'm spending time with Antony though, even if I didn't catch him after the meal this morning. When I went to look for him I was told by another monk that he'd gone into the town with the Abbot. Didn't say why.

I'm slowly getting used to being around monks but they're so sombre and lacking in expression. They don't smile back when you greet them and most of them don't even acknowledge you are there. I walked past one this morning, said "Hello", smiled at him and got nothing in reply, not even a nod. His expression didn't even change. They're even worse than the old Yorkshire men back home who might give a slight dip of the head as you pass, if you're lucky. At least I know what they mean by it. They mean, "Hello, how are you doing, haven't seen you for a while but it's good to see you even if I'm too embarrassed to say it, so be grateful I even nodded." It's like an ancient code that only Yorkshire folk understand and we ridicule outsiders for being too thick to grasp the finer nuances of it. But this lot? I haven't a clue what to make of them. They just make me feel awkward, like I'm an alien or something, which is a bit rich since they're the ones who look like they've just stepped off a ruddy space ship.

The other morning, I went for a walk on my own when I found out Antony wasn't about. Not really knowing my way round and concerned that I'd wander into somewhere I wasn't meant to and break yet another rule, I decided to follow part of the route we had taken the other day, round the perimeter wall. On the way out of the gate, I bumped into Mae Li, the Thai woman who's been looking after my room. She's been sweeping it most days and yesterday placed

fresh flowers on the shrine.

Mae Li was wearing a white blouse, flower print sarong, enormous black Wellington boots that drowned her knees and ankles, and a crumpled, golden straw hat that looked like it had seen more of life than even Mae Li had. She was beaming her infectious smile at me and her small dark, wet eyes twinkled with life as she chattered away in Thai to me, bowing and placing her hands together, in a greeting which I returned and which only made her smile even more. She grabbed my arm with her wrinkled hands and looked earnestly into my face as she again rattled something off in Thai. I love Mae Li's face. It's all happy, craggy and full of laughter lines which gather round her eyes and her cheeks. Wrinkly, twinkly, kind Mae Li.

I assumed she wanted to know where I was going, so I waved in the vague direction of the path ahead.

"I'm going for a walk," I told her, shouting like an idiot and I pointed up the path. This made her turn and look to where I was pointing. Seeing nothing, she looked back at me and grinned again, quizzically this time, twisting her eyebrows and clearly thinking this English woman was mad. Thais don't go for walks.

"Why are you going up a path that leads to nowhere only to be burnt by the hot sun?" her face said.

But that's what the British do, isn't it? Go for walks to nowhere. In the midday sun.

Mae Li bowed again, polite as ever.

"Sawat di kha," she beamed as she shuffled away, her straw hat hiding her tight black curls. After a few paces, she paused and turned back to face me. She took a deep breath, giggled endearingly and then, thrilled at herself for summoning up the courage, said in unpractised English,

"Hello, Miss," and her wide mouthed grin revealed an array of gappy teeth, blackened from an addiction to betel nuts.

Then she turned, chuckled to herself so her shoulders shook and shuffled off up the dusty path, a vision of fashion in sarong, sun hat and Wellington boots.

Once again, the morning was beautiful and the breeze gently whispered through the rice fields that brushed along one side of the path. To my right was the wall of the monastery about six feet high with long grasses and foliage that had begun to creep over the top. My thoughts turned to home. I liked Thailand and, despite the uniqueness and strangeness of my surroundings, I was starting to get used to it all. I still missed friends though and I wished I could phone someone, just to see how they were doing and to tell them what I'd been up to. I've written a few letters but I know they take ages to get through and I haven't received any thing from home yet. I was beginning to feel very cut off.

As I walked, a butterfly chased the breeze in front of me, its colourful red, orange and white wings flicking their way through the hot air. I was following its progress when I became aware of the faint sound of someone singing. A boyish, deep voice trying to sing high and it was coming from the other side of the wall. The singer obviously thought he was completely alone and he was singing without inhibition and way off key.

 "The finger of blame has turned upon itself!" he yelled. "And I am more than willing to offer myself!"

It was awful and I couldn't help but laugh out-loud, having to cover my mouth to stop from being heard.

"Do you want my presence or need my help," he continued and then, for the high pitched painfully off key

finish, "I FALL, at, your, fee - ee - eet," and with that the singer came flying over the wall and crashed to the ground only missing me by inches.

I fell over as I jumped out of the way and landed on my bum in the dirt. I don't know who was more stunned.

"OH SHIT!" he shouted, as he realised what he'd done. He was a monk, I think. He was wearing white Nike trainers on his bare feet and was listening to an MP3 player. The earpieces were still stuffed in his ears with the music still playing. Very loudly. It was Amaro in what looked like an orange, off-the-shoulder shift dress.

"JEEZ, I'M SORRY! ARE YOU OK?!" he shouted, forgetting he was still wearing the earpieces.

"I think so," I managed. "Are you?"

He clicked the music off and took out the earpieces, a slightly concerned look on his gentle, muscled features.

"What was that?" he asked, more quietly.

"I said are you OK?" I repeated.

"Me? I'm fine. Hey, look," and, to prove the point he leapt lightly to his feet and jogged on the spot.

"I can't offer to help you up, rules is rules and all that," he added playfully in his Australian lilt, his face now full of sunshine and him still jogging on the spot.

Was it me or did no one else think that behaviour here was a little weird. Who the hell was this guy and what sort of a bloody monk was it who leapt over garden walls singing to Crowded House, when surely he should be meditating in a quiet hut somewhere or sweeping leaves or chanting or something. Anything but this. He wasn't like any monk I'd known before.

"I've shocked you, haven't I?" he continued when I didn't respond.

He was astute.

I remained sitting in the dust, looking up.

"Not what you need, I imagine. This place is rough enough without you being shaken to your boots by a leapfrogging, screeching baldy like me. Am I right?"

I nodded, still unable to make decent conversation with the screeching baldy. He wasn't as skinny as Tikaro or Antony come to that and thankfully, unlike Tikaro, he talked a lot.

And, he was still bloody jogging on the spot.

"Finding it a little tough, huh? All this "monky" stuff? Hey, you should try living here for keeps!"

He finally stopped jogging.

Amaro moved swiftly between the roles of cheerful clown and caring counsellor. The cheerful clown tended to gesture with his arms a lot and be very animated while the caring counsellor clasped his hands sensitively in front of him, leaning his head on one side, listening with genuine concern.

Arms open in an expansive gesture that took in the place he now called home, Amaro said, "I'm only teasing. It's hard sometimes here but I wouldn't change it."

Then, looking directly at me, he said, "You've come to scatter your Uncle's ashes haven't you? At the River Kwai."

I nodded.

"Wow, what an honour."

I suppose it was. I hadn't really thought of it like that. I'd thought of it as a duty.

"I've come here to find Antony first," I explained. "We're going together. I've been reading about the river and the bridge in my guide book." And then, nervously, I added, "I've never done anything like this before."

"I know," said Amaro, nodding gently. "Your brother told me."

For a few moments there was silence between us and I realised how much warmth I felt coming from this unexpected new friend. A young, toned-up, tough boy, living in a surreal world of monks, meditation and monsoons.

"So, you're a monk too, are you?" I stated the obvious, dying to know how he could get away with the trainers and the music.

"Not strictly, I'm a novice," he explained in caring counsellor mode. "Which means I get to wear the funky robe but I haven't yet taken all the vows that Thanavaro has. This is my summer wardrobe." And he gave an accomplished mock curtsey as he showed of his dress. "I'm supposed to get ordained next Pansa."

I raised an eyebrow, bewildered. Pansa? More strange words.

"Right," he laughed with affection. "You're new at all this aren't you? Pansa is the rains retreat which we have every year during the monsoon. Three months of strict meditation, routine and achy knees. But, I suppose it's good for me."

"Will you ordain?" I asked as I got to my feet and dusted myself down.

"Straight for the Achilles!" he called out and began to gesticulate again, swiping one palm against the other. "I hope to but I almost left after Pansa this year. Packed my bags, dug out my old trousers and booked a ticket to Bangkok."

"What stopped you?"

"Your brother."

I'm sure he knew that this would surprise me.

"He's an angel, your brother. He can see when a hard time is just a hard time and he knew I didn't want to leave really, I'd just had enough."

"Seems a good enough reason to me."

"You are new at this!"

He'd lost me but I liked him already and felt I'd found a friend.

"It must be hard for you here," he said. "I find it difficult too. People expect just because we're all monks and all westerners that we should get on but why should we? We're thrown together in the middle of the jungle in a foreign country, each of us with our own individual struggle and journey, each with our own hang ups and insecurities, and then we wonder why sometimes it doesn't seem to work."

"So why do it, then? Why be here?" I offered.

He paused before responding, gently,

"Why not? Is your world any better? Look around you," he explained. "It's beautiful here, the people are beautiful and where else in the world can you go where all the people want to do is to live life with a good heart. Nothing else. They just want to be good. Is that so strange?"

He spoke with an integrity I had not yet come across in anyone, here or at home. So wise yet so young.

"Aren't you breaking the rules by being alone with a woman?"

"Yes," came the frank reply. "But I wasn't expecting to bump into anyone and, anyway, I'm a novice so they shouldn't be too hard on me."

This I realised straight away was an endearing, blatant and feeble excuse. I'd rapidly learnt that he was wearing a robe and that was what mattered. He shouldn't be breaking any rules, novice or no novice.

"And you like Crowded House," I said.

"Sure do, although some of the other monks think I shouldn't be listening to music. Not very monky of me." Amaro was young but the head on his shoulders and his view of the world was very old. I wondered where he'd got it from.

"Why can't you listen to music?"

"We can but it's supposed to be music that's appropriate to our way of life as a monk."

"And Crowded House isn't?" I asked.

"It is for me. It helps me work out a whole heap of stuff but some of the others don't see it like that. I checked it with the Abbot though and what the Main Man says, goes."

"And they're Australian like you," I quipped, referring again to the band.

"You Pommie!" he fired back, good naturedly. "They're Irish Catholic New Zealanders! You all make that mistake!"

I managed a smile for him, grateful for his kindness and for his attempt to make me laugh.

"I'll let you finish your walk alone," he said, looking serious again. "But no more motorbikes, eh? Tikaro and your brother got into trouble for that." And he pointed his finger at me, sternly.

"I thought it was allowed!" I protested on their behalf.

"It wasn't the bike thing that was the problem. They missed tea with the Abbot, that was the problem!" and I realised he'd been teasing me. "I doubt "Riding a Harley with my little Pommie sister" is a reasonable excuse for missing one of the Main Man's invaluable talks to the Sangha."

Amaro rolled his eyes at himself, hands on hips, beginning to jog slowly on the spot again.

"Now that was a bit bitchy of me." And he looked at me with a "you-won't-tell-on-me-will-you" kind of a face. "But hey, I'm still only a novice," he finished.

Before he left, I asked him if he knew when Antony would be back from wherever he'd gone. Amaro paused before answering. He didn't know but said he and Tikaro would come and visit in the afternoon for tea.

"Don't worry if Thanavaro's gone a while," he reassured me, seemingly knowing something I didn't. "He will be back."

I wasn't worried, just re-adjusting.

Amaro jogged off after giving me some directions for cutting through the monastery grounds without stumbling into the monks' sleeping quarters. He pointed me towards the Outside Sala, a meditation room on the edge of the forest which I found easily. It wasn't what I expected but I was quickly learning that not much about Thailand was ever what I expected.

The Outside Sala was outside. Strange that. It was a building with no walls, only pillars and a high ceiling. To one end there was the now familiar sight of a shrine from where Buddha looked over me as I knelt self-consciously before him in this mysteriously moving place. The Sala was completely open to the breeze. It had no inside and I felt uniquely vulnerable as I lifted my head to gaze at the shrine and became aware that something other than me had entered.

I didn't know what it was but I could feel something. It felt eerie but safe.

As I knelt there I could hear the breeze in the nearby trees and although I was sheltered from the rays of the sun, I could feel its heat as it climbed into the clear sky and began its daily

duty of scorching the earth. Apart from that, there was nothing. Just Buddha and me. And still they looked at me, those incredible, penetrating eyes, piercing my soul and cradling my heart as I knelt there for about half an hour. Half an hour that was a lifetime and a fleeting moment.

As I left the Outside Sala, I noticed the shed skin of a visiting snake lying intact by the steps leading away into the forest.

 October,
Wat Pah Chatanan

Tikaro and Amaro did come for tea. We sat outside next to my kuti for hours and we chatted easily about all sorts. They were lovely company and they're helping me to get used to being here. Amaro sat like a young, solid oak tree and told tales of a painful, glorious life before Buddhism, while Tikaro perched like a quiet willow, listening to it all before calmly interjecting a thoughtful observation on whatever was being said. It was clear that these two liked each other and were friends, but it was also clear that they wound each other up. Amaro would get annoyed because he seemed to think Tikaro was judging him simply by being silent and would get irritated when Tikaro disagreed with something he said. Tikaro would then retreat further into silence, unable to articulate his frustration at being misinterpreted. And hence, the spiral continued.

"You don't agree with me do you, Tikaro?" said Amaro to his orange robed friend.

"About what?"

"About what I was just talking about." He'd been talking about the life he'd lived before becoming a monk, including

the sex trade in Bangkok and how different cultures reacted to it. He'd also admitted to learning a few secrets of that trade himself and clearly felt that Tikaro disapproved.

Tikaro just looked into the air, trying to remember what it was that Amaro had been talking about when in fact all he'd been doing was sitting and staring into space, lost in his own thoughts.

He stumbled, trying to think of a reply but seemed to get lost between not wanting to offend Amaro by admitting he hadn't actually been listening and defending himself against being accused of not agreeing, when in fact he might agree with Amaro, if only he knew what it was he'd said.

Amaro just took offence. "You lived a sheltered life, didn't you Tikaro, before joining us here."

"S'pose so," replied Tikaro, looking confused, his mouth closed tight over his two front teeth, his eyes looking lost through his glasses.

"Suppose so what?" fired Amaro, more like an unfriendly friend than a clown or counsellor.

"S'pose I did have a sheltered life."

The sheltered life that Tikaro led before he joined the monastery, I learnt, was spent in Savannah, Georgia. A quaint, straight-laced town where his father was a school head teacher and his mother a school head teacher's wife. The only challenge that Tikaro had ever made to his parents' authority was buying a Harley-Davidson. It didn't go down well with his parents who equated the purchase of a motorbike with a pact with the devil. They thought their precious son had been brainwashed by the local chapter of Confederate flag-waving Hell's Angels. All it proved was just how little they knew their son. All Tikaro wanted to do was ride a Harley.

Tikaro was one of two sons. Up until a few years ago he'd followed the path laid down for him at birth. He did what was expected of him, went to high school, went to college and was aiming for medical school when he told them he'd become a Buddhist. They were appalled, thinking he'd joined some strange religious sect. They were worried that he'd again been brainwashed and that he'd have to give over the large financial fund they'd set up for him as a child. When he came to Thailand to ordain as a monk, they disinherited him and broke all contact with him.

"Been easier if you'd been one of them there gays," was one of the last things his father had told him before he left the States. "Thought that was why you ain't never brought no girl home."

His mother had said nothing at all and simply wept, silently.

"My brother writes," Tikaro explained in his drawn out, sad and distant way. "He's a lawyer. I get to know what's goin' on, but it ain't the same. I'd like my folks to visit but I guess that ain't never gonna happen."

I asked Tikaro what had made him become a monk. I was intrigued by how a boy from Forrest Gump Land had ended up being interested in the faith of a completely foreign culture. He looked at the floor for a long while and then at his hands and I began to think that he hadn't heard the question. Then I noticed that his down-turned, goofy Jesus face was a picture of concentration and I realised he was thinking hard about his reply. Amaro sat with me, patiently awaiting Tikaro's thoughtful answer. When Tikaro eventually stirred and lifted his head to look up at us, all he said was,

"I guess I don't know."

It was a reply which surprised each of us, not least Tikaro

himself.

Amaro was more sure about what had made him join the monastery. He'd been brought up in a children's home, where he'd been regularly beaten up and assaulted by the other kids and, just for good measure, sexually assaulted by the staff. At fifteen, he ran away and lived hand to mouth on the Sydney streets for a year, finally ending up as a rent boy. Early one morning, when he'd been up all night and had collapsed on the street after taking too many chemicals, an Australian Buddhist monk on alms round found him and took him back to the friends' house he was visiting in the centre of the city. The friends fed Amaro and looked after him. When the monk went back to his monastery outside Sydney he took Amaro with him and in return for his keep Amaro worked for them, cooking meals, tending the garden and cleaning. He lived with the monks for three years, learned to meditate and soaked up their way of life.

"I learned a whole new way to be," he explained.

He became a novice in Australia and the monks sent him to Thailand a year later.

"And what do you know?" he piped, arms outstretched, beaming. "Here I am!"

Jesus and the Rent Boy. What a pair.

"Has the Abbot been enlightened?" I asked them, naively as it turned out and I immediately regretted it. Amaro and Tikaro said nothing, they just glanced nervously at each other. It was clearly another rule I'd unwittingly broken. Neither of them seemed to know how to respond to a question that to me seemed perfectly understandable but appeared never to have been asked of them before.

"I thought that was the whole point," I added, searchingly.

"Enlightenment isn't really talked about," said Amaro, his

serious counsellor head firmly back in place. "How would you describe it? You can't, it's like explaining what the colour blue is like, or asking you what a banana tastes like. Until you've experienced it you can't understand the description."

"But surely you want to know if your teacher, your Main Man, has got it right?"

Tikaro fidgeted. My question had rattled him.

"But then we'd be looking for fault," continued the wise Amaro, old for his years. "It's like looking for a chink when all we should be doing is concentrating on our own practice. Why should I be concerned about what someone else has achieved or not achieved?"

"An' if I find out he hasn't been enlightened," piped up Tikaro, "does that mean I should stop trying or stop being a monk?"

I wasn't convinced by the reply but, being the new girl, I went along with it.

Later, on our own for a few minutes while Amaro had gone back to the kitchen to find more tea, Tikaro also confided that he had had a hard time with himself since our Harley ride.

"Y'know, I jus' loved my Harley so much," he drawled. "An' being reminded of that thrill an' all, I didn't want it to end. I craved more an' that's not good. Not good at all."

I suppose sheer, self-indulgent fun wasn't what they were aiming for here but I could also tell that his Harley had been Tikaro's only ever taste of independence.

Antony didn't come back to the monastery until late so I didn't see him until the next day. I didn't really like him not being around but that was how it was. The boys left after a couple of hours and I sat down with my book, War and Peace, which I was determined to read once in my life, and

as I read, I waited for the sun to set. I'd got into a routine of sorts. Getting up early, going to the meal in the morning, seeing Antony when I could, taking a walk, reading, writing cards, and then coming back for tea.

I don't need to see Antony all the time but I would like to see him more. I wondered what he got up to with the Abbot when they're in town and why so many visits, why him and why not the others?

I'd been feeling a bit more adventurous of late, having found my Thailand feet, and I decided that I too would venture into town. I caught the bus into Ubon. The bus was a simple open truck with wooden benches in the back. Everyone climbed in and when it got full, they hung off the back or scrambled onto the roof. More than often, someone loaded a bale of hay on or some produce they wanted delivering and the driver would drop it off for them. I spent most of the trip sharing a bench with a dustbin full of ice that was being delivered to a local restaurant.

The school kids got on the same bus as me and stared. One small boy stared for a whole twelve minutes. I timed him as he sat opposite me about two feet away, staring into my face, innocent eyes wide, not smiling, not frowning, just staring. They all looked very smart in their white shirts, khaki shorts and black plimsolls and they chattered away, occasionally looking over to me and whispering amongst themselves. Eventually, one of them brokered the courage to speak to me.

"Wat Pah Chatanan," he said, and at first I struggled to understand. I'd only heard westerners say it.

"Wat," he repeated, pointing to where we'd just come from.

"Wat Pah Chatanan," he said again and then pointed at

me. "Wat Pah Chatanan."

"Yes," I replied, assuming, arrogantly, that he could speak English. "That's right, Wat Pah Chatanan, I've come from Wat Pah Chatanan. My brother is a monk there."

And then, thinking he was up for a chat and feeling incredibly relieved that I'd found someone who spoke my language, I asked what his name was. What I got in return was a polite smile and a small Thai boy nodding to me, pretending he'd understood what I'd said when clearly he hadn't at all. I realised, with embarrassment, my mistake and resorted to common ground again.

"Wat Pah Chatanan," I nodded at him.

"Wat Pah Chatanan," he nodded back and smiled, happy to have received a comprehensible response which was rapidly followed by his school friends nodding and smiling at me too, before all calling out in an overwhelming chorus of grinning faces.

"Wat Pah Chatanan! Wat Pah Chatanan!"

"Wat Pah Chatanan!" I sang back.

"Wat Pah Chatanan! Wat Pah Chatanan!"

Wat Ba Ba Loo Bop, Wat Bam Boo.

Shake, rattle and roll all the way to town.

Ubon, like Bangkok, was dusty and dirty. Cars screamed past on the pot-holed roads, throwing fumes and grime into the shops and onto the many roadside food stalls. I enjoyed wandering round the town and trying to negotiate the prices of things in the shops. It was fun getting used to a different way of life.

As I was leaving the indoor market, a bustling, busy, loud colourful arrangement of stalls selling fresh fruit, vegetables and what seemed like half-alive meat and fish, I thought I caught a glimpse of my brother through the throng of

market goers. He was getting out of a minibus with the Abbot at the gates of a large, white building down the hill on the far side of the wide road. There was a group of three Thai men waiting for them on the steps of the entrance and each bowed in greeting as the two monks approached. I blinked as the bright sunlight hit my eyes, not sure if it was him, but soon saw from the familiar posture and familiar way he wore his robe that it was indeed Antony.

Something, however, stopped me from calling out or running over to them. I have no idea what it was that kept me rooted to the spot with shoppers and traders scurrying past me, some bumping into me, some pausing to stare at me, some grinning, but I think I knew that whatever my brother was up to, I was not invited. It was like watching him caught on camera on a silent screen without him knowing he had an audience.

I watched Antony gracefully accept the greetings from the Thai men and then follow the Abbot as they were both shown into the building, the door pulled open for them by their uniformed hosts as they entered. As they disappeared into the building, the sun caught the glass of the doorway as it slowly fell closed.

A Tuk-Tuk sped past kicking dust up at the pavement where I stood and when I was able to open my eyes again, the scene in my own little mini-film had finished. Antony had gone. That brief glimpse into the life he led when I wasn't around had ended and I was left with my shopping.

A woman behind me, who had emerged from the market building, loudly spat some juice from the betel nuts she'd been chewing into a plastic bag and it shook me back to the here and now. I'd ask Antony about it later I thought and wandered further into town, eventually finding a tiny

regional tourist office which sold postcards I could send home – one for Captain Archie, another each to the girls, and one to the Boatyard and Joe.

As I wrote, the woman I'd seen at the airport also came into my mind again. I could remember her smile and her dark black hair. I also began to think about going to the River Kwai. It was time to start planning, to sort things out with Antony about exactly when and how we were going to get there and where we would stay.

Strangely, despite the fact that we would be scattering the ashes of our dead uncle, I was looking forward to it. It would be a chance to be alone with Antony and to share some rare time with him. I didn't get that very often. I knew too, that I couldn't face scattering the ashes alone. Tough as I have had to be, I would find that too hard.

 October,
Wat Pah Chatanan

I'm loving this place but I'm still missing home. Listening to familiar music helps to connect me. It's the Killers' first album at the moment.

Destiny is calling me. Open up my eager eyes.

I went on my first Pindabah alms round with the monks the other day.

"The Buddha lived in the forest on nothing other than what he was offered," Antony explained to me, as we were leaving the monastery that morning. "He wore a robe to indicate to others that he had chosen a separate way of life and our custom of going on Pindabah every morning has grown from that. If it wasn't for the local people, none of the monasteries could sustain themselves."

At first, listening to my brother explain how things worked here, my reaction was cynical. Yeh, great Antony, I thought. You live here, pay nothing, earn nothing and what's more, you seem to do nothing in return. Nice one. Then I remembered what Amaro had said to me about everyone just wanting to be good and thought about Mae Li and the other lay people I'd met. They were kind, loving people and this is what made their world tick.

Pindabah opened up my mind to all this stuff a bit more but, before we set off, it didn't stop me cursing Antony at four-fifteen that morning when my alarm went off. This'd better be worth it, brother, I thought.

My humour was sweetened when I caught sight of the little green gecko that had been in my room since I arrived. At first it scared me. Another creepy-crawly that I didn't know whether was friend or foe. I wasn't used to sharing my bedroom with small, lizardy reptile things. However, after a few days and learning that Gecko was completely harmless and emitted an endearing soft croak every now and then just to let me know he was still there, I got used to him and now he's become my room-mate. He clings to the facing wall like a plastic toy with suction pads which stay stuck wherever you put him. I still giggle when Gecko decides to go for a vertical run up the wall, his small, delicately splayed feet sucking him in place. Off he shoots impatiently as if someone has flicked his tail and he can't wait to get away. He's become my pet.

They don't have cats in Thailand after all. Lots of stray dogs and geckos but no cats.

It was dark as I made my way timidly in the early hours through the forest paths to the Main Sala where I was due to meet Antony and some of the other monks for the start of

Pindabah. There were two alms rounds that left the monastery every morning, each to one of the nearby villages. We were to go on the longer one and were therefore setting off earlier. Antony was already in the Sala.

"Morning," he beamed in a whisper. "I wasn't sure if you'd make it."

"Charming," I retorted, playfully. "I seem to remember that this hour was nearer your bedtime not so long ago."

It was true. The Antony I knew would rather have gone without sleep all night than get up at this at early hour. He was crap at getting up.

"I've changed," he said, smiling and without an ounce of defensiveness.

We were joined by four other monks. As far as I could make out in the dim light they were all westerners, busy adjusting their robes and their bowls which they put in a sling carried over one shoulder. Some of the monks wore sandals, others, including Antony, had bare feet. None of them bothered to say "Hello" or offered a greeting so for the first ten minutes I just thought they were miserable buggers.

Eventually, after watching them get their robes ready in silence, Antony introduced one of them to me. He must have been in his late sixties and when he turned directly to me, I realised he wasn't miserable at all and actually had a very warm, smiley face. He had soft grey stubble that was just beginning to creep through his hairline and he spoke softly with a deep, syrupy voice and an American accent. It turned out that he was the Abbot of Wat Pah Chatanan, the Main Man.

"So you are Thanavaro's sister," he said and as he did so, his eyes, as well as his face, smiled. "We are pleased you are here. How are you finding it?"

"A little strange," I responded with nervous understatement.

"Only a little?" he asked, wryly raising one invisible eyebrow.

The other monks laughed and I realised he was joking.

"I hope you are happy here and please treat it as home. You are family now."

I could only smile back and nod my gratitude, intimidated by his status.

As we set off, the sun was just beginning to dawn, creating a strong golden glow through the trees. I followed the monks along the dust track leading to the village. Dawn happens quickly in Thailand. One moment it is dark, the next the sun has risen and before you is a spectacular, honey-edged, new day. We walked silently in single file, the monks' robes echoing the amazing radiant tones which were beginning to reveal themselves in the daylight. Dark gold, sandy gold, shiny gold, soft gold. Ahead of us were lush, green trees which formed a bank of colour against the dry rice fields and masked the wooden structures peeking out from the green in the village ahead. A stray dog began to follow us lazily as we made our way along the road and just as I was beginning to think that things really couldn't get any more beautiful, a rainbow emerged in the blue haze above us. I walked and gazed wordlessly and took in the last few moments of the dawn before entering the village.

One of the monks ahead of me turned. It was Amaro. I hadn't noticed him at the Sala and was surprised he hadn't greeted me before. I was learning not to take offence at something that may seem rude at home but, when you thought about it, wasn't really such a big deal.

He smiled at me, his boyish face happy in the sunshine.

"You see," he said, holding out an open hand as if offering me the day. "We've even arranged a rainbow for your first Pindabah." And he quietly turned back to focus on his walking.

Approaching the village, I saw that the street was lined with kneeling men, women and children at intervals along the side of the road. They each held something in front of them. As the monks approached, one by one, the person kneeling placed offerings in each monk's bowl and then gave a Wai, the traditional bowing that I'd learned to emulate. It was all so graceful, honest and humbling. I also gave a Wai as I passed them and the response I got ranged from a gleeful grin to a bashful smile.

The whole ritual was carried out in silence. The people offered and the monks accepted. No thank you was uttered, no thank you was needed.

The village, a ramshackle cluster of wooden huts and corrugated iron thrown together, had clearly been awake for hours. We passed one lady dressed in a thin, scruffy blue sarong and a once-white blouse who, with her children helping, was busy stripping and preparing bundles of pink spring onions that were laid out on the ground beside us. They were preparing their day's produce for selling. Further down the street, a man was having his hair cut in a barber's shop which consisted of a propped up mirror and a chair placed in the street.

The higgledy-piggledy streets were so narrow they seemed to carve a path through the villagers' living rooms and at every corner children stared at me. A tiny young boy, who couldn't have been more than two years old, was being held by his older, caring sister. Two brothers stopped mid-breakfast about to dip their doughnut-like biscuits into a

bowl of hot soup, staring as I went past, mute. And they continued to stare like unmoving statues when I turned to look at them. It was only when I responded with an awkward, westernised Wai that they broke their silence and burst into fits of giggles, feeling free to break their pose, as if the music had started again in their private game of musical statues.

"Hello, miss," said another boy bravely as I passed him squatting with his friends under the floorboards at the side of a wooden house. He was subsequently chased and playfully swiped at by his friends when he received a "Hello" back from me.

Everywhere too were scrawny baby chickens, running about between the legs of the children or scampering ahead of us and disappearing in a cloud of squawks and dust. I approached one lady who was kneeling, offering some rice from a bamboo steamer to the monks. She was unsmiling and her sun-drained face carried the mask of hard work and a hard life. My interpretation of her expression and demeanour was loathing. She hated me. Who do you think you are, you jumped up, pathetic, white western girl, coming here and invading my home like it is some kind of theme park? I was sure she thought I was trash. Then, as I passed, her face broke into the widest, loveliest, heartfelt smile I have ever seen in my life and she chuckled, unself-consciously as she offered me an orange. I hadn't expected to be offered anything and this woman's pleasure at giving something to me moved me in a way I find hard to describe. She had nothing except a wooden hut built on stilts and a few bundles of leaves to sell to earn a living, yet she wanted to give an orange to me, the rich westerner, who could afford to buy more oranges than she'd ever see in her whole life.

On the way back to the monastery, Antony waited for me and walked beside me.

"You know you can come again tomorrow," he said, upbeat and happy, the sun shining on the side of his smiling face.

I smiled with him, sharing a very a unique moment, both knowing that the four-fifteen wake-up call had been worth it.

"I'm not sure," I replied, trying to put into words what it was that I was feeling that morning. "I want to keep this special, Antony. I don't want this to be routine. I can't ever repeat today and I don't ever want this to begin to feel normal."

"Benedict," he said gravely, and I noticed him stop himself from reaching out and taking my hand. "I've been coming on Pindabah everyday for nearly four years and there are moments when it still moves me to tears."

I wanted to ask him about his visits to town to get an idea of what he did there. Seeing him the other morning had felt a bit eerie and I felt like teasing him about visiting a brothel or something and for not telling me the real reason why he'd come to Thailand. He couldn't fool me. All this monk stuff. It was a scam, really wasn't it? He'd just come here for the sex shows and to see the tricks with the ping-pong balls. I didn't get to ask him, though. The moment was lost as Amaro joined us and wanted to know what I'd thought of my first alms round.

There was so much I could have said to him about how it had affected me, about how humble it had made me feel, about how insignificant my western life had begun to feel but, like Tikaro the other day, the only words I could find to describe what was going on for me were,

"I don't really know."

I didn't want to trivialise what I felt by using inadequate words.

When we arrived back at Chatanan, the place was heaving. Battered cars and pick-up trucks filled the driveway and what seemed like hundreds of men and women were busy in the kitchen or fetching and carrying buckets, boxes and flowers from the cars. There were extra orange robes around too and more Thai monks than usual. Scores of children were running around and the normally whispering atmosphere of Chatanan had been transformed into a loud, bustling village.

"It's Kathina this weekend," explained Antony as two young monks, who could only have been about ten or eleven, dashed past us playing tag. "Every year we have a robe ceremony where new, handmade cloth is offered to the monks for their robes. Each Wat does it on a different day and will have visitors from the other Wats. It's traditional and as you can see, it's party time."

It was indeed. More cars, crammed with lay people, were arriving by the minute and the kitchen was buzzing. Tables were being laid along the path leading to the main Sala and a fire was being prepared beside the kitchen in the open air.

"That'll be for the tea which they make from wood bark. There'll be a pot on the boil all day. You'll have to try some," said Antony.

I wasn't so sure.

"I'm going to be chanting at the ceremony tonight," he said. "Would you like to come?"

"Sounds like the best gig in town," I teased and Antony explained that he had to get ready for the meal and needed to leave.

"I need to practise my chanting today, so do you mind if we make our tea visit short?"

"That'll be fine," I reassured him, biting my initial reaction to complain about not seeing him enough.

He smiled that damned Buddhist smile at me and I was certain that there was something else he wanted to say but he couldn't quite find the words so we stayed silent, surrounded by the organised mayhem that was Kathina.

"You'll have to start thinking about going to the River Kwai soon," he said.

"I beg your pardon?" I replied frostily.

"The River Kwai. You'll have to start thinking of going."

"What do you mean I'll have to start thinking about it? We'll have to, Antony. You and me. We'll have to start thinking about it." I noticed him hesitate slightly. "You're coming with me, Antony."

He nodded sheepishly but didn't answer and I thought of Uncle Erno, sat in his box, waiting unnoticed in the corner of my kuti.

"But not for a while?" I added, trying to lighten things. "We can make the arrangements later. I'm enjoying spending time here with you."

And I was. Yes, it was weird. Yes, they were odd but I knew I'd never get a chance to experience this again, and anyway, it beat shivering my bones off in an English winter or drinking the night away yet again down at the King's Arms.

Antony smiled warmly in the way only a brother can and I again experienced the pang of missing out on a hug. He left and I headed for the kitchen to see if I could help. As I entered, the now familiar warm smell of chilli and coriander swept over from the cooking area where a melee of people were stirring enormous pans of curry and steaming

bucketloads of rice. On the floor before me there must have been fifty women crouched over bowl upon bowl and tray upon tray of different foods. The colours and the aromas were intoxicating. Heaps of shiny red apples, mountains of rice sweets wrapped in bright green banana leaves, piles of ripe yellow bananas, pink melon, luminous pineapple, crispy cakes, pastries, white bread sandwiches, peanut cookies, sesame toffee, cartons of milk, boiled eggs and enormous clumps of sticky rice being collected and taken away to be resteamed. It was overwhelming.

Christopher came whizzing past in his usual, speedy manner.

"Hello, miss. You like here? You eat good food today? Good Thai food?"

I beamed back and nodded.

I like Christopher, though I only ever get a fleeting glimpse of him before he dashes off to what always seems to be another important, urgent job.

He grinned back at me, bowed and sped off.

No one let me do anything. I kept getting ushered to the nearby table and chair every time I made an attempt to help. I was a guest and they wanted to show me how well The Isaan treated its guests. The white haired lady who had chatted to me on my first morning here came up to me, still chatting away as usual. I wished I knew her name but we hadn't got that far. She had such a mischievous, cheeky face, like a cheeky kid really, wrapped up in an old woman's wrinkles and grey hair. I was convinced she was telling me some joke or saying something rude that the others wouldn't appreciate. I wish I could understand her! I laughed with her, teased her back as she tugged at my western clothes and she waved over here, over there, pointed at me and

hugged my arm before shuffling off to assist with the washing up.

The thing that struck me most about watching all these rituals unfold is how simple they are. The locals give food, the monks eat, the locals then eat and they have a bit of a chant to mark it. Similarly the setting is very simple too. It's a few huts thrown together amongst a few trees. The dawn breaks, the sun shines, the sun sets, the monastery goes back to sleep. And all the people in the monastery seemed to concentrate on is being a good person.

It isn't what I'm used to. A religion that seems to work.

I've already learned loads. I've learned that the daily morning ritual of sweeping the labyrinth of footpaths was not only to make the place look tidy but helps to spot snakes and scorpions before you step on them. So, the people sweep.

I've learned that fetching and carrying the water from the deep well located in the forest is a luxury few Thais have in this area. So, they fetch.

I've learned that the insects I so detested on my first night and which instilled such fear in me, have become my companions on lonely nights, and that the scream of the forest as dusk descends is only the insects' nightly call to remind you that all is well in the world and that life is ticking over as usual. The forest looks after you and befriends you, asking for nothing more in return than to be respected.

The first night I heard the insects' scream I thought it was a car alarm going off. It was that loud. I couldn't believe a few insects hiding in the trees could create such a din. On the edge of the forest you can hear the scream as you approach. It's like a mad, whirling frenzy of crazed witches and after only a few days you're so used to it that you have to

concentrate to even hear it.

The other big thing I've learned is that I could go for this long without lager. I haven't had any alcohol since I arrived in Thailand and the funny thing is, I haven't even missed it. I don't think Antony would appreciate it if I asked him to join me for a pint in downtown Ubon one night. Somehow, I don't think it's his thing anymore. He told me that alcohol isn't even allowed in the monastery but I'd really fancy a drink, one night at least.

On the way back after the meal, a group of children were playing amongst the parked cars. There were about twenty of them playing on an open-topped truck that doubled up as a peoplecarrier. They were clambering on top and swinging from the frame which held the luggage on the roof. As soon as I was spotted, they fell silent and watched me. A small girl giggled but all of them stood still in their tracks or sat motionless. Self-consciously, I nodded towards them and said,

"Hello."

No answer, just tiny elbows dug into a neighbour's tiny ribs and more tiny giggles. One boy was clinging horizontally from the frame up on the roof at the back of truck. He was balancing by pushing his canvas shoed feet against the back strip of iron and his outstretched arms against the frame at the sides. The poor kid's strength was giving out but still he dared not move. You could see him straining not to fall, his young face distorted by the effort. Silence and stares prevailed as I walked on by when the boy's pre-pubescent muscles finally gave out. He yelped as his body dropped vertically onto the children below who laughed as he tumbled and disappeared behind them.

When the laughter subsided, they all turned to me and silence fell again.

I was concerned that the poor kid had hurt himself. Then his tiny grinning face bobbed up from behind the shoulders of the other children.

"HELLO MISS!!" he yelled at me and they all collapsed into hysterics, their silence finally replaced by the relieving sound of children's high-pitched, playful chatter. The boy who had fallen was still shouting at me as I walked away through the trees.

"HELLO MISS! I LOVE YOU!!"

I love you too, matey.

At eight o'clock this evening, I watched the robe-presentation. The room was full with monks sat in the centre and easily over a hundred Thais around the outside. I hadn't realised that Antony wasn't just chanting, he was presenting the robe and was the focus of all the attention. Listening to him chant, I could see why he must have been nervous. He was chanting in ancient Pali with another monk, just the two of them in perfect duet. Most of the crowd listening probably knew the chant backwards and, knowing Antony, he would have been bricking it beforehand, not wanting to let anyone down by getting it wrong.

God, it's weird watching him do all this sort of thing. My brother, the monk.

I arrived a little late to the ceremony so the other people who were watching ushered me forward so I could get a better view. They all seemed to know that it was my brother who was doing the chanting. The Sala was lit by candles and incense was burning. I could also smell the flowers that the women had been preparing that morning and were now placed in tall vases around the room. Some were placed at the foot of the Buddha statue. The Abbot sat next to Buddha.

Antony was in the centre of the group of monks and he half-smiled at me, sheepishly, when he noticed I'd arrived. His chanting was wonderful, an hypnotic nasal two-tone song, performed calmly with love and grace and sounding like a far-away call from a beckoning, un-visited place. He still looks so strange in his robes, shaven head and bare feet. Haven't got used to it yet. Not sure I ever will. And he looks so thin. Fair do's, he's bound to lose weight out here but still, he does look scrawny.

 October,
Guest Villa, Wat Pah Chatanan,

Since last writing I've moved house. Instead of my little, one roomed kuti, I now have the run of the very palatial guest villa. Two stories high, about a five-minute walk from the main part of Chatanan, it has, wait for it, two bedrooms, each with their own bathroom, a shower in each bathroom with hot water and a sit down loo - not one of those holes in the floor I've had to get used to lately - a kitchen with a fridge-freezer, a normal sink - not just a hole in the floor again - and a stove, albeit more of a Bunsen burner than a top-of-the-range Smeg.

Downstairs consists of one large room with a tiled floor and, as ever, it is open to the air apart from mosquito screens which act as serene, transparent walls. You can hear, see and smell the forest from in here and you can feel the breeze as it gently whistles through the wire mesh. It's as if you are sitting in the forest. Upstairs has polished wooden floors and a shrine at the far end of the landing which looks out over the forest through the screens.

I'm in a palace.

The villa itself is about the size of large family house and it felt way too grand for me as I approached it for the first time through the forest, its white structure looming up through the green of the trees. Antony and Amaro were with me, helping to carry my bags from my kuti. The house sat on an immaculately kept green lawn which was bordered by an array of colourful plants and there was even an attendant caretaker to look after me.

"He lives with his wife down there," said Antony pointing to a tiny, scruffy hut at the end of the garden path that led outside the gate.

I was shocked. Their whole house was the size of my old kuti and was propped up on wooden sticks, had a grass roof and consisted of two rooms separated by a white sheet. There were no walls, no mosquito screens, no bathroom, no fridge-freezer, no cooker and they shared their veranda not with a statue of Buddha but with a water buffalo, a few chickens, thousands of mosquitoes and probably the odd scorpion or snake.

What a contrast to my new home.

I missed my kuti at first, the new place was so big and to begin with I thought I wouldn't like it but it took all of thirty minutes for me to get used to this new level of luxury. I brought Gecko with me in a matchbox and he settled in nicely in the upstairs en-suite bathroom. I chose the bedroom on the left. Might try the one on the right another night.

After the boys had left and as I was sorting out my stuff, I heard someone call gently from the garden in Thai. I looked down through the shutters which protected the bedrooms from the harsh sunlight and saw a Thai woman shuffling down the path. She was still calling out and from above I saw

a familiar, flower-print sarong, Wellington boots and an old straw hat. It was Mae Li. Yeh! And it turned out that she was the caretaker's wife and would be my neighbour during my stay here.

"Sawat di kha," she bowed, grinning away at me as I met her downstairs in the living room. "My house," she said in English, pointing proudly to her hut at the bottom of the path.

I greeted her with a beaming smile as she let herself in and she followed me upstairs to help me unpack, peering quizzically at my clothes and belongings as she did. She showed me round the house but when I offered her a cup of tea to say thank you, she wouldn't accept, screwing her face up into a wrinkly frown and waving a stern index finger at me. No, she didn't take tea, thank you. She kept hugging my arm like the white haired old lady from the monastery kitchen and it felt lovely to have a friendly, tactile person to spend my time with.

When my brother arrived again later with Tikaro, I was taken aback when Mae Li immediately knelt down on the floor and offered a Wai to each of them. She changed from the grinning, huggy woman I knew to one who was incredibly formal and deferential. Clearly the presence of the monks took priority over everything else. She stayed kneeling, saying nothing while they each arranged their robes in silence and sat down at the coffee table in the middle of the room. It was only once they were settled that she shuffled backwards on her knees towards the door, bowing as she went and saying something quietly in Thai.

"She says she is very happy that you are staying here," Tikaro translated.

Me? I love her to bits but you can forget that bowing crap.

✠ October, 1943
Chungkai Camp

Charlie was sent back to Singapore with a working party under orders to take part in an operation to clear up the dead. I fear for him. He left me his wedding ring to look after and I hide it along with mine and beside Arthur's. I pray that the Nips do not find them for I could not put up a fight if they did. The knowledge of this drains me. How could I not fight for the one thing that means more to me than anything? How could I not fight for the one thing that Charlie and Arthur have left with me to protect? The fear of a beating, of death, and the sheer hopelessness of our situation has dragged my natural reactions from me. They have taken rings from the men and we know they keep them in the Commander's tent. One of the Nips was taunting an Australian about taking his wedding ring while he was being forced to stand outside for three days for stealing a bowl of rice. He bragged that they were saving it with the others to be melted down after the war. They know only too well how to break a man. The Australian was already ill and he died two days later.

I don't know when I will see Charlie again. Arthur remains with me, although he is desperately weak. He has an ulcer from a leg wound and a fever. The Doc is marvellous but we know he can do very little despite efforts to clean dressings and irrigate the wound. Maggots infest the flesh and clearing these and the pus from the lesion is a procedure which Arthur has to endure night and day. He is in luck since the hospital now has some anaesthetic, although I don't imagine the supply will last for very long. They will surely have to amputate and in these insect ridden conditions I fear

for him. He is so emaciated and weakens with every day.

We are still being sent up country to work on the railway. Sick men have to go before inspections every morning and if they can stand, they are not exempt from work. Often they depart, never to return, falling by the wayside, dying before our very eyes. Very few are buried and the bodies pile up in the jungle. Two officers escaped a few weeks ago and all of us prayed for them. But they were recaptured and the Nips made us all stand outside and watch as they were hauled back into the camp. The sense of hopelessness which we could see behind the officers' eyes as they were being dragged back into captivity affected us all and the camp sank further into a deep, bleak numbness. The officers were beaten within earshot of the rest of us and we tried to cover our ears since we all knew where the screams were heading. The silence that followed their screams lay heavy with us for days.

Morale is so low but we still try to maintain discipline. There are many times when orders have been disobeyed, and I can't blame the lads, but without discipline survival would be even harder. I am not proud to admit that often I have wished that survival would elude me. It would be so much easier just not to be here anymore. I know not what awaits me on the other side but at least it would not be this. And who knows, maybe my Muriel will be there to look after me. How I wish to be with Muriel, lying with my head in her lap and gazing up at her gentle, loving eyes. How I wish her arms would cradle me and her lips caress me as I let her warmth envelope my being. How I wish.

Take me Muriel. Take me, away from here, away from the pain, the horror and the everydayness that is my existence. Take me. I think it is only this thought that keeps me alive,

and the distant hope that we will indeed one day be together again in this life. I would not want to live if to live meant to be deprived of this. If that were so, I'd take my chances on the other side.

Death no longer stays at a distance, waiting politely to take us only once we have seen life, loved it, watched our children grow and enjoyed three score years and ten of English summers. Instead it lies all around us, seeping into every pore and gnawing at our brains. I know Arthur will die, here in this hell. His ulcer spreads from his knee to his ankle and has devoured the flesh, which has all but disappeared save for a raw strip where his calf should be. You can see daylight between this and the bare bone. But it is not the ulcer that will kill him. It is the cure for the ulcer that will take him away. Only a few more days and they will have to amputate his leg and I have not seen any man, yet, who has lived here beyond a fortnight of such an operation. The Doc has to take the same saw used by the cookhouse to chop wood, sterilise it as best he can, perform the operation in the outdoors, and return the saw for chopping wood when he is done. If he doesn't amputate, Arthur will die an agonising death, poisoned by the festering menace which is eating him alive. If he does amputate, Arthur will surely die from infection and disease which, in the course of time, will also eat him alive.

Today I found myself thinking that maybe it would be better for Arthur if he died now, quickly, while there's still a chance to relieve his pain. I have no faith that our situation will improve. For weeks now, I have had to watch men die. Men I have been living with, working with, slept alongside and with whom I have shared the unimaginable.

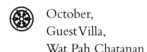 October,
Guest Villa,
Wat Pah Chatanan

Mae Li helped me with my washing this morning. I gathered my stuff together, dirty clothes, the washing powder I'd bought in Ubon, a bowl I'd taken from the kitchen and took it all outside to the tap on the lawn. It was fiercely hot already so I wore a baseball cap and covered my arms and legs with sun cream. It seemed OK to wear a T-shirt and shorts at the guest house, there was no one nearby to offend and I think Mae Li enjoyed having this snow white westerner around.

"You Farang," she'd told me the other day, stroking my white arms and then, with trademark grin, placed her own alongside to show how pale my skin was next to hers.

"Farang," she repeated.

"Farang," I nodded back.

Mae Li giggled infectiously when I tried to speak Thai, her gappy mouth making her look like a small child who'd just begun to lose her milk teeth. Then, with no warning, she whacked me on the bum with her hand and laughed.

"Big Farang!" she grinned madly, her eyes bulging for a moment. "Big Farang!"

Thanks Mae Li. She might as well have called me a big, fat, white lump of lard.

As I filled my washing bowl from the tap and felt the cool water splash against my big, fat white legs, I glanced up at the harsh sun and I figured I'd sooner be tipping this bowl of water over my head, never mind over my washing. It was so hot. Mae Li shuffled over in her wellies and showed me where she kept her bar of soap.

"This good," she told me, pointing at the half-used bar and taking away the box of powder I had brought, shaking her head as she did. She brought an extra tin bowl, filled it and mine with water and began scrubbing at some of my clothes, every inch handcleaned until it gleamed in the bright sunshine. Then each garment was plunged into the second bowl to be rinsed, while the first bowl was emptied and filled again with clear, crisp clean water and my clothes were then taken and plunged into that bowl, rinsing away the suds, eliminating the dirt. Then she started the whole process again, giving everything a second wash.

It was a bonding experience for me and Mae Li. The steady routine and rhythm of washing and rinsing, the splash of the fresh, clean water on my bare feet and the silence within which she and I worked together was almost meditative. I watched how she washed and followed the process, the sun beating down through the trees and the fresh, green grass tickling my toes. My big, fat, white, Farang toes.

Working our way through my load, we came across my dirty knickers, next in line for a wash and scrub. As much as I loved Mae Li, I couldn't possibly let anyone other than myself wash my dirty knickers and I picked them out of the heap and began washing. Mae Li began to chatter at me in Thai, shaking her head as she did and then in her broken English said,

"No good, see?"

And she took my dirty knickers from me, added some soap and began scrubbing. Scrub, scrub on the cotton gusset, scrub on front and back and plunge into clean water, then scrub, scrub on the cotton gusset again just for good measure. Now we'd really bonded. I didn't know anyone in

the world who could wash my dirty knickers like that.

"Beautiful," she beamed as she picked up a pair of my now clean best Marks and Spencer white cottons. "Beautiful," and she held a pair of them up to her chest, closing her eyes and cuddling them like a small child cuddles a new soft toy. For Mae Li, one hundred percent cotton was a rare treat.

"You go," she said, suddenly. "You go."

And she gestured with her arm over towards the fields, flicking her head and her hand up towards the sky. What was this? Was she stealing my knickers? Surely not. I thought we were getting on so well.

"You go," she said again, the arm waving towards the fields in an arc. Then I realised that Mae Li was trying to say something else.

"Me," she said, tapping her chest. "Me." And she waved her arm in the reverse direction and held up the knickers.

Translation: You go home on an aeroplane and when you do, you send me some beautiful white cotton Marks and Spencer knickers just like these.

"Size 'S'," she informed me helpfully and grinned and twinkled like there was no tomorrow.

"Of course I will," I replied. And I meant it.

Airing my dirty linen in public is something I only ever want to do in Thailand and only ever with Mae Li.

 November,
Poo Jom Petch Retreat,
The Isaan

This country is so beautiful, so peaceful and I've finally got to spend some time with my brother too. At last. I'm having an incredible time and I've come to a place I thought I

would only ever see in my dreams. We've come to a retreat monastery high up in the plains over looking Laos and the Mekong River.

I keep mentioning to Antony about going to the River Kwai but he suggested visiting here first and spending a few days.

We left early morning two days ago with Tikaro. Dawn hadn't broken as we set off from Chatanan and it was still dark. Our minibus, with our driver at the wheel and filled with food and supplies for our journey, rattled its way across the dirt tracks to the main road. No monks lived at the retreat permanently so there were no provisions and the local villagers were very excited about us visiting.

Life was waking up near Chatanan as we left in our truck, Antony and I sitting in the back on benches. There was a bit of traffic on the road. A pick-up truck laden with workers about to start their long day passed us, a petrol wagon went by and you could hear the familiar sound of small motorbikes revving up in the distance. I opened the window to have a look at the kids on the bikes that had screamed up behind us and were about to overtake. Their screeching engines were at full throttle as their riders hurtled the machines past us in the cool, dark morning. Weary headlights barely lit their way as they passed. Antony noticed them too and turned from his seat in front of me to catch my eye, his soft, silent smile reaching me through the half-light and showing me that he remembered, too, that those were the days we thought would never end. Kids on bikes, living the life of Riley.

Once they'd gone, we were left with the dark again and all we could hear was the sound of the engine.

Silence hung between Antony and I for a while as we

rested in each other's gaze, the cool, dusty morning taking us back to years gone by, years when he wasn't a monk, when we were still brother and sister, and when he was tearing around in Levi's on a battered old Honda Superdream.

It was always summer, that image I had. Antony's bike was shiny, metallic green and you could hear him coming up the street long before you saw him. Neighbours complained about the speed he rode and they complained about the revving noise coming from the back yard while he played about with the engine, tuning it, make it rev louder, getting oil all over his jeans, all over the floor. Once, he let me ride it, once and only once because I was too small to really get a hold of it and as I trundled down the back lane, scared to even try and change gear, I negotiated my first corner. I was going far too slowly and as I leaned into the bend, like Antony had forever told me to do, the Superdream fell over. Sin of sins. I'd dropped his precious bike. And I'd marked the paintwork, and it was the first and last time Antony let me anywhere near his Superdream. It was at that moment that I vowed to pass my bike test and get a bike of my own, just to show him and the world that girls can ride bikes too.

I was still holding Antony's gaze as all those tender moments flooded back but Antony couldn't hold the moment any longer and his eyes fell to the floor. The last thing I expected though was for him to reach out, find my hand with his and squeeze it.

I knew he'd been remembering what I had. It wasn't until we'd travelled another mile or so that he finally let my hand fall.

It was still dark outside, still silent and I still had my window open, so I rested against the frame and let the breeze flow against my face and allowed the air of Thailand's pre-

dawn minutes to fill my lungs. The early morning air smelt very clean and fresh. It was warm enough to let my head fall onto the window frame and feel bathed by it. I spent at least fifteen minutes with the air rushing over my face, occasionally pulling open my eyelids to watch the roadside flash past beneath us.

Then, I thought I could hear something. I wasn't sure if it was a memory or not at first but, lifting my head up to hear better, my ears caught the sound again, so unmistakable that I thought I'd drifted into a dream. It was that wonderful sound of shake, rattle and roll, chocolate and Mozart. Foreign and familiar all at the same time.

Not here surely, I thought, but as I woke from my half-dream, I could hear it more clearly, getting louder, getting braver, getting here.

Antony heard it too and without him even turning round I could see he'd raised an invisible eyebrow and that his jaw was dropping ever so slightly with surprise. It was as if his ears had pricked up like an anticipating, excited puppy.

Tikaro, who'd been perched in the front seat next to the driver and had been characteristically silent up until now, suddenly turned round. The side of his face was lit by the orange and red lights from the minibus dashboard and his expression was almost fearful.

"You guys hear that?" he drawled, his forehead furrowed.

We nodded together. Tikaro, we're ahead of you.

The sound of the Harley-Davidson grew closer and a single, round yellow light appeared behind us, shining out of the dark into the minibus and onto our excited faces. The soft orange glow of Antony's and Tikaro's' robes grew brighter, reflecting off the truck's windscreen as the light behind us grew larger and the sound grew stronger, until

eventually the machine it belonged to began to overtake us and the transport of the gods came into view.

Christopher was riding it, his hair streaming away from his face as he sat in his shorts, poised on the leather seat, arms outstretched to reach the wide handlebars and his thin bare legs straddling the teardrop tank. The Harley engine was singing a loud proud song of diesel and oil and motoring along with ease through the dark morning, reminding us that this was what it was born to do. To shake, to rattle and to roll. And I'm telling you, if chocolate could make music, this would be what it sounded like and Mozart would've written the tune.

Christopher stayed alongside us for some time, escorting us, while Tikaro, Antony and I stared out of the windows like three awestruck children. He looked so serene as he rode the enormous bike through the early morning darkness, his expression calmer than I'd ever seen him, calmer even than in the Sala when he was meditating. Finally, without changing a single facial muscle, an aloof Christopher nodded slightly at us, leaned the bike over to his right and then arced away from us, disappearing into the blackness and making his way up a different road. All we could see as our truck continued along the main road was the shaking beam of the Harley's headlight as it got smaller and smaller. Shaking, rattling and rolling into the dark beyond.

It made my day, my week and my month in fact, seeing Christopher out on the Harley. A Harley's meant to be ridden, not locked away in a garage and polished every Sunday. The image had felt like water in a desert.

And he hadn't been wearing a helmet. Imagine that? A Harley and no helmet.

Apart from the bike, travelling in the truck with Buddhist

monks wasn't a bowl of cherries. When I first got in, I sat myself next to Antony up front next to the driver but immediately the driver started protesting and pointed towards the back seat, a poky little area with hardly any room for my long, Farang knees and no chance of a decent view.

"I'm afraid, you can't sit on the same seat as a monk," explained Antony, waiting nervously for my reaction.

"But you're my brother!" I protested predictably, irritable in my early morning crabbiness.

"I know, Benedict, but I don't want to offend him. You might touch me or my robe by accident."

"And we couldn't have that, could we?" I said, sarcastically, folding my arms in a huff.

"Benedict, please. It's him I'm thinking of," Antony replied, gently glancing at the driver. "We can swap places though, if you want. You can sit next to the driver and I'll sit in the back with Tikaro so you can get a better view."

"Antony, it's four thirty in the morning. It's pitch black. There is no view."

We resolved it by Tikaro sitting in the front and Antony climbing in the back with me. The driver seemed happy with that because we weren't sitting on the same seat.

Poo Jom Petch was a day's drive away, which meant stopping at dawn in a nearby town so that the boys could go on alms round. There were other monks in the busy market as we pulled up and they nodded towards Antony and Tikaro as they got out of the truck, adjusted their robes and began Pindabah. They were given heaps of food. Chicken, curries, rice, banana cakes, soya drinks, oranges, biscuits and when they arrived back, I left them for an hour or so while they had their meal.

Later, we also stopped for a drink in a roadside restaurant.

The driver left us alone. He said less throughout the whole journey than Tikaro. I ordered a rare bottle of cold Heineken, and I bought some drinks for the boys. Tikaro wanted Coca-Cola, Antony orange Fanta and they each asked for a straw. I've never seen anything quite so incongruous as two bald headed Buddhist monks in sacred orange robes, sitting in a bar in the middle of remote Thailand, sucking pop 'til it slurped.

Back in the truck, heading for Poo Jom Petch, Antony and Tikaro, who had joined us in the back and sat next to Antony, offered me something to eat from the morning's Pindabah, explaining that none of what was offered was allowed to be stored for the next day.

"In case you become squirrels and start hoarding food in your rooms?" I asked.

"That's a heap closer to the truth than you think," said Tikaro seriously, peering over the top of his glasses. "It helps to be reminded everyday that our subsistence is dependent on the loving kindness of the lay people around us."

Lighten up, I thought disrespectfully. I was joking.

"But they're not doing it just out of kindness, are they," I protested. "They just want brownie points to help them get to the next stage of wherever it is this Buddhism stuff takes them."

"In a way, I guess, but it ain't quite as simple as you make it sound. An' anyways, at the end of the day we would starve without their generosity. An' I don't ever wanna take that for granted."

Point taken.

It's easy to criticise another culture and I didn't really understand the ins and outs of this faith, but I could already see that there was a difference between the fundamentals and

what was left when that got messed up and turned into an institution. Maybe I was too ready to mock this stuff when what was actually staring me in the face was a country of very kind, very generous, smiling people.

A few of the villagers greeted us when we arrived at Poo Jom Petch in the late afternoon. Tikaro disappeared somewhere quickly while I was offered a drink of rice milk. Antony then showed me to my room. My expectations when he had referred to it as a 'room' were my downfall. We were in one of the most remote parts of the country, high on a hill where a lonely goat herder was a far more realistic proposition than a double en-suite.

My room was about a hundred a fifty metres down an unmarked, unlit path over rocks, through a small stream and up through the undergrowth. It was a small wooden hut on stilts with a single mosquito net and a few candles. During the few minutes it took us to gather my bags and walk there, Thailand's night fell like a stone. Bam! And it was pitch black. There were no other huts anywhere near and the bathroom was somewhere down a different path which Antony indicated at with the beam of his Maglite. I had no intention of making a visit that night.

"Is this it?" I asked, foolishly, squinting up at the frail, wooden hut and just making out a set of slatted steps and a long, railed walk way running along the side.

"Yes," replied Antony.

Even though I couldn't really see his face through the darkness, I knew his worried eyes would have been flitting nervously from me to the hut to the floor to the trees and back to me.

"Where will you be sleeping?"

Not that I was worried or anything. It was just that we

were in the middle of God knows where and I was supposed to spend the night on my own with only the insects for company in this ramshackle wooden hut miles away from anywhere, where the local villagers knew the rich westerners had arrived, where anyone could wander along for a visit and I wouldn't have a clue where anyone else was until dawn.

"I'm not far away, Benedict, and you'll be fine here," he said, unconvincingly.

"Where will you be sleeping, Antony?" I repeated, raising my voice.

I could hear his eyes rolling in the dark and see his mole twitching. He sighed in anticipation of my response to what he was about to tell me.

"My kuti's the other side of the Sala," he said.

"That's miles!!" I shouted.

"Shh!!" And he added, quickly, "Don't worry. Nobody comes here, they leave the place well alone."

"This is ridiculous," I told him impatiently. "How do you know that, Antony?" I tried not to shout, not to show him that I was scared. "Antony, anyone could wander up here. They know we're here. They know I'm here, a big fat white western woman sleeping all on my own 'cos she's not allowed to go anywhere near you lot!"

"But they respect us," he insisted. "It's more than their life's worth to come here."

"You're too trusting," I told him, cynically. I didn't want Antony's faith in the good nature of the Thai villagers tested out on me.

"And you're not trusting enough," he said, a cold, fed-up edge to his voice. "They won't come here," he repeated. "They're far more scared than you. You'll be OK, I promise.

They never come here."

And his deliberate tone finally began to reassure me.

"You're sure?'

"Positive."

And, eventually, I could hear a smile in his voice.

My big brother's knowledge of and blind faith in this country were impressive. Perhaps it wouldn't be so bad sleeping out here after all. Perhaps I would be safe after all. Perhaps I'd enjoy being out in the open and at least I'd have something to write home about. It's not often you get to sleep in a wooden hut with no light, no lock and no loo. I was coming round to the idea until Antony casually added,

"Anyway, it's haunted."

"That's it!" I shouted, picking my bag up off the floor. "You just blew it. I'm not sleeping here!"

And I started to stomp off back towards the Sala but had to stop when I realised it was pitch black and that I couldn't see where I was going without Antony's torch.

"Benedict, they just think it's haunted. That's what stops them coming. Thai's hate the thought of ghosts."

"So do I!" I shouted.

"Shh!! Look, it's just rumours and even if there were ghosts you've got a feel of the place, haven't you?"

"What do you mean?"

"I mean follow your intuition, Benedict. Trust it. Does this feel like a place that's going to harm you?"

Antony calmed down, standing with his hands resting in front of him, the beam of the torch now shining up at our faces. He had absolute faith in what he was saying.

"Well, does it?" he asked me again.

I was speechless, open-mouthed. He was right. Poo Jom Petch felt sublime. It didn't feel scary at all. It felt like a place

that would look after me.

"If there are any ghosts, they're nice ghosts," he said comfortingly, clearly concerned for me now and no longer irritated by me. "It's only the dark that's frightening you, Benedict, and you can cure that."

"How can you cure darkness?" I retorted, stubborn to the end. "Even Buddhist monks can't make that disappear."

Antony just smiled at me, knowing I was being proud.

"You just light a candle," he said and he did just that, taking a candle from inside his magic robe, lighting it and placing it in the centre of a large canvas lamp which hung on a metal wire from underneath the balcony of the hut. It cast a pale yellow glow in a circle all around us, a pool of light to massage my fears. He'd obviously thought ahead.

"I'll hear if anything happens which it won't," he said. "And if it makes you feel any better, I've brought you a whistle. But Benedict you won't need it. I promise."

And like a soft focus, browny orange Santa Claus, he produced more gifts from the folds of his robe. A small black whistle and a spare torch.

Antony helped me to carry my stuff up the wooden steps to the first floor room where I found my bed already made, the mosquito net suspended over it hanging at four corners from the walls, and fresh flowers sitting in small glass jar. Tikaro, you're ahead of us, I thought. So that's where he'd disappeared to.

"I love having you here, Benedict," Antony said as he was about to leave. "This is a very special time for me."

A tiny bit of me nearly stepped forward to hug him but I wasn't sure whether I should and I couldn't face the thought of getting it wrong again. I watched from my balcony as Antony descended the steps, a thin, notably frail-looking

robed figure slipping out of the pool of light that came from my lantern and disappearing silently into the darkness down the path. I kept watching as the beam from his Maglite slowly swung in time to the rhythm of his steps, silently dancing in the dark until finally it was gone.

I was alone in the jungle. In the night. In silence.

I'd received two letters this week so I reread them, huddled on the floor under my mosquito net. I needed the distraction. One letter was from Michaela and it filled me in on all that had been going on since I left. Stella had got a new boyfriend, which seemed to have caused considerable excitement. The weather in England had finally started to turn cold after a mild October. There was to be a new landlord at the pub. Michaela had seen Captain Archie who had said everything was all right at the house and Molly The Cat was fine. Captain Archie had informed her in graphic detail of exactly what time he went round in the morning and evening to carry out his daily assignments and what he had accomplished. She said she'd also bumped into Joe in the pub and he'd grunted that he was missing me, thought of me often and that everyone at the Boatyard hoped I was having a good time.

What Joe'd actually said was, "How's t'daft bugger doing, then?" But Michaela had translated for me.

After reading my letters, I felt very homesick and sad so I dug my iPod out, found "Where is the Love" by the Black Eyed Peas followed by the dance version of Guns 'n' Roses' "Sweet Child of Mine" and blasted away my sadness. Exhausted, I fell asleep.

In the morning, as I was walking from my kuti to the small Sala where the meal would be served, I again caught a glimpse of my brother's life without him being aware, like

the time I'd seen him in Ubon, disappearing into a building with the Abbot. This time he was stood at the far side of the Sala building, underneath the wooden pillars which held the structure in place and he was with Tikaro. They were arguing, exchanging hushed, shouted words. It was a bit like watching a foreign film with the sound turned down, only someone had forgotten to show the subtitles. They weren't very animated in the argument. There were no waving arms like Amaro, no clenched fists or exchange of blows. They were both far more restrained than that, keeping their arms firmly under wraps inside their robes.

It was the colour of Tikaro's face that gave things away. He was bright red from the top of his bald head to the top of his chest, his redness vanishing in a sweeping line around his neck, a feint vein pulsing at the side of his temple. Occasionally, as he turned his head, the sun glanced off his spectacles and for a split second he became a mad vision of flashing orange, red and yellow. The poor guy was clearly upset about something, something major.

Antony on the other hand hadn't coloured up. Instead, he was pacing, precisely and impatiently, creating a track in the dust where he walked to and fro in a neat, twelve-foot line, listening to Tikaro, flicking his head up every few steps to look at him then looking back down at the floor as if he didn't really want to hear what he said. I couldn't hear what they were discussing and only caught my brother's words once.

"But you know why I haven't said anything," he insisted with a tone of irritation. And the quiet argument continued. It shocked me seeing them like that. Monks don't argue, I thought. They're not supposed to, and I felt a pang of guilt for having caught them at something I thought they weren't

supposed to be doing. And it upset me.

I crept quietly around the back of the Sala towards the kitchen so that Tikaro and Antony didn't see me but I wasn't sure whether it was for my sake or theirs that I didn't want them to know I'd seen them.

When I arrived at the kitchen, a few yards away from the Sala, there were three women from the village in there already, cooking the morning meal. I helped them as best I could until it was time to eat.

Tikaro and Antony had now entered the Sala and sat down. No sign of anything that had been going on earlier. They were offered their meal first and I joined them a couple of hours later, after I'd eaten with the villagers and helped to wash and clear up the kitchen.

"How goes it Tikaro?" I asked.

Tikaro just looked at me thoughtfully, his gaze lost in the space between us. He didn't reply but after a few silent moments he focused on me again, caught my eye and just smiled and nodded. He then tugged at his robe, pulling the bit that hangs down behind the arm up over his shoulder, and left us to go and sort out his bowl. Antony and I watched him and we caught each other's eye. My brother's eyes told me, "Best leave him be for a while."

"Antony," I asked later when we were out walking. "Why did you become a monk?"

They were taking me to see Tikaro's kuti on the edge of the cliff nearby. It was hotter here than down in Chatanan and there was no shelter from the heat. The monsoon rain had long since vanished into the rocks and the heat bounced off the surface of the dry river beds we were walking on, scorching the soles of our sandals.

Tikaro was up ahead and I was alone with Antony.

He didn't reply straight away and we kept on walking, his face serious and his soft smile barely perceptible. He'd never told me why he'd become a monk. I got letters from him telling me what he was up to, where he was, what it was like. But he'd never explained why, never explained exactly what made him kiss goodbye to his old life, want to wear a funny dress and live in the middle of a wood on the other side of the world.

Finally, after a few glances in my direction as if he was checking whether or not my question was sincere, he said,

"It just made sense."

I jumped straight back in.

"What did?"

Again there were more pauses from Antony and more deliberations. We scrunched through the dry river bed, twigs and lifeless leaves cracking under our feet and filling the spaces of our conversation with brittle, unhelpful punctuation. Short on gestures, I think Antony was searching to find the right words. There were no other sounds and but for the crunching of dead leaves I'm sure you would have heard our pulses beating.

"I've never spoken about this before," he said warily. "It's like I know in my heart why I became a monk but I've never had to explain it to anyone. Everyone here knows without needing to explain."

"Like riding a motorbike," I said.

He looked at me, clearly not understanding what I meant.

"If someone has to ask you why you ride a motorbike," I reminded him, "then they'll never understand the answer."

He smiled.

"A bit like that I suppose," he said.

"So try me Antony. I just want to understand what made

you become a Buddhist monk."

Antony just gave me the same, changeless expression, and I felt like he was sussing me out, assessing whether I was worthy of an explanation, whether I was intelligent enough to understand. My patience snapped far too soon.

"For God's sake! Why did it just make sense?"

"And why are you always angry with me?" he asked, pained, raising his voice. A rare show of emotion making his features tremble and his face colour up in a way I'd never seen. It shocked me. I hadn't ever realised that my anger was so near the surface. I always thought it was buried deep inside, away from reality. I never for the life of me thought that it might upset him. I felt humbled and eventually managed to explain.

"Antony, I just want to understand. You never came back. You said you would but you didn't. You never came back and I simply want to know what it was that kept you here. Is that so strange? I've come half way round the world. The least you can do is try and explain. Please?"

Finally, realising I was getting upset, my brother decided to spill the beans and decided that maybe his kid sister just might have the sensitivity to understand after all.

"I suppose before I came to Thailand nothing really made sense."

"So you ran away?"

"No," he said, taking a deep breath. "It wasn't running away."

He was struggling to find a way of explaining, his head bowed, so I bit my tongue and gave him time to say what he wanted to say.

"Yes, I needed to get away. After Dad died, I couldn't make sense of anything and away was as good a place to be as

anywhere. I didn't want a life that just gave me a good job, a wife, kids, a mortgage. I wanted a life that could also explain to me why Dad died. Why Mum died. Why one day I'll die too."

He spoke slowly, careful about the way he explained things, emotion creeping in. He clearly meant every word as he picked his head up and looked directly at me.

"Is this making sense?" he asked and I could see that he really was concerned that I understood him.

I nodded. There was no need for words from me. I'd only say something crass that I didn't really mean. I won't pretend it was easy listening to him. It was actually very hard because I knew that while he was living out all that he was describing, I'd been at home on my own, agonising about when he, the only member of my family left alive, was coming back. Listening to him talk about that time, with no reference to how I might have felt, was painful. I still wanted to scream at him. Wanted to hit him. Wanted to stop the pain from disappearing into my stomach and giving me cramps. But I was good. I clenched my jaw and kept listening.

"I was heading for Ko Tao, a tiny island off the coast. On the way, I stumbled across a temple in Ko Pha Ngan, and something just made sense," he continued, now more confident and with relief in his voice.

"I'd visited loads of temples in Thailand. In Bangkok, in Krabi, in Chang Mai. You've seen what it's like here. They're everywhere. Everywhere you go in this country there are amazing temples that are full of people my age."

This was the first time I'd seen Antony so animated since I arrived. This time his arms had appeared from under his robe and he was using his hands to emphasise what he felt.

"There was something in those temples that worked for them and I wanted to learn what it was. So I began reading.

I never expected to find the temple on Ko Pha Ngan. I'd hooked up with some other travellers and we island hopped from Ko Samui. One morning I took a moped up the mountain and found the temple. It was pouring with rain all the way up but as soon as I got there the clouds lifted and the sun shone on me and on the face of a golden Buddha. It was the first thing I saw when I got to the top of the mountain and it looked at me, right at me."

Antony was fighting back tears now as he spoke, breathing hard, almost spitting out the last few words.

"I just fell to my knees. I knew I'd come home."

Then after a few calming, deep breaths he continued. "There was a monk watching me, Ajahn Bramadho. He invited me to stay."

I felt Antony glance at me, checking my reaction as he described the moment he decided not to come home. Finally, in an effort to lighten the mood, he said, "I never did make it to Ko Tao. After spending a few months with Bramadho I knew that I'd ordain. Something inside me shifted and I found a way of looking at life that finally made sense to me. It didn't take away all the pain, but it gave meaning where before there'd been none. Absolutely none."

I was silent, unable to find an appropriate response. I'd never imagined something so emotional had happened to Antony. I thought he'd just bummed around Thailand for a while, eventually found a cushy number in a cosy monastery and had got so used to it that he'd stayed. But Antony had described a brother I hadn't yet met, one who'd taken charge and one to whom I was slowly being introduced, here, in Thailand.

"So you see, Benedict, it's not really like riding a motorbike."

"No," I said. "Do you miss home ever?"

"Sometimes."

And what about me? I wondered. Do you miss me?

"I miss my bike like crazy."

Bastard. And I kicked a stone that was in my path and watched as it careered across the rocks and bounced off the boulders up ahead.

"But not as much as I miss you," he said gently and knowingly. On hearing that, my tears arrived too.

Tikaro was waiting for us as we approached the scraggy little bamboo kuti that sat at the top of the plain. The sun was behind him as we approached and, silhouetted in his robe with his arms tucked inside, he looked like an Oscar statue sitting on a giant mantelpiece.

It wasn't until we reached the kuti that I could appreciate exactly where we were. About twelve feet in front of us was the cliff, a hundred feet high and looking out onto the widest, most breathtaking view I'd yet seen – the magnificent Mekong River, winding its mighty way round the eastern edge of Thailand, cutting through the plain far below us and nestling up to Laos which lay on its other side. From up here it looked like a deceptively mild river but from the way it had sliced through the rocks that edged its banks and the way in which there was no traffic on this river, you could tell that it was in charge. The Mekong ruled the countryside for hundreds of miles and it cared for nothing except its own endless flow and its own continual renewal.

I must have stared at the view for nearly half an hour while Antony helped Tikaro mend a hole in the roof of his kuti.

I'm typing this up as I'm sitting on the balcony of my kuti. It's dark and I've only got the light of the battery powered laptop screen, the candle lamp and my torch to

write by. I know what Antony said about friendly ghosts but it's still a bit spooky here. It's the fact that I feel so exposed, like everyone can see me but I can't see them. I do like it though. It is so peaceful and it's as if this place feeds you by just being here.

The moon's out and the stars seem so close. Whenever I look at the stars I always think of home. I know that at some time soon, in a few hours' time, there'll be a similar view above York. Captain Archie will be walking his spaniel and there'll be Joe on his boat and they'll be looking up and seeing what I'm seeing. It's really comforting and makes me feel like the world is not so big after all.

I've just come in off the balcony and locked the door because I heard footsteps and it's spooked me. Someone's trampling through the undergrowth. I can't see a bloody thing. He's got a dog. I can hear it panting.

I've got Uncle Erno's pen-knife out now and if I die this will be my final record of what happened, so listen up. I can hear them only a few yards away. Antony! You swore no one would come up here!

Shit. That was a gunshot. He's shot the dog!! He's shot the damn bloody dog!! Antony, where the hell are you?

Now he's digging, I can hear him digging. He's burying the dog, the cold-hearted bastard. Antony, you promised no one would come. You promised. You always make promises that you never keep. Where the hell are you.

Oh shit, what's that now?

 November,
Wat Pah Chatanan,

'That' was Antony, carrying two cloth lanterns which were

dangling in the distance like the eyes of giant rabbit in the headlights.

"I heard the gunshot. I thought you might be a bit worried," was the first thing he said, his face eerily illuminated from underneath by the lanterns.

Antony climbed the stairs and stood on the balcony. The digging had stopped and the man with the gun hadn't appeared.

"He's shot the dog, Antony," I whispered. "He's shot the damn dog."

"He didn't shoot the dog," Antony calmly replied.

"He shot the dog!!" I repeated, pointing to the spot where the noise had come from, my heart beating loudly. "He shot the dog and then he dug a grave and he buried it! I heard it. I'm telling you he shot the goddamn dog!"

"Benedict, calm down," he said gently. "He hasn't shot the dog. He was hunting. That's all. I should have mentioned it. They find an animal hole and send the dog in. He'll have been digging out the hole where the dog went and he'll have shot whatever animal came out. He hasn't shot the dog."

It took a while before I believed Antony and for the picture to fit as I played it out in my mind.

"You sure?" I asked grumpily.

"I'm sure. He was hunting and he's gone now."

"Thought you said they never came up here. Thought you said they were afraid of the ghosts."

"Well he probably won't ever come back now. He probably thought you were a ghost."

"I was scared!"

"I know and I'm sorry. I should have warned you. Do you want to sleep in the Sala? I'll help you move your stuff."

"No, I'm all right."

And I was. Finally. Poo Jom Petch was special. It will always be special in my memory because I had time to spend with Antony. For the first time in four years, I got to know him. For the first time in four years I could share his life with him. I could joke with him, go for walks with him, eat with him and listen to the tales he had to tell me over candlelit times in the Sala. And I could tell him about the life I'd built up for myself in York. I told him about my life on the river and how the gentle rhythm of the water had put a rhythm back into my life after all the hard times of the last few years. I told him how much I loved the river and how, when I was away from it for too long, life was not so easy to navigate. Without the river, too many eddies found me, too many rocks got in my way. Without the constant flow of the river to renew me, life made less sense.

After listening, Antony said he'd take me on a river trip up the Mekong and I cried, feeling that finally my brother had come home to me.

We climbed the plain early one morning after the meal and descended the cliff down a thirty minute, near vertical walk to the edge of the Mekong. I'd never been near such a vast, powerful piece of water. As it made its way from Tibet and China, through the distant hills near Burma, through Cambodia and down to the Mekong Delta flowing out into the South China Sea, it made my river at home look like a trickle.

The boat we hired, skippered by a man from the village, was a tiny, wooden, handbuilt one with an engine hanging over the back built from a modified aeroplane propeller.

"They're left over from the Vietnam war," explained Antony.

Once in the boat and away from the shore, the silence on the river was very strong, making its presence felt on my shoulders as if loading me with the weight of the entire landscape as far as we could see. I felt like a privileged soul being given a glimpse of an untouched world that had kindly allowed me to visit for a short while.

We travelled low in the water, gliding magically across the wide, strong flowing current. We were so close to the river that I could trail my hand over the edge as we moved past sunken islands, a straggle of small trees peeping out of the water. Antony sat in front of me, his back towards me, his robes bright orange in the sunlight and his head and the tips of his ears catching the sun.

In silence for most of the trip, we just drank in the view.

It moved me. It was a journey through a timeless place. The river at home puts sense into my everyday life, keeping me calm, keeping things in place but the Mekong helped me to make sense of me, of my place in time and the tiny role I play in the great big scheme of this universe.

Speaking of rivers, I must pin Antony down about going to the River Kwai to spread Uncle Erno's ashes. I'm looking forward to planning it with him. It'll be difficult but special and I bet that being a monk he'll have some ideas about how we go about it. I'm not looking forward to it but carrying out Uncle Erno's wishes with Antony will make it OK. Not sure I'd manage it on my own and it's beginning to hang over me a bit now. I want to get it over.

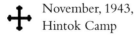 November, 1943,
Hintok Camp

We moved camp and Arthur died. He didn't survive the

journey though we tried to save him. My wish for him to be taken early was not granted. He died painfully, as expected and as have many. I am empty. I would like to cry and to feel what it is I should feel at the loss of my dear friend but I am empty.

I must bury him. I must dig a grave for Arthur. I cannot let him be thrown on the pyre with the heaps of other bodies. Death has lost its dignity for the men working in the cremation party. They have become callous and mechanical. So many dead, so many young bodies thrown away. The men tell stories of corpses acting like chimneys in the fire, smoke funnelling up through rib cages still covered in flesh, flames filtering up through eye sockets. They roast wild sweet potatoes in the embers, use a spare bone to retrieve them and toss back any nuisance toe or finger that mistakenly finds its way into their meal.

I will bury Arthur. I will give him dignity, if it's the last thing I do.

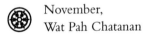

November,
Wat Pah Chatanan

I used to think Chatanan was quiet but having spent time at the Poo Jom Petch retreat, it feels like a busy train station in comparison. We're back at Chatanan now. Back to the old routine of early morning greetings from Gecko, early morning meals and teatime meetings in the guest villa with the boys. And today we had someone new for tea too. She's a Buddhist nun. Called Susan. And at first she scared the living daylights out of me.

Susan, an Austrian, is the only other western woman who has visited the monastery since I've been here. Her bald, stark

appearance, married with her brusque, staccato accent, was very intimidating. Women shave their heads and eyebrows too when they become a nun and the result can look fierce. I wasn't sure I wanted to get to know her. She looked so scary. She arrived this afternoon with Amaro, Tikaro and Antony, who for once hadn't done a disappearing act into town with the Abbot.

"I will sit here, ya?" Susan announced with a nod. "I think this would be best, ya?"

She made me nervous. Antony hadn't warned me he'd invited her and I immediately switched into being extremely polite and very English and began worrying if the house was clean enough for this visitor who kept ordering me about.

"It is very good you invite me for this tea with you," she told me with a nod, scuttling determinedly across the tiled floor of the guest villa, swishing her white robes out of the way very brusquely and perching herself very precisely in one of the wooden chairs by the coffee table in the middle of the room. Knees together, shoulders back, bolt upright.

"It is very good for me to have another western woman to speak English with, even though, of course, English is not my first language. Still it is less difficult than to speak Thai."

So glad to be of use.

"You speak Thai well?" I asked, not sure if I was meant to ask questions.

"Of course. Why not? I have lived here for two years."

How very stupid of me not to know that.

Then, she was silent. I waited for her to elaborate, expecting more after her rat-a-tat-tat entrance, but no, she just sat there, still, like the others who had now joined her. No one said anything for a very long time and I fell into a

panic about being a useless host and was sure that people weren't enjoying themselves. Should I make conversation? What should I say?

I heard Gecko scamper up the mosquito screen and it made me smile. That's right, mate. Run away.

"Would you like some tea?" I asked them eventually, not having a clue what I'd do if they said no.

"I'll give you a hand," offered Amaro, smiling and he got up and followed me to the kitchen. It was so good to see him again.

"You're so English, you little Pommie," he teased me once we'd escaped and I leant against the kitchen wall, breathing a sigh of relief at having got out of the painfully silent living room.

"Is it me, Amaro, or is all this weird?"

"It's just different," he said, his tone affectionate and reassuring. "Don't worry about the social chit-chat bit, it doesn't work like that here. If someone's not got anything to say, then silence is very appropriate. There's no need for embarrassment. We're so used to filling the gaps with fluff, it just takes a little time to get used to."

"Amaro, I'm not sure I want to get used to it." I only realised the deep truth of what I'd said as the words left my mouth.

Amaro, God bless him, stayed silent. When we returned with the flasks of tea and some sweets on a tray, Susan was deep in conversation with Antony and Tikaro. Susan was visiting from nearby monastery, Wat Nong Pah Pong, where there was a big community of Thai nuns. Unlike the monks, they all wore white robes and as far as I could see, they definitely got the raw end of the deal because, from what I was hearing from Susan, they also tended to do a lot of hard

grafting. They did the cooking for the whole monastery, chopped wood and charcoal for the fires and generally kept house and home together. Keeping that white robe clean must have been a nightmare.

"Susan has asked if you'd like to go with her to visit Wat Nong Pah Pong," Antony informed me. "It's where I was ordained and you'd get a chance to see a proper Thai nun's community. It'll be a good experience for you."

Antony had slipped into his let's-educate-my-younger-sister-in-the-ways-of-Thailand-and-improve-her-cultural-a wareness role and I had to stop my knee-jerk reaction of telling him to piss off. I was convinced he was trying to convert me.

"You can stay as long as you like," added Susan, smiling.

"Stay? You mean overnight?"

They all laughed.

"It's eight kilometres away, over the fields, and no buses," explained my brother. "If you go, you'll have to stay at least one night."

Susan had lived for three months at Wat Nong Pah Pong where the nun's community was sixty women strong, all Thai except for her. The monastery had been run by the top man, the Ajahn Chan, until he died and as far as this particular tradition of Buddhism went, it was the bee's knees. A chance to visit and to stay was rare indeed for a western woman.

"You come for tea at my kuti tomorrow," ordered Susan, "and we can talk. Thank you and now I must go. I wish to hear the Ajahn speak this evening."

Abruptly she came, abruptly she left.

Mae Li hovered in the dust at a distance. She smiled beamingly at me and bowed to Susan as she passed. And then Mae Li shuffled in her Wellington boots over to the outside

closet to collect some water.

Tikaro had been quiet the last few days, ever since we'd returned from Poo Jom Petch. Of late he'd begun to get quite animated during our afternoon tea conversations but now he chose to be present in person only, sitting patiently, sucking his teeth every once in a while and polishing his glasses. Occasionally he chipped in but it was usually only to make a sarcastic dig at the faith which his robe told everyone he belonged to. Something was bugging him but he chose not to share it with us.

Antony told me that the other evening, after he and Tikaro left the guest villa, they had sat in the dark on the footpath between here and the monastery, talking until two in the morning. He didn't elaborate on exactly what they were talking about but clearly, since they had to get up an hour or so later, it must have been something important. Was it something to do with the row I'd witnessed between them at Poo Jom Petch, I wondered. Or was something else bugging him as well.

Darkness had fallen by the time Susan, Tikaro, Amaro and Antony had all left so I sat alone in my palace, the warm breeze gently whispering through the mosquito screens, the silhouette of Mae Li sat by a glowing fire outside her hut and Gecko keeping me company. War and Peace was getting surprisingly gripping.

I was becoming increasingly impatient about going to the River Kwai and sensed that Antony was avoiding it for some reason. But that was why I'd come to Thailand in the first place. If it hadn't been for Uncle Erno, I wouldn't be here, wouldn't have got to spend time with my brother and to get to know him again, even if it was in this weird and wonderful place.

But, while we remained without any fixed plans to leave Chatanan, Uncle Erno rested on the table next to the shrine upstairs, waiting.

 November,
The Nun's Community,
Wat Nong Pah Pong

This morning Susan and I left Chatanan early to travel, as planned, to Wat Nong Pah Pong to help prepare the meal. A meal prepared every day for over a hundred people. I can't believe the regime here. I thought I'd got used to all this Buddhism stuff but now, something new and unsettling was being thrown at me. The women do all the fetching and carrying for this monastery and then they aren't even invited to the party. The kitchen shutters are closed, locking the women inside when the monks line up to collect their food so that the men don't lay their eyes on the women. The nuns then have to stay in the kitchen while they listen to the main ceremonies going on in the Sala through a loud speaker system.

"What kind of woman could carry on like this and keep her self-respect?" I threw at Susan, insultingly and ignorantly, when we were alone.

"You look at it only as western woman," she retorted. "For these nuns it is very different. For them, to serve gains merit and that helps them on their path. It is not subservience."

"It's crap," I said, walking so fast that Susan had to nearly run to keep up. "You told me you'd been to Antony's ordination here. You didn't say you had to listen to it through loud speakers because they wouldn't let you in!"

I was flailing my arms about in disgust so much I think I nearly swiped her on the face by accident. I saw her duck out of the corner of my eye.

I carried on, regardless. "What's it all about? Are we supposed to accept that men are higher spiritual beings than us? That we can't make the grade and we should be happy cleaning up after them because that's as near as we'll get to the real thing? Is that it?"

"I know to you it must seem very, what is the word?"

"Crap?" I offered, slightly more calmly, but not much. I knew I had to stop from shouting too loudly. Nobody shouts in the Thailand I was visiting, nobody except big, white, fat, female Farangs.

"No," replied Susan. "I mean patriarchal. At this moment in their cultural history, this is how it is for them. It is a good way to live."

"Susan, it is pre-historic shit! I can't believe you want to live here. How do you manage it?"

She paused. I know she'd been really enjoying having a lively chat with me and a naughty grin began to appear beneath the stern, formal surface.

"I have a doctorate in anthropology," she explained. "It helps."

We both relaxed and laughed.

"You talk like an anthropologist," I teased her. "A German one."

But at that, she stopped laughing.

"I am Austrian," she corrected me sternly, and for a few moments the air between us was a little chillier than it had just been. Then, having forgiven me my blunder, she continued.

"Really, this is a good place and the women like to serve.

For them it is like to meditate, a tool to help gain deeper understanding, to help ease inner suffering. It is only because to you it seems subservient that it upsets you."

She pointed over to two nuns who were passing us, shyly dipping their heads.

"Look," she said, "They are not upset."

She was right. They looked content. Not happy in a sense that I knew but definitely content and anyway, what did I know? Maybe their type of happiness was longer lasting than mine.

Then Susan looked at me wryly and, in her clipped, sucking and by now endearing, Austrian accent, she added,

"Then again, it could all be crap."

 November,
Wat Pah Chatanan

Back at Chatanan today, having escaped from the Nun's Community with the aid of a lift from one of the lay people, I took the path that led to the Outside Sala, heading away from the main monastery and out to the edge of the trees. As I approached the gap in the forest where the Outside Sala sits, I saw a monk standing in the centre of the polished wooden floor. He had his back to me and was wearing a simple robe, like the one Amaro had on the first time I met him. It left his arms and one shoulder free.

The monk faced the statue of Buddha, the sharp morning sun filtered by the trees falling on the floor behind him and the breeze playing quietly with the leaves as if singing. He slowly began to lift his arm in a very gentle, calm sweeping circle, his hand following the arm, pulled upwards wrist first, fingertips trailing in the air. He stretched the limb as far as he

could from his body and then allowed the other arm to be lifted in the same slow, mesmerising arc. Once his hands were resting high above his head he locked his elbows, cocked his wrists and began to lower his arms simultaneously, his palms facing out to the side, his arms straight and powerful. He turned his head to the side, away from me, in a slow, deliberate movement and lifted one leg to start a sequence of movements which carried him silently on a self-contained, physical and spiritual journey. The sequence lasted for about twenty minutes and I watched this vision of golden brown as he danced with his own energy, surrounded by light and the singing breeze.

He finished by returning to the original arm sequence, his hands high in the air until he gracefully drew them to him and knelt down to bow three times towards Buddha.

When he stood and turned to leave the Sala, I saw the monk's face. It was Antony and I hadn't recognised him. He didn't see me as I rested in the trees, covering my presence with the branches.

It was Antony I saw but it wasn't my brother. This wasn't my teenage biking hero whose dream of heaven had been a loud, greasy Harley-Davidson roaring across the Golden Gate Bridge. This wasn't my big brother who swatted scary wasps that terrorised his little sister and who punched the school bully who'd tried to tease her. This wasn't Antony. This was a monk. This was Thanavaro.

"Gets to you don't it?" a soft voice said, making me jump.

It was Amaro. He'd crept up behind without me hearing, on his way to ring the eight o'clock bell over at the tower next to the Sala. My brother had gone and Amaro thought I'd just been sitting admiring the view and I didn't realise, until he pointed it out, that I was crying.

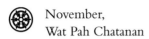 November,
Wat Pah Chatanan

I killed Gecko this morning. My poor little, adorable Gecko.
I can't believe what I've done.

He'd been living in my bathroom where it was warm and
wet, and every evening when I came home he'd be there to
croak hello, and every morning he'd scurry out from behind
the pipes or wherever he's been resting to greet me. I didn't
feel alone in the villa because I had Gecko. He listened
attentively as I brushed my teeth or chatted to him. He'd stay
clung to the wall as I asked his opinion about things and his
silent wisdom helped me in a strange and foreign land. It was
only once I'd finished talking and the sound of my own
voice trailed away, that Gecko would flinch and choose to
wander further up the wall or shoot off down to the tiled
floor below.

This morning I didn't see him in the bathroom. He didn't
appear from his overnight hiding place to greet me and I'd
assumed he'd simply slept in or was in a grump, so I trundled
off to the main Sala, half awake.

He wasn't there when I returned this evening and I began
to be concerned. I began looking for him. It wasn't like him
not to be around.

I checked the bathroom again, this time turning on the
overhead light and as the door swung open, I found him.
He'd taken to resting in the door well, clinging to the inside
of the frame where the hinges open and close. As I'd
absentmindedly closed the door, I'd killed him. He was still
clinging there, his body rigid and intact. Shock hit me as I
took in what I'd done.

I projected all my feelings onto Gecko. I was alone. I was

lonely. I'd had enough. I hadn't realised how much I'd been missing home. What the hell was I doing here anyway? Why was I in the middle of the jungle in Thailand staying in bloody wooden huts with no one to hug me when I could be at home with friends, by the river with a drink in my hand? I could feel the heat in my face rising and my head began to pound with a million hand drums beating a heavy, angry bass against my temples.

My tears stung as I collapsed onto the bed. There was no one here to listen to me, no-one I could turn to for emotional support, no one who really understood how difficult all this was for me.

At that moment, I hated these monks and this monastery with its stupid bloody rules and its stupid routines and those stupid bloody robes! I hated pretending to be calm when actually I was feeling like I'd just swallowed rocket fuel. I hated being rational. I hated not being allowed to do things just because I was a woman. I hated having to offer things formally, why couldn't they just bloody take it? I hated not having a TV. I hated not being able to phone anyone, not being able to run downstairs to see if any mail had come for me, not being able to call out to Molly The Cat. I hated being here in this villa on my own when my brother was just around the corner and couldn't even come and visit me without a bloody chaperone.

But mostly, I hated remembering something Amaro had told me the other day. He'd told me that one of the most difficult things for a human being to do is to return love for hate and I began to feel very small. Very small indeed.

When I looked up, I saw that the bedclothes were in a complete mess. I was sweating and still angry. I'd killed Gecko.

My iPod was by my bed, so I picked it up and disappeared into an hour of heavy duty Nirvana.

Load up on guns and bring your friends.

 November,
New Samui Guest House, Bangkok

I can't believe all that's happened since last I wrote. I don't know what Uncle Erno had in mind when he asked me to come here but as far as I'm concerned, this trip has descended into hell.

I must have cried for another hour the night I killed Gecko before finally falling asleep and I didn't wake until twelve hours later, missing the morning meal and sleeping right through until after nine o'clock. I felt drugged on sleep as I heard the clunk of the gate and saw Thanavaro and Amaro through the mosquito screens, walking up the footpath, their robes translucent in the sunshine.

"Morning," beamed Thanavaro. "I wanted to check you were OK. You weren't at the meal."

"I'm fine," I lied. Why do we say that? Too right I'm 'fine' – the fucked up, insecure, neurotic and emotional kind of fine. "I'll make a drink," I said coldly.

"No worries," said Amaro, as he entered the house. "I'll do that. You two sit down."

He made it sound like he'd been planning what to say.

"You don't look fine," my brother told me as I slumped into a chair and he arranged himself on the bench opposite. "What's the matter?"

His faced reflected his concern but irritated by questions, I replied, "I'm just tired, Antony. I had a bad night and this place is getting to me. I needed to lie in and catch up on

some sleep."

And then, just for a dig, I added crossly, "It hasn't been easy adjusting to all this, you know. I don't even know what to call you anymore!"

"I know," he said affectionately. "And I think you've adapted really well."

He paused, nervously looking at the floor and then said, "Benedict, I really appreciate you coming. It's meant a great deal to me, more than you can imagine."

I did know it meant a lot to him and I did know that he struggled to convey it but I wasn't in the mood for making things easy for him so I made no response.

Despite the gentleness in his words, I could feel an unspoken tension in Antony.

"Look," said Amaro, appearing from the kitchen with forced melodrama, "I've brought some of the finest chocolate in the world with me, shipped in all the way from Switzerland by kind donation of one of the novices' parents no less."

But my enthusiasm that morning wasn't easy to find and I didn't reply. I was tiring of all this. I was touched at the thoughtfulness of Amaro's innocent gift but, sensing something might be going on that I wasn't quite party to, I felt a tear coming but managed to keep it in check. I played along with the cheerful charade and went to root out some caramel rice sweets I'd bought in the village the other day to go with the strong tea Amaro had made. I needed a sugar boost.

When I returned, Amaro had skipped off with his drink and was sitting alone in the garden, his back facing the house. Antony looked very serious and things suddenly felt very ominous.

"I need to talk to you alone," said Thanavaro, and I could feel the air grow heavy.

He glanced over at his friend through the mosquito screen. "Amaro can act as chaperone from outside."

I slurped some more sweetened tea. What was it now? What rule have I broken? Who have I offended now?

"Uncle Erno asked you to scatter his ashes, right?" Antony said.

I nodded, tentatively.

"He asked you and that's why you came to Thailand, and why you're going to the River Kwai," he continued.

Again I nodded, and added clearly, "And to find you, so we can scatter the ashes together."

And at that, my brother's face fell.

I could sense what was coming but I didn't want to hear it and all the sugar in the world couldn't protect me from the final, inevitable body blow that was to send me reeling.

"I can't handle this on my own, Antony," I began to insist. "The whole idea of me coming all this way was so that you'd come with me. We arranged it."

Anxiety was rising in my chest.

"You know this country," I continued. "I'm a stranger here. You know what to do."

Antony remained sitting in silence, his head down.

"I can't do this on my own, Antony. You're my family. Don't do this, Antony!"

Don't say what I know you are about to say.

"I can't come with you," Antony said.

Silence hung for a few moments while I let the information register.

"Can't or won't?" I asked, unable to go near the pain.

"Can't," he replied.

I didn't believe him. He was leaving me on my own. Again. Just like he always did. Just like every member of my family always did.

Thanavaro's voice broke into my void.

"Benedict,"

"I killed Gecko yesterday."

"Pardon?" he said, caught off guard.

"I killed Gecko. I squashed his head against the door frame and he's still stuck there, hanging."

My brother looked bewildered, shuffling uneasily in his robe. Amaro was still waiting outside.

"I did it, you see," I explained. "I killed him."

"Benedict,"

"Go away, Antony."

"I can't come with you because there's somewhere I need to go," he said beseeching me, but I didn't want to hear.

"Just go."

"It's important, Benedict!" It was his turn to plead now. "I wouldn't just leave you."

"But you already have, Antony." The words punched themselves out of my mouth. "Don't you see? All of you have. You, Mum, Dad, Uncle Erno. All of you have left me!"

"I can't come," Antony still insisted, a thin, forlorn figure and I remember making a mental note that he'd lost even more weight. "I want to," he said. "But I can't."

I wasn't listening.

"Go, Antony," I said.

He looked at me.

"Go. Don't drag it out. Go wherever it is you have to go but leave now."

Antony's head dropped into his hands and he started to sob.

Out of the corner of my eye, I noticed Amaro, listening to every word. He still faced away from the house, his knees pulled up to his chest, his big, brave shoulders hunched over and his face in his hands. I remember now, although at the time it didn't register, that Amaro too was crying.

I got up, unable to handle the situation and went upstairs, back to my darkened room, back to abandoned, dead hanging Gecko and back to bed. As I locked the bedroom door, I shut the world out and blasted my eardrums to pieces.

Arctic Monkeys screaming at me.

Suede. Trash.

Garbage. Stupid, stupid girl.

Don't believe in fear, don't believe in faith.

Don't believe in fucking anything. Fuck off. Fuck off. Fuck off.

I wouldn't let Antony in when he knocked on the door. I stayed in my room for hours, refusing to hear him. Demons took me over that night but I fought them away with loud, desperate bursts of the loudest, most desperate music my iPod possessed. I packed my bags in a frenzy of anger, alone after they had left. I didn't say goodbye to them and I left Chatanan early the next morning to catch the bus to Ubon. I was numb. Mae Li helped me carry my bags and she didn't say a word as we crept away from the monastery. I gave her an old white cotton T-shirt that she could wear and she hugged it to her chest but without any of her usual glee, only a sad, concerned furrow on her once wrinkly twinkly brow.

"You have good heart," she finally said as the bus came into view. "You come back Chatanan."

I tried to smile back. I doubt it Mae Li. I doubt it.

And I climbed aboard.

As the rackety old bus pulled away and with dear old Uncle Erno sitting on the bench beside me, I looked back and watched Mae Li and Chatanan slowly disappear behind a cloud of early morning South-East Asian dust. I didn't cry. I was fine.

I arrived at the train station in Ubon around six, in time to see the sun rise while the almost full moon still hung brightly above the roof. I was expecting it to be fairly quiet at that time in the morning but, no, it was heaving. People were milling about, buying tickets, buying breakfast at one of the many food stalls that were set up by the tracks or sitting, waiting for the train.

My vague plan was to head for Bangkok and then work out how to get to the River Kwai in a couple of days. So much of me wanted to go straight to the airport to catch the next flight home but the sight of the box with Uncle Erno's ashes in it stopped me. I was here now. I'd got this far. I had to do it.

I doubt he'd have minded me going home with him and with hindsight, it may have been a better idea, but my brain wasn't working well. I was tired, upset and angry beyond belief.

I managed to explain to the man in the ticket office that I needed to go to Bangkok today. There was a group of Thai soldiers waiting with me, swanking along the platform, hovering around their bags, laughing and chatting. I got a fair few stares but they were friendly, unthreatening stares of simple curiosity. One of the soldiers offered me a cigarette. He looked very cute, as they all did in their tight blue cotton uniforms, navy berets and shiny boots and buckles. I nodded a thank you for the cigarette and the soldier offered me a light before leaving me in peace. I don't smoke. Sitting on

my backpack, I felt like shit. Numb shit.

The train to Bangkok pulled in. I was still operating in a daze and it was only with the help of a kind, middle-aged man who recognised me from the monastery that I was able to sort out my allocated seat.

He helped me load my bags onto the carriage.

"Sawat di krup," he bowed and gave me a bottle of water before he left.

I stared out of the window as a guard passed. He waved a flag and the train groaned into motion, dragging itself out of the station in a cloud of smoke and whistles. I closed my eyes.

Make the world go away.

It took fifteen hours to get to Bangkok. We left the houses and shacks of Ubon behind as our train chugged relentlessly into the countryside, weaving like a manmade, noisy snake through mile after mile of golden rice. A couple of hours into the journey, I spotted two elephants at work in the fields and they stopped and lifted their trunks towards the train as we went past. The transport of Kings, my brother had called them and I shook the memory of him away. I stared at rice fields for hours. Five solid hours of nothing but rice. The countryside didn't alter except for a gradual shift from the dry, straw-like fields of the north-east to lush, wet paddy fields once we'd got further into the centre of Thailand.

Rice, rice everywhere and not a drop to drink.

The scenery became far greener as we came south. Palm trees and sugar cane were now the backdrop to my view and I could taste the moisture in the air and began to feel it lying heavy on my lungs. The Isaan had been far more arid and its heat sharp. The mass of giant, water-rich leaves and groves

which I now saw, were a vivid contrast to the sparse, thirsty twigs and shrubs I'd grown accustomed to.

Closer to Bangkok, we passed an enormous, golden Buddha as big as a church sitting in one of the fields, miles from anything. It was squat and solid, an incongruous, ostentatious emblem of the country's devotion to its faith. A faith I was struggling not to resent.

My travelling companion for most of the journey had been a fat, friendly looking young man who sat on the seat opposite. He didn't say a word throughout the whole trip. While I munched, drank, read and listened to my music, he sat calmly and upright, a gentle contented smile on his face, sitting and waiting. At first I thought he was a bit odd, the inevitable railway carriage weirdo but, no, he was simply doing what most Thais do and what very few Brits can do. Sit and wait for fifteen hours. The only movement he made was a couple of times to have a drink and to buy a fresh curry and a piece of grilled chicken offered by one of the food sellers who boarded the train at each station.

The train shuffled and shunted its way noisily through the outskirts of Bangkok towards the central station. Gone were the rich, lush forest vistas of the last few hours. Gone were the luminous lagoons and the bountiful paddy fields. Here was filthy, dirty, stinky, noisy, wonderful, alive Bangkok. Chatanan could have been on another planet for all I cared.

Funny though, how life has a way of reminding you of the things you most want to forget. While I was flicking through my guide book deciding where to stay, a dried pressed Bodhi leaf which Antony had given me fell out. It was such a perfect shape and I had to force myself to forget how he'd given it to me one day while we were walking near the Outside Sala. The monastery's Bodhi tree, he told me, sat in

a corner, protectively overlooking the Sala. The story went that it was under such a tree that the Buddha was enlightened and so, in honour, every Buddhist monastery planted its own Bodhi tree. The heart-like leaf that Antony gave to me had a small hole in it and I screwed it up, the leaf disintegrating in my fist. I threw it out of the window to be swallowed up by the noise, the dirt and the activity of the busy Bangkok street. I needed to leave Antony behind, in Chatanan. The hole in my own heart would just have to remain there.

Bangkok felt familiar even though I'd been here for one night only but I knew I could now put The Isaan and Chatanan behind me and get on with the job in hand. A couple of nights here and then on to the River Kwai. I'd be OK on my own, I convinced myself. I'd always managed on my own before, somehow coping without my family, but now the resentment began to weigh heavily.

"Awright with that, love?" said a whining voice ahead of me, shocking me back to the here and now.

The taxi I'd taken from the station dropped me off at the steps of the New Samui Guest House, and I was trying to drag my big fat rucksack and the bag with Uncle Erno in it up the steep flight. It was a sticky, sweaty night and despite sleeping a little on the train, I was almost beside myself with fatigue.

"Need a hand, love?" came the voice again.

Oh for Chrissakes! What does it bloody look like?

"Yes please, if you're free," is what I actually said.

"Free to you, love, charge anyone else," and he laughed, tickled by his own, corny humour. He helped me up the steps, a short, sweaty, sticky man with flattened greasy hair scraped back across a bald patch. His glasses were thick-

rimmed black plastic and he wore cream slacks and a red fake Lacoste T-shirt. Overall, he resembled a wet fish in fake designer clothing.

"No problem, darlin'. There you go. You staying 'ere, then? Been 'ere long, have we?"

"Just got here. I need a room."

"Ooo, darlin'! Lucky to find a room this late. You can always share mine!" Again, the self-congratulatory laugh, until he saw my face. "Only a joke, love. Only a joke."

I wondered what this fella's wet greasy head would look like once it'd been slapped around the gills a few times.

He hovered while I checked in and found that there were plenty of rooms available, and I had to be quite insistent about not having him help me to my room with my bags. I managed to give him the slip.

My room was very clean and had a fan and shutters over the tall window, which overlooked the lower roofs of the adjoining buildings. It sounded as if there was a working kitchen or a restaurant down there, spoons scraping against metal bowls, pans being thrown on a hot flame, a heavy chopper hitting a wooden board with a decisive thud. So this was it. Backpacker land. I had friends who dreamt of being here. It was their idea of paradise. It was the last place on earth I wanted to be at that moment. I was operating on autopilot, emotionally depleted. I was so tired that I didn't even make it to the bathroom to clean my teeth or have a pee.

I had weird dreams that night. Dreams of trying to evade a never-ending flow of cockroaches which were swarming over the bed like a blanket of brittle black treacle and following me as I ran out of the door and down the corridor.

I woke early and weary, around six, got up and went in search of breakfast. There was a stall round the corner of the street and I bought some fried rice cakes and a drink. Opposite, there was a small entrance leading down to the river and it drew me down. Familiarity in a faraway land. The quay had hastily laid wooden planks for a walkway and I followed this through to a turnstile where I paid a few baht to enter. I was standing on the edge of the Chao Phraya River, which flowed through the centre of Bangkok. On the train, I'd read about the Chao Phraya Express, a river bus that ran the length of the river. The platform was already full of besuited commuters on their way to work, briefcases in hand. It was like catching the tube in London, everyone cramming themselves in and rushing to get a seat. I simply got carried along with the crush and found myself hanging on for dear life as the whistles screeched to let the ferryman know everyone was on. The engines splashed into life and we heaved away, onto the river.

Didn't know where I was going. I just needed to be near the flow of a river again to try and find a rhythm to my disturbed life.

After a couple of stops I got a seat and was able to watch the river life of Bangkok. Two monks sat in front of me, their backs to me as they looked out silently over the river. I had to work hard at throwing away the memories of the morning I'd spent with my brother on the Mekong. That blissful, special morning.

I swallowed my tears, refusing to let them be born.

The stretch of water we were on was a giant, six lane free-for-all of barges, ferries, tankers and small wooden, two person taxi boats with a driver at the rear steering a route through the waterway and a smartly dressed customer sitting

at the front. The barges were deathly looking bruisers, black, flat, square-fronted platforms which took on all-comers and very often we had to wait for ten minutes to let one of these unstoppable dinosaurs past. It was as if the whole river came to a halt and held its breath while one of these creatures slid silently by. Once it had gone, the taxi boats sped again and the ferry fired up its engine, straining to be let loose on the open water.

I was happy to watch the life of the river but it didn't feed me, didn't nurture me like at home. It was too busy, too exciting, too much.

We cut under a bridge and the mood of the river changed yet again, but I couldn't change with it. Ahead, about another mile and spreading like a giant spider's web spun dramatically across the sky, was the Rama IX Bridge, the longest of its kind in the world. I'd never seen anything so big. Two awesome New Age skyscrapers, fifty, sixty floors high, sit at either end of the bridge, one walled in blue glass, its upper floors sloping off to an angle, creating a diamond which reached upwards towards a thin mast which pricked the apex. It reminded me of something invented from Lego, only it was real and hundreds of feet high.

I could hear the warm buzz of the traffic overhead as I craned my neck to see the enormous slabs of engineering sliding by. The water swirled around the pillars, lashing against the new concrete and I wondered just how long it would be before it began to grind away the stone and take the legs from under this manmade mountain.

I closed my eyes for the return trip and let my face rest in the warm sun. When we reached the stop where I'd got on, I watched as we came to a slow halt amid a screech of whistles from the man on the quayside and lots of loud,

sputtered manoeuvring. No one tied the boat off, it just waited there precariously on the choppy water, straining at the leash to be let go again.

There was a crowd of people waiting to get off and a crowd of people waiting to get on. As soon as the boat got within striking distance of the quay, everyone pushed forward and the two sets of waiting people met in the middle. It was difficult to get on or off and at one point I thought I wasn't going to make it off and I would get stuck on the boat while it set off for the next stop. I gave one final push forward and leapt on to the quay. As I gathered my bag to me and made my way through the melee of oncoming passengers, I saw her, the woman who I'd seen when I first arrived in Thailand. Bangkok Airport Woman.

She didn't turn my way and I watched, as she got on the express, alone. My eyes followed her as she dipped her head to avoid hitting it on the roof of the doorway and made her way to find a seat. Just as the boat fired up its engines and the whistles began to sound again, she glanced up at the quay. She saw me. It took a while for her eyes to register and I thought she hadn't remembered. But, as I took my sunglasses off, she smiled at me.

I could have got back on the boat at that point. Could have maybe changed the course of my journey through life but I didn't. Instead, the boat pulled out and Bangkok Airport Woman, like everyone else in my life, was gone. That was it.

I saw your face in a crowed place but I have to face the truth.

James bloody Blunt.

I had a beer at a street side cafe and thought of writing home. What on earth would I tell them? I imagined some of

them might be a bit concerned that they hadn't heard from me for a while, but what would I say?

"Having a wonderful time. Bastard brother left me again. Going to throw Uncle Erno into the river alone. Wish you were here."

I thought of Joe and how he had picked me up out of the river that time. I wished that his strong arms were around me now, lifting me up and keeping me out of harm's way.

I spent a difficult second night in the New Samui Guest House. It was hot and noisy. Fish Features came to annoy me again while I was watching the TV in the reception area so I left, and went to my room. I could hear the other travellers coming and going, sounding like they were having a fun time.

I thought of Gecko, and wondered if Mae Li had found him later as she was cleaning up. I thought of Mae Li sitting round the fire in the darkness, waiting for her husband to come home. I thought of the grey haired lady in the kitchen, of Christopher and Susan, and I thought of Amaro and Tikaro.

I tried not to think of my brother. I tried with all my heart not to think of him and not to let the anger and hurt find me. I tossed and turned on the bed. I shouted out loud and I thumped the mattress with my fist but he still got through to my head. I still saw his bald, thin face and brown mole, his orange robe and bare feet, and his thin wrists and bony hands.

What was it he hadn't said to me? What was it that could possibly keep him from coming with me? I didn't understand. What did he have to do that was so important? More important than me. "I can't go with you," he'd said and I knew he'd wanted to say something else but I'd stopped

him. I was too hurt. I wondered if I'd ever know what it was he'd wanted to tell me.

I cried then, like a child. A motherless child, a long, long way from home.

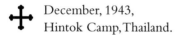 December, 1943,
Hintok Camp, Thailand.

This is the third week we have been at Hintok. Of my party, fifty have died in those three weeks, we have one hundred and fifty in hospital and only fifty are left working. The Nips have reduced the food given to the men in the hospital so that they can give more food to the working men. It is still barely enough to keep us going and every grain of rice we eat, we know a dying man goes without. I am convinced that the doctors are sending the sicker men to work, knowing that they will die anyway, and sending those with a better chance of survival to hospital. Every morning, broken men stumble to work knowing for certain that it will kill them, if not that day, then the next. Survival has been reduced to such choices and life has sunk to depths unthinkable, yet again.

I managed to bury Arthur. In a frenzy of numbed madness I took him into the jungle in the darkness of night and collapsed asleep on the grave when I had finished. The Doc gave me three days in the hospital afterwards and it has revived me to a state where survival is possible again. I went back to the grave and marked it, making a mental note of its location, how many yards from the camp, how close to the cliff which edges on to the valley. When all this is over, I'll be back for him. I can't leave him abandoned forever in this forgotten hell-hole. Beriberi is now taking us and dysentery

has led to such a lack of hygiene.

I struggle to write these pages on scraps of paper stolen by the Australians. But I know I must. If I do not write this, no one will believe these events but, please, I beg, don't let Muriel see this. She doesn't need to know.

 December,
The River Kwai,
Thailand

Kanchanaburi, the town where the bridge on the River Kwai is located, lies a hundred and sixty kilometres from Bangkok. It took two and a half hours to get there and cost eighty pence. The train journey was unremarkable apart from two very cute children who were travelling with their mother and started playing peek-a-boo with me from behind the back of the wooden seat opposite. A small brother and sister, I got the inevitable, "Hello miss," and, "I love you!" followed by enormous grins and added to which the boy threw in "Manchester United."

They offered me some chewing gum so I swapped it for some biscuits I'd bought at the station. The children got off after a few stops and I sat alone watching the Thailand countryside trundle past.

Arriving in Kanchanaburi, it was like any other town in Thailand. Rough and ready, dusty and dirty. It reminded me of Ubon only greener. The monsoon, now over for this year, ends later here. The station was quite a way from the main road through the town and I struggled as I carried my bags. There were a few other people who got off at Kanchanaburi, mainly Thais and a couple of other backpackers. It was a long, hot walk into town, far further

than I thought from the map I'd picked up at the station. It was around five in the evening and very humid and I knew that in about an hour or so the sun would disappear and daylight would be lost. I was worried I would be too.

My backpack and Uncle Erno were getting increasingly heavy as my energy waned and I reached the end of the street. The sun was sinking fast and I was worried about where I would stay. All the hostels I'd tried were full.

I sat on my rucksack and in the fading light, which I knew was about to vanish in a blink, looked at my useless map. It indicated a large road joining this one at the point where I was but all I could see was a dusty, dirt track to my right, disappearing around a curve and with no street lighting to guide my way. It also indicated that there was a guest house down there but it looked so dark and desolate that I didn't trust what the map told me. My other option was to go back the way I came but there were no Tuk-Tuks or taxis around, and I was so tired that I knew I would struggle to walk the mile and half I'd just come.

My optimism faded fast and I felt like crying. I was lost, it was getting dark, I had nowhere to stay and I could feel tears pricking my eyes. How had life turned out like this? How had I got here? A few weeks ago, life had been simple, nothing more exciting than floating up and down a river in York and getting pissed occasionally. It had been a bit boring sometimes but safe. I'd had no greater problems to sort out than Molly's dodgy teeth or my leaking radiators and the nearest I'd got to thinking about going abroad this year had been to look at a few brochures on Prague and a few fewer on Italy. You had a lot to answer for, Uncle Erno, sending me out here on your last errand. You didn't mention I'd end up here, on the other side of the world, on my own, in the

bloody dark with nowhere to stay for the night.

I felt a pang of déjà vu as I remembered being with my brother at my hut up at Poo Jom Petch, a memory I struggled to let go.

I looked at the bag with Uncle Erno in it.

Cheers, mate, I told it sarcastically.

"Don't give in, Benedict," a quirkily familiar voice said, shocking me to alertness.

I spun round on my bag to see who was there. No one. The road was empty.

"Trust in yourself," I heard it say again.

I thought I'd finally begun to go mad. I was sure it was Uncle Erno talking to me in his half-Yorkshire, half-Lancashire accent.

In a dazed half-mad blur, I picked up my bags and headed down the dirt track. Just after the bend in the road, there was a hand-painted sign nailed to a tree, saying 'Guest House'. It looked more like someone's back yard. Then a short, smiling, middle-aged Thai man appeared wearing a T-shirt and sarong, and he greeted me with open arms and a gentle face.

"Hello, Miss," he said. "You look very tired. I am Mr Joo. I take your bag for you. Come, you rest, take your time, I show you room."

He led me past a wooden building which, on the side hidden from the road, had a large balcony tucked away and in which were three or four western travellers, sitting on cushions on the floor and eating or drinking from low, wooden tables. The path ran alongside the edge of the balcony and down a steep set of open slatted steps which bridged a channel of water and led to a series of bamboo huts built close together.

I followed him round the edge of one hut. I couldn't

believe my eyes when we turned the corner. The amazing, stunning River Kwai burst into view two feet in front of me. I had no idea it had been so close and had been running parallel to the long road I'd just walked down. The huts sat on rafts on the river, water lapping a few inches below my feet and splashing against the stilts which moored the rafts in place. There was an empty hammock swaying between two wooden posts in front of the room the man showed me. In the room was a double bed with a decent mattress and a mosquito net draped overhead. Three other rooms shared the raft.

The sun was beginning to set on the opposite bank across the dark, wide river and I knew without a doubt that I'd come home.

"You rest, miss, take your time, pay tomorrow," and before my angel disappeared, he placed my bags next to the bed, explained where the shower room was, told me the price of the room and gave me the key.

I spent my first evening on the River Kwai relaxing in a hammock, listening to the hum and whistle of the insects and watching a magical, golden red sunset spread over the horizon, turning the water into liquid fire and melting my fears into oblivion.

God bless you, Uncle Erno.

I slept well, surrounded by acres of muslin suspended from four corners hanging down in a tent over my wooden bed, protecting me from the many mosquitoes. The remnants of a mosquito repelling spiral coil that my Thai host had given me and which I'd burnt overnight lay collapsed in a forlorn little heap next to Uncle Erno, a pretty pattern of ash waiting to disappear in the morning breeze.

My room was still dark, with just a chink of morning light

poking in through the gaps in the wood but as I opened the door, the view swept in, filling the room with the magic of the river. It was still there. The River Kwai. In the bright, silent light of the Thailand morning, the water still flowed swiftly and strongly and the lush green forest on the far bank was today vibrant and clear whereas the evening before it had been a dark mass, sitting in a long, heavy strip on the horizon.

A wooden boat buzzed past on its way up river where there was a long sweeping curve, which swallowed the boat, hiding its progress from view. Down river, about a mile away, I could see the main part of Kanchanaburi, far more urban and built-up than I'd envisaged. Where I was staying was a grass village compared with the hotels, concrete and traffic down stream.

The River Kwai wasn't as wide as the Mekong but it was strong, calm and powerful and flowed with a timelessness that brought solace to my aching soul. It began to put a slow rhythm back into my aching heart.

It was already hot by the time I set off to find the bridge. I wanted to see where it was located and get my bearings before deciding when to scatter Erno's ashes. I hired a mountain bike and set off down the road I'd walked the previous evening, through the edge of the town and out into dusty country road.

After a couple of miles, I came across some smart hotels and about a dozen cafes, drinks sellers and gift shops. The road met a railway crossing where it took a right hand corner and followed the tracks, running in parallel alongside. Still no sign of any bridge. The railway crossing had been pedestrianized so I stopped and looked around.

I nearly missed the bridge. It sat tucked away to my left, a

series of black metal arches set on solid pillars of stone neatly stretched over the river which flowed unseen a few metres below the railway line. The blackness of the bridge camouflaged it against the forest, the trees diminishing the impact of this manmade construction, and it was only the few people walking across it in their brightly coloured T-shirts that helped it to stand out.

This was it, the Bridge Over the River Kwai.

I fleetingly thought of Mr Hollingsworth, my solicitor and corrected myself. On. The Bridge On the River Kwai.

I locked the bike and walked up to the railway line towards the bridge. It was single track railway, built on heavy wooden sleepers with smooth, weather-worn planks of wood running parallel inside the rails. It swept over the bridge between the iron arcs, each not more than ten feet high and held together with giant rivets like a child's giant Meccano construction. It was eerie. Despite its history, there was a very strange peace about it and a deep sense of human experience. I could almost feel the bare feet that had walked these wooden sleepers and I could feel the bare hands that had worked them into place.

Uncle Erno had been here. An Uncle Erno I didn't know.

Looking down the track, which passed through the metal gateway into the depths of the jungle beyond, I was moved and I'm sure it was the presence of death that touched me. I stared between the sleepers at the river flowing underneath, and then carefully picked a route between the rails, avoiding the many Japanese tourists who had descended from a tour bus that had pulled up close by. They were posing for photos. Surreal tourist shots of a monument built by slaves slaughtered at the hands of their forebears.

I walked to the centre of the bridge and leant over the

rails, looking upstream. It was so stunning here, so incredibly tranquil. Hard to believe that this stretch of water now running beneath my safe feet once ran red with blood.

Two Buddhist monks were walking towards me, the soft material of their robes glowing bright in the sunshine making the colour stand out dramatically against the blackness of the iron. Their presence added extra serenity to the scene as they silently passed over the bridge but it churned up unwelcome feelings inside me, and I felt anger towards them for choosing this moment to remind me that my brother wasn't here with me. He'd chosen the call of that bloody robe instead.

I couldn't tell if the monks were from a local monastery or if they had just stepped off a sightseeing bus too. Again I thought of Poo Jom Petch, and of catching Tikaro and my brother that morning. It was such a strange setting for two men in sacred cloth to be found arguing, that haven on a hillside. I never got a chance to ask Antony what it had been about and I now wondered. My mind came back to the River Kwai as the sound of the river under my feet once again began to register.

And the story is told of a river that flowed, made me sad to think it was dead.

By a band from America, called 'America'. I loved that old song. I used to sing it with my brother all the time as we dreamt of Highway One and the Golden Gate. Good job the band hadn't come from a place called Poo, I thought and as I began to smile to myself, my brief taste of frivolity was brutally measured by a sad vision of happier times, special moments with my brother that had been shattered.

I arrived back at my raft hut after lunch, crashed onto the bed and after an hour's snooze, sat and watched the sun's

glow over the river through the open door. I read a little and enjoyed the peacefulness of the setting. The water oozed by, turning from a fiery red to infinite black as the sun dropped behind the trees and finally disappeared altogether. It seemed to last longer than the sunsets at Chatanan. Maybe it was the countryside, maybe it was the clouds. Who knows.

Later, lying in the hammock, watching darkness, I remembered an evening at Chatanan, just before sunset. It was shortly before I left and I'd had a day alone, mooching, washing with Mae Li and cleaning the guest villa. We'd arranged no tea that day and I hadn't seen my brother as he'd told me he'd be away.

I took a walk on the familiar route, following the path round the walls of the monastery. I'd brought my torch with me as I knew that once the sun had disappeared, there'd be no light to guide me back. I was coming round the curve in the road where, just ahead, was the shed that housed the old 1938 Harley. I was still some distance away. Light was beginning to fade rapidly and as I got closer, I realised that there was someone inside the shed. Christopher, I thought. I crept up.

What I hadn't expected was to find Antony.

He hadn't heard me approach and I watched him in the dim light through the door. He didn't seem to be doing anything in particular. All he did was walk slowly down the length of the bike, trailing his finger along the handlebars, over the tank and across the seat. He looked deep in thought as he gazed at the Harley, as if lost in a memory, in a place all his own. When he reached the seat, he stopped. He stood, not moving for about five minutes. I barely breathed, afraid I'd break the magic spell of the moment he had created for himself.

I didn't let him know I was there. I just watched. Tikaro had talked about how riding the Harley had been too good and how it had made him restless, made him consider his future at the monastery. Was that going on for my brother, too? Was that what they were talking about the night they'd spent sitting until two in the morning outside the guest house? Maybe the Abbot had persuaded him to stay at Wat Pah Chatanan rather than come with me to keep him from disrobing?

It all churned over in my head as I lay watching the light fade over the River Kwai. I remembered how I'd hidden by the side of the shed when eventually Antony made to leave. Darkness had descended and it hid me completely as I heard him close the door and watched as he walked back towards the monastery, the small beam of his Maglite showing him a route and its light catching the orange edges of his robe. A silent shadow, walking away from me.

I woke at around two, restless. A full night's sleep wasn't on the cards. The mosquito coil had already burned away and it was pitch black in the room. There was a faint shift in the blackness round the edge of the door. I knew I wouldn't sleep, so I crept out of the bed and carefully opened the creaky door so as not to wake any visitors in the nearby rafts.

Once outside, I realised that the shift in light was because the moon was out. It was bright silver, shining high in the night sky and casting a crystal sheen over the water and the trees. I could see remarkably well and walked over to the hammock by the water's edge. Gently rocking in the swing of my own weight, I rested, letting my ears relax into the sound of the flowing river and looking up at the sky and the many stars that shone there. There were a few clouds but not too many to interrupt the space between me and the great

big galaxy in which I began to let my mind rest. Who's out there? I thought. Who's up there, watching all this going on? Who's letting it happen?

A slight breeze picked up and the River Kwai stirred below me. The ripples hit the side of the raft and I felt the hammock move ever so slightly. I looked into the darkness of the river again. Maybe it could give me some answers.

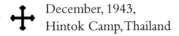 December, 1943,
Hintok Camp, Thailand

We have tried to maintain a sense of order in the camp but disease is making it impossible. The latrines are dug one at a time, since we have neither the labour nor the materials to build more. Even now, it is the sick from the hospital, working in half hour stretches who have to dig them. It only takes a week for a trench to fill to the brim and become infested with squirming maggots and flies. They fester on the surface six inches deep and swarm over your bare feet and along the wooden slats which we have to squat on. There is excrement everywhere. Many men don't even have the strength to make it through the trees to the latrine and the bushes and undergrowth nearby are squalid. It's not just physical strength that they lack. Many have ceased to care and the resulting filth and stench is overwhelming. That area of the camp is a human pigsty of excrement where the pathways and drainage trenches are filled with the sordid mess. And, now that the monsoon has stopped and the oceans of water that so unrelentingly fell on us simply vanished within days into the earth beneath, we have no water and no way of cleaning ourselves. Self-respect is abandoned and many

men are little more than animals.

Survival. We hope for nothing more.

 December,
The River Kwai
Thailand

I was joined at breakfast by a few other guests. There was Dave, a tall, calm, dark haired and very good looking South African with incredibly smooth skin and a male model's jaw line, and his Spanish girlfriend, Anna, also very good looking with long dark hair, and she too had incredibly smooth skin, and a female model's jaw line. Also in the restaurant were two bespectacled, blonde Dutch girls but they kept themselves to themselves, studying their guide books and whispering to each other.

Mr Joo, arrived mid-meal and offered us all a day trip in his pick-up truck. "You lucky," he told us all. "Monsoon finish early this year. Mr Joo drive you."

I wasn't sold on the idea at all until he told us more about where we would be visiting. He said he'd take us to see a few of the nearby sights, one of which was the Death Railway and as soon as I heard him say that, I picked myself up from the slump I'd fallen into and listened to what he had to say. He mentioned Hell Fire Pass too, a section of the railway built by POWs which cut through solid rock in the hillside and he also mentioned the 'Famous Railway Curve,' a part of the railway I'd seen in a photo at Uncle Erno's house.

He was talking about all the places where Uncle Erno would have been when he was a prisoner here.

All the time I'd been in Thailand, I'd felt the presence of Uncle Erno close to me, locked in that small casket, like a

benevolent being watching my every move. It had been because of him that I'd come here and met Antony again, yet I knew so little about him. The Erno I knew was old, frail, even silly. He was always forgetting why he'd phoned you and by the time you'd worked out it was him on the other end of the line, he'd got all flustered and had usually put the phone down.

Once when he rang my number, I picked the phone up and all I heard was him saying,

"Is that you, Muriel?" over and over again.

I didn't have the heart to explain that it was only me and that Muriel had passed away so I didn't say anything and waited until he realised there was no one there and put the receiver down. That was the Uncle Erno I'd come to know in the last ten years of his life.

I'd heard stories of a different Erno. Dad had told us about Erno when he was younger, a young handsome man, strong and virile with a sharp sense of humour and an eye for the ladies. He was intelligent too, passed his exams and was about to start a job as a teacher in the local boys' school before he went to war.

"God knows what happened to him," Dad had explained one evening over supper. "He came back a wreck. A complete wreck." Antony and I listened in silence.

I learnt over the years that it had been Aunty Muriel who had nursed Erno back to health when he turned up. He'd been presumed dead by the whole family because they'd heard nothing from him for years, even after the war had finished. Everyone had been surprised when he arrived out of the blue, like a ghost. Muriel was able to nurse him physically but the rest of Erno had long since been left in the faraway jungle of Thailand, sacrificed under the weight of an

unforgiving, foreign war machine.

There must have been so many like him, I thought, as I listened to Mr Joo sell us his special price, all-day, sightseeing trip and realised that I was on the edge of the world Uncle Erno had never spoken about.

While the others squeezed themselves into the cab of Mr Joo's pick up truck, I sat on a rug and cushions outside in the back. It was chilly as we set off but I really couldn't understand why the others would choose to sit inside when they could have had the wind whistling past their ears, the smell of the countryside streaming through their nostrils, and an unimpaired view of the spectacular mountains and forests through which we drove.

Other cars and trucks zoomed scarily up to our bumper, inches from our truck, before swerving out to overtake with barely enough room. One car was so close as it passed alongside me that I could've reached out and nicked the cigarette that the driver was smoking. A tinny motorbike hurtled up behind us until all I could see was the shaking head of the rider, the flesh on his face pulled back by the force of the air and his hair streaming. He was also so close that I could've nicked his cigarette too and I laughed at the sight of a man on a moped, smoking.

Christopher on the Harley didn't feel far away.

About two hours up the road, Mr Joo pulled in at some natural hot springs which bubbled out beneath the rocks, piping hot steam rising into the tropical air.

"Now you take bath," he told us, a warm, kind smile on his face. He knew that none of us had seen a hot bath in weeks, maybe even months. And boy, were they hot. It took a while to get used to the heat but the luxury of relaxing in an outdoor steam pool, sprinkled with the sunshine as it

found its way through the layers of leaves above, made it worth the wait. It was like a nostalgic homecoming.

As I sank into its depths, the heat opened my pores and I began to feel a heap of pain ooze away as my aching limps were rested, and I felt the familiar lap of warm water in the nape of my neck, licking at my ears. Bath time for Benedict.

Dave and Anna were at the far end of the pool, playfully splashing each other and the two Dutch girls clung together at the side, sitting on the edge and dangling their toes, too nervous to actually get in.

A Thai woman who was bathing with us lent me some soap and a bowl so that we could wash. She indicated to us to sit on the edge rather than in the water so that the suds didn't go in the pool. Like how Mae Li had washed my clothes, first soaping them, scrubbing them and then rinsing them off with clean water. Only this time, it was not my clothes that were being washed. I was being cleansed.

A stream flowed a short distance below our feet and I could feel the cooler air from it as the fast flowing water hit rock after rock and crashed downstream. It provided a vivid contrast to the hot pool we'd just come from, and its rush was a reminder of the life that lay waiting for me once these few weeks were over. A life, maybe, without my brother. Like any river, it just kept flowing no matter how hard you tried to ignore it. I turned my back on the rush of the stream and returned to the temporary sanctity of the hot pool. I sank into the soft, liquid heaven and would've stayed there all morning if Mr Joo hadn't insisted that we left. None of us wanted to get out and we groaned as we each lifted our wrinkled bodies out of the water and went limply to fetch our clothes.

We reached Hellfire Pass about an hour later. It was

approached on foot through the trees and down a pathway which led to a steep set of steps plunging down into the jungle. Once at the bottom, the ground levelled out into an area less than ten feet wide. The rocks we'd just climbed down were on our right and there was a steep tree-lined valley disappearing into nowhere on our left. You couldn't see where the valley ended, it just descended into a lost mass of trees and undergrowth. Mr Joo explained that we were to walk about a kilometre along here and to be careful not to trip over the wooden sleepers which were sunk at irregular intervals into the earth beneath our feet.

The pathway ahead cut an unnatural line through the forest which was beginning to be encroached by eager young trees, leaning over until some of them touched each other, forming a green roof of branches high above our heads. It was peaceful and pretty but as we set off to make our way down the pathway, I felt a dreadful icy grip take hold around my heart.

I was about to walk in death's dark vale where a young, strong Erno had once walked before me.

Hellfire Pass is a narrow railway cutting carved by prisoners of war through solid rock which rises vertically twenty to twenty-five feet on each side. In some parts, the cutting is only about six feet wide. All that the prisoners were given to carry out the inhuman task of slicing through the rock were pickaxes and hand-drills, and occasionally a small amount of explosive. More than two-thirds of the men working on the pass died creating it. It was self-evident why. We were miles from anywhere, in the depths of a hot, unforgiving jungle where disease thrived and if the sun didn't get you then the torrential rain would. The only way out was down into the unfathomable abyss of the deep

valley below.

And this was where my dear old, quirky-voiced Uncle Erno had been a prisoner. He never spoke about it, so we never did.

What hell had he been through here?

I caught up with the others who had stopped at the entrance to the pass but none of us spoke. Mr Joo halted his commentary and fell respectfully silent as we entered between the steep rocks and even the hushed whisper of the rustling trees ceased. Once between the great walls of solid cliff on either side, you could see how the rock had been chipped away, painstakingly slowly by hand, not blasted away in huge chunks or removed by machine. You could see how human hand had scraped tortuously at the brutal sheer face which every so often bore the mark of a pickaxe that had been smashed down through ages of hard stone. There was the head of one drill still embedded, snapped off and stuck there for eternity, and all along the length of this human torture tunnel you could feel and see the evidence of brutal labour and eventual death.

It was shocking. And it was a tourist attraction.

It took a while for the impact of where I was to sink in. It seemed so far removed from the tranquil shores of the River Kwai and the stunning sunsets that greeted us every evening. It was hard to put the two places side by side. Heaven and hell are such unexpected bed fellows but, in this subtropical haven, dark images began to colour my heart. Here was horror staring me in the face.

Halfway down, at the very centre of the pass, there was a tall thin tree. It had been planted by relatives and colleagues of those who had perished here and it stood defiant, perfectly vertical, a branchless tree reaching way, way up

beyond the sharp edge of the rocks, beyond the other trees that hung from the top of the cliff and out into the blue sky above the canopy of the forest. It had grown like a beacon of hope, a symbol of triumph nourished by the bodies of the men who had fallen here.

I stood at the base of the tree, craning my neck to see its leaves which were high in the sun above and I let the others leave me. I needed to be alone. If I'd believed in God, I'd have prayed. If I'd been a Buddhist, I might have meditated but I was none of these and so I was just still, alone with Uncle Erno, Mum, Dad and the thousands of men who had died here. I thought of Antony too and of how this place put our differences into sharp relief. I'd come back to Thailand to see him, I thought. When I'd calmed down and forgiven him, I'd come back.

A plaque had been placed explaining the history of the pass and told us how work had continued twenty-four hours a day, and at night was lit by burning torches. To the prisoners the lit pass looked like the fires of hell and so the name was born. To most of the prisoners it was the fires of hell, a hell in which they lost their lives.

I stayed in the pass a long while, alone with my thoughts and with the slow realisation of what Uncle Erno may have been through. I doubt I'll ever know war, I thought. Yet this had been the reality of Uncle Erno's life and none of us had known.

Everyone was moved by the visit to Hellfire Pass and our collective mood was very sombre as we made the return walk along the railway and climbed the steep steps up to the car park. Dave and Anna joined me in the back of the truck as Mr Joo set off again but none of us spoke.

We followed the direction of the railway as it made its way

towards Kanchanaburi and picked up the track at its most western stop, Nam Tok.

"Now I take you to see Famous Railway Curve," Mr Joo told us while we were eating. "Very impressive," he said. "Very impressive."

And sure enough, it was. A death defying section of track which followed the curve of the cliff high above the river on a fragile, wooden frame. Over a kilometre long, it wound a route about a metre away from the rock. It was a sheer drop down either side to the rocks below where the fast-flowing river carried tiny boats and rafts far, far away below us. They looked like children's toys bobbing in the water. The rickety wooden pack-of-cards railway bridge snaked its way round the rock, and grew smaller in the distance.

I stared, the sheer magnitude of this engineering feat finally hitting home. How did they build this? How did human hand achieve this impossible construction and what cruel mind even dreamt of the idea? I could only wonder at the depth of misery that lay on the price tag of this bridge and at the reasons why Uncle Erno had kept a photo of it on his mantelpiece at home.

I ate with Dave and Anna and the two Dutch girls in the guest house that evening. We didn't say much but it was good just to spend the time together.

Next day, to learn more of Uncle Erno, I visited one of the museums in town, of which there were many. I could've gone to any but this one appealed. It was a rough and ready affair run by Buddhist monks and was a reconstruction of the type of long grass roofed hut that the prisoners would have lived in. There were thin beds made of reeds and meagre cooking utensils amongst the displays. There were also sketches drawn by some former prisoners, depictions of

horrific conditions, paintings of torture techniques, men force-fed with buckets of water until their bellies swelled and were then stamped on by a guard, medical drawings of primitive amputations, legs eaten by ulcers and skeletal men with their bellies swollen from starvation.

It numbed me. I'd come such a long way since I'd set of from Manchester Airport. First the monastery, seeing Antony, then leaving him. Now coming here and finding heaven on earth by the river, only to have it shattered by what I was seeing now. What had happened to my idyllic, sub-tropical free holiday?

I was still looking at the terrifying exhibits as I slowly made my way round the museum when I came across a photo that made me stop and stare. Old, weather-beaten, smiley men, standing stiffly for the group memento to commemorate their reunion here.

It was the same photo that Uncle Erno had left for me with the solicitor and there he was, in the photo, Uncle Erno, smiling out at me.

"Miss, are you all right?" said a monk behind me.

He was a wise-looking, concerned, old Thai monk. There was grey hair peeping through at his temples and the first, rough bristles of a white beard brushed his tired chin. He was due a shave.

"Please, drink some water," and he placed a bottle on the table in front of me, next to the photo.

"You are Benedict, yes?" said the monk, his kind, soft features close to my face.

My jaw dropped.

"I am Ajahn Sumeno," he said. "We have been expecting you. First you drink and then I will explain everything."

With that, the Ajahn called over to a Thai man who was

waiting close by and who scuttled off, returning later with some sugary tea. The Thai man hovered by my arm protectively as the monk led us out of the darkness of the museum and headed into the sunlight and over to a building on the far side of the footpath. The large room we were in had a stone floor, bare walls and was far cooler than the museum. Down at the far end there was a large gold Buddha statue and I realised we were in the main Sala of a monastery.

The Ajahn took some floor cushions from a large wooden cupboard by the entrance and invited me to sit with him while the Thai man chaperoned us.

"Your uncle visited the museum many times when he was here for the reunion and he became a benefactor. Over the years he provided some of the exhibits and much of the information we have. Six months ago he wrote to us to explain that he hoped, one day, you would come too. We didn't know when that would be but we hoped you would find us."

Six months ago would have been shortly before Erno died. Ajahn Sumeno also said he knew the Farang monastery in The Isaan and, after I explained that I was alone and that Thanavaro hadn't come with me, he suggested that I didn't judge my brother too harshly.

"You are angry with your brother but your anger is in the wrong place," he said.

What the hell did he know, I thought, but kept my mouth shut. Instead, I told him that I'd visited Hellfire Pass and about how hard I'd found it. He nodded in empathy, the soft folds of his elderly skin creasing on his forehead.

"It is hard to know that something so ugly can happen in somewhere so beautiful," he said. "But always, this is so."

"He never told us, you see," I explained. "He never once

said anything to anyone."

"Yes, it is hard. But child, remember that you only see pictures," he responded. "You don't have to feel the pain as well."

I looked at this kind, humble man, so wise in his words and so warm in his energy.

"Ernest made a diary when he was a prisoner," continued the Ajahn, in a matter-of-fact tone, the wrinkles in his old face folding softly as he spoke. "It was very dangerous. If his captors had known, they would have killed him. He donated the diary to the museum."

I swallowed hard. A diary.

"Can I see it?" I asked, naively, not considering what the diary might contain.

"Of course, you may," said the Ajahn. "We keep it safe because it is so fragile, but I suggest you are tired and can see your strength for such things is low today. Come again tomorrow and I will show you your uncle's diary."

And he called over to the waiting chaperone.

"My friend will take you to your guest house. We will see you tomorrow."

And he smiled, got up and left, a guiding light in the lost sea that had become my Thailand. I wasn't making much sense of my trip. I'd set out to scatter a dead uncle's ashes and carry out his final request. I'd ended up falling out with my brother and so full of rejection that I'd never known anything quite like it. I'd be home soon, I thought. I'd look at Uncle Erno's diary, scatter the ashes and then go home. I'd do what I set out to do but I was ready to go home.

Uncle Erno was a postman. He knew everyone in the village, knew their birthdays, their red letter days, their

goings on. For almost forty years he could be seen early morning pushing his bicycle from house to house, and early evening pushing it to the local pub on his way for an early doors half-pint. He had a smile for everyone, had time for everyone, except for 'Nips'.

"Can you have a word with the officer, dear?" he'd phoned one morning.

He was seemingly trying to arrange a police escort for his Welsh dresser, the one he'd bought with Muriel in the early days, and he was trying to get it delivered to our house. Erno lived five counties away. Five counties, five police authorities, five hours and five irritated but patient police officers trying to fathom why they'd been called to escort one not particularly impressive Welsh dresser to Yorkshire.

"They said I'd need an escort," he told them.

We have no idea what he meant but Uncle Erno was a lovable soul with a quirky voice, who did quirky things.

Uncle Erno was a postman who, after the war, had really wanted to be a history teacher but who now had a wobbly voice and a shuffling walk and never spoke about the war. Uncle Erno had been a prisoner of war, malnourished, humiliated, stripped and tortured, forced to watch the flesh fall from his friend's bones and who'd been presumed dead for over five empty years. No one heard anything. No one knew anything.

Then, as if heaven had started sending mail, a postcard arrived, delivering life:

"James Ernest Taylor, 1st August, 1916." Erno was alive and had been found.

James Ernest Taylor left me one hundred and thirty-

nine thousand pounds and asked me to scatter his ashes. I still don't know what was going through his mind when he did that.

I went back to the museum to read Uncle Erno's diary. I took the tattered, fragile scraps of paper from Ajahn Sumeno and held them for a few moments. I recognised the familiar, laboured scrawl of Uncle Erno's hand, barely legible in places but written with a determination that was evident in the sparing use of every available space. Every inch, every tiny gap was filled with his words, every letter an etching of defiance and a prayer for hope. Every small scrap a testament to the enormity of the pain he and his fellow soldiers had endured.

It put me to shame, reading the words of the uncle I'd never known, the uncle who had existed before war had wrenched the spirit from him and destroyed him, leaving a wrecked shell to find his slow way home and introduce himself as the Erno we thought we knew. Erno the Postman, the small, quirky little man who stammered at any word beginning with 'T'.

He'd been an officer, you know. I hadn't known.

The final entry was not written in Uncle Erno's hand. It was written by someone called George Smith and it told how Ernest Taylor had been caught by his captors with a stub of pencil hidden in the seam of his tattered shorts. Ernest wouldn't tell them what it was for and so they tortured him in front of the whole camp. Forcing him onto his knees, they tied his hands and left him in the blistering heat for over a day. They kept asking him his name and each time he replied, they hit him. He knew that if he said anything different they'd also hit him so, proudly, he said,

"Taylor", knowing they were trying to break his spirit by getting him to the humiliating point where he couldn't even say his own name.

"Taylor," he told them. A rifle butt in the face.

"Taylor," he told them. A stamp in the groin.

"Taylor,' he told them. A smashed jaw, a shattered shoulder, a ruptured spleen. A broken man who ever after could not pronounce any word beginning with 'T' without seeing an image of a Japanese officer aiming a rifle butt at him.

Uncle Erno, the Postman, blessed thereafter with sterility.

 December,
The River Kwai
Thailand

It's been a shock discovering Uncle Erno's diary, discovering his past. I suppose though he wrote it to be read. It wasn't a secret diary, it didn't reveal a sordid past. It revealed a brave, strong man who'd survived.

Ajahn Sumeno and the other monks at the museum have been very kind to me. They let me go there whenever I want to and I've re-read the diary several times. Each time it hits me in the stomach but rather than depleting me, strangely it gives me strength. He made it, you see. He survived and went home.

"Some visitors to our town prefer not to know," said Ajahn Sumeno to me as I was sat on the landing stage by the river, Erno's diary in hand.

"They prefer just to see the river, eat something, drink something and then leave. But sometimes it is important to remind ourselves what man can do to man. One hundred thousand Thai people died over there in the jungle, and

more than sixteen thousand western prisoners. And it will happen again. Somewhere."

I didn't need to ask him but I guessed that some of Sumeno's family had died on the railway.

I spent a few days at the museum. In the evenings I'd retire to the guest house and swing in my hammock, finishing War and Peace or listening to music. I'd usually take a bottle of beer down to the water's edge, light a mosquito coil and drift into another world, gently rocking to and fro, lulled by the creak of rope against wood or drowned in a musical carnival that swam inside my head. The sunsets were relentlessly stunning and the river was forever calming. I lost count of the days as I slipped into the routine of being here and found a rhythm to my life that had been missing for the last twenty or so years.

I often wondered what Antony would have been up to at that time, up there in Chatanan. I'd lost the need to completely banish him from my memory but I was still angry at him. Still hurt by him. I still wished he had come with me.

The visitors to the guest house had followed their natural rate of turnover and the familiar faces of Dave, Anna and the two Dutch girls had left. New faces had appeared and I enjoyed their company at meals but mostly I relaxed into my own company.

At the weekend the calm of the setting was often blown apart by the arrival of large rafts which cruised up and down this stretch of the river, blaring out disco music so loud that it drowned out any conversation. They heaved with Thais who came from Bangkok for the weekend and who took it in turns to belt out their favourite hit through a microphone. A kind of Karaoke on the Kwai.

At first I was annoyed that my peace could be so

obscenely ransacked by the tinny, disco music but who was I to complain? They were doing exactly what customers on our boats in York did every Friday and Saturday night. We would hire boats to customers who would spend three hours on the river, with no greater intention than to get as supremely pissed as they could manage and dance for as long as they could stay upright. One evening, I was working a boat which had been chartered by the staff of the local frozen chicken factory. They were on their annual social. By the end of the night, three of the blokes were on the top deck stark naked, standing on top of the tables and shouting at the beautiful people on their yachts as we cruised past the Marina. When they came downstairs, their friends joined in and we had a full strip show in front of Mad Malcolm's pulsating disco lights. Clearing up afterwards, Joe found a pair of underpants under one of the tables. It was just an average night out on the boats in York.

I was eating my supper on the balcony one evening, along with a few other guests, when one of the rafts came down stream. It had a digga-digga tink-tink disco beat pumping out of its small music system and it filled the valley for miles. The song filtered through the night, gradually growing to fever pitch as it neared the guest house. The singer sang in barely recognisable English and he either guessed at words or completely mispronounced them. I still couldn't quite place the song as every few words were punctuated by the digga-digga tink-tink beat. Digga-digga tink-tink. Digga-digga tink-tink.

The party-goers on the raft jumped up and down and shouted to their friend who was screeching into the microphone at one end of the floating disco, which throbbed with flashing, strobe and coloured lights. Digga-

digga tink-tink. Digga-digga tink-tink.

As the blaring raft pulled level with us, I named that tune.

"A - a - maze, digga-digga, Zing - in - ing Grace, tink-tink, How sweet, digga-digga, The sound, tink-tink, That saved, digga-digga, A - a wretch, tink-tink, Like MEEEEE!"

All of us on the balcony joined in as the party drifted past and the loud music crashed into the air. I haven't a clue what the Thais thought the words were about. I'd never heard a disco version of Amazing Grace before. Doubt I ever will again.

I visited the bridge frequently, sat on the river bank, looking at it, letting its energy soak into my veins, preparing for the moment when I'd scatter Erno into its depths. There is a resigned serenity about the bridge itself. It is at peace, stretching comfortably across the water, resting solidly on the history of its low stone pillars.

As you look down the railway track, it disappears into the trees on the far bank, a slight gap in the branches as it carves its way deep into the jungle. The track is lost a few metres in, swallowed up by the disappearing darkness. The peace on the bridge is taken with it, devoured by the secrets of the jungle, lost to the misery of time. Hell waited at the other end. I never once felt like wandering further down the track, as some visitors did. It didn't feel safe and I'd seen the unholy savagery that lay beyond. If I ventured too far down there, I wasn't sure the jungle would ever let me return.

Nearly every time I visited the bridge, the same thought crossed my mind. Why did Uncle Erno want to have his ashes scattered here? Why come back? Of all places? And, why me? If I'd been him, I'd have wanted to be kept on safe ground back home not returned to a place of so much pain. I'd have wanted to be buried with my loved ones where

people could come and visit me and put flowers on my headstone.

"Are there any loved ones to visit Ernest's grave?" asked Ajahn Sumeno when I mentioned it to him.

There weren't, apart from me. And my brother, but he lived here.

"Not everyone views death the way you do," continued Sumeno. "When I die, I will not be put in a box as you Christians. My body will be placed on a fire and burned in front of the community."

"Oh my God!"

The wise old monk only smiled and said slowly, "We don't need to hide death from our eyes. It is only a body that is burning, only flesh and blood. It is not I who is burning. I will no longer be."

"Are you saying people here aren't afraid of death at all?"

"No, just that we try to accept that we are to die and that is how it is. For every beginning there is an ending."

"Don't you mean the other way round, for every ending there is a beginning?"

"No. It is how I say. For every beginning there is an ending. When we accept this, suffering eases."

I loved my chats with the Ajahn. He was so kind, so knowing and he'd clearly lived a fulfilling life.

"It doesn't stop you being sad when someone dies though," I said.

"Of course we miss them, but all death comes from birth. If we are to cry, we should cry when someone is born because we know they will suffer in life. Death means that their suffering in this life is over, so we should be happy."

"I still think it is strange to want to have your ashes scattered in a place where you suffered so much pain," I told him.

"They are only ashes, my child. You will not be throwing Ernest into the river."

"But I will be. It's all that's left of him."

"My child, they are only ashes," he repeated but I wouldn't let it drop and later I tackled him again.

"But what is he trying to achieve? Does it mean he's forgiven them?"

"Benedict," chuckled the old Ajahn, "You are like a dog scratching at a wound. You do not need to know why, but if you loved your uncle do as he asks."

"I'd just like to know."

Sumeno laughed at me and swung the rolled end of his robe back over his shoulder.

"Scratch, scratch, scratch," he teased, slowly picking himself up off the step. "You look for problems which do not exist. If a dog is scratching at something, he keeps scratching because he knows no better. If we scratch at something, we should not keep scratching. We should take away the flea."

And he chuckled as he turned and patted up the steps in his old, bare feet.

After a week or so of being by the river, I made a decision to scatter Erno's ashes. I wasn't relishing the thought but I knew I wanted to do it. I'd put my life in England on hold for too long and it'd been fine to suspend it all for a while but I'd begun to miss it too much.

I decided that I'd sort out my tickets when I returned to Bangkok but first, I had a date with Uncle Erno.

Back in my room at the guest house, listening to the water lap at the sides of the raft, I lit some candles and closed the door. As well as a mosquito coil, I lit some incense that Ajahn Sumeno had given to me and took the bag containing Uncle Erno's casket out from the corner of the room. I lifted

the casket out of the bag it'd been in throughout the trip and sat it on the floor in front of me. The dark, wooden casket was shining like new, still highly polished and you could see the reflection of the candles on its surface. There was no plaque or inscription on the top as I was half expecting, just a solid brass clasp at the front which I undid. The hinges slid smoothly as I pushed the lid back until it rested with a gentle click.

Inside was a thick, translucent polythene bag, folded over at the top and neatly tucked in and sealed. There was an envelope placed on top with my name written in familiar, handwritten, laboured scrawl. I opened it.

My Dearest Niece,

With my ashes you scatter gold from the rings of the brave men with whom I served. I throw myself at their feet.

May we all rest in peace with Our Lord.

Your loving,

Uncle Erno

Sitting in the dust, I read the letter twice and I felt very close to Uncle Erno in my makeshift shrine. I assumed when he spoke of gold, he was using it as a metaphor. I had been dreading opening the box. It felt akin to opening a coffin and I had an irrational fear that once open, I'd be letting a whole heap of dead spirits escape into my world, pestering me, not leaving me alone and I'd never find peace while they menacingly whispered in my ears and swiped past my face with their poisoned wings. It was only the memory of Uncle Erno's innate goodness that pushed aside my irrationality

and allowed me to peel away the square of tape that was sealing the ashes.

As I pulled the edges of polythene apart I could see the ash sitting inside and I drew the casket nearer to the candle to catch the light. Flecks began to glisten in amongst the ash, glinting golden in the candlelight, firing sharp beams of brightness out at me. This was Uncle Erno and he had a glint in his eye. Looking closer, I could see flakes of bright gold leaf mixed in with the soft ash and they glittered, sending any dark spirits flying and filling the casket with happiness. They defied my morbid mood and told me to cheer up.

I might have guessed that Thailand held a few more surprises for me before I left but I hadn't banked on discovering gold. What was it doing in there? What's going on, Uncle Erno?

I closed the bag, being careful to seal it fully and leaned back against the wall of my hut. With that, I heard someone's carefully placed footsteps coming down the steps behind the raft and I closed Uncle Erno's casket, pushing it under the bed. I heard Mr Joo call from outside my door.

"Miss Benedict, please, a friend is here."

I had no idea who he'd meant when he'd said friend and thought maybe it was someone from the museum or maybe he was playing a joke on me. I didn't have any friends here. Opening the door, I found an excited Mr Joo eager to usher me up the steps and into the restaurant.

When we reached the restaurant, in the far corner of the balcony a man was standing with his back to us, looking over towards the darkness of the river. He was tall, white, and in the dim light I saw that he had very, very short cropped hair and was wearing jeans and a thin cotton shirt. I didn't recognise him and turned to Mr Joo for help but he simply

waved me towards the man again, excited and grinning.

The man turned round and smiled. He had the start of a thick, dark beard covering his jaw and he was wearing John Lennon glasses. As his smile widened, an unmistakable, goofy grin smiled at me and his face reminded me of Jesus.

"Hi there, Easy Rider," he said in a slow, American drawl. "How ya doin'?"

"Tikaro?" I gasped.

He nodded.

"I disrobed," he said in explanation and grinned even wider as he pretended to ruffle his head of growing hair, which was far too short for ruffling.

"I ain't alone," he added and nodded over to the door.

"Thought we'd call in for a cup of tea," said a young, muscled monk in a sing-song Australian accent as he dipped his head to get through the low doorway.

"Amaro!" I yelled and it was all I could do to stop myself from going over and throwing my arms round his orange robes and giving him a great big smacker on the both cheeks. My heart beamed at the sight of them both.

Then, confusion.

"What are you doing here?" I asked.

And where's Antony?

Tikaro and Amaro stood together by the balcony. The river was pitch black, not a light or sound other than the gentle, distant lap of the water as it brushed the sides of the rafts a few metres down the bank. The nervous silence that had descended on our small reunion was beginning to concern me.

Time hung in the air. No one said anything for a long while. Slowly, I became aware that Amaro was wiping his eyes with his finger tip. He'd begun to cry, very, very quietly

and Tikaro, I noticed, was biting his lip, staring down at the river as if his life depended on its very presence.

"Tikaro?" I said.

He looked up.

"This isn't easy," he explained.

"Come on," I joked, trying to dispel my growing panic by making it easier for them. "Can't be that bad. OK, so Antony didn't want to come. It's OK, I'm used to being on my own."

And at that, I felt Amaro flinch.

"Benedict," said Tikaro, reaching out to me, stepping forward and taking both my hands in a tight grip.

But again he stalled. He needed to breathe deeply before continuing.

"It's your brother, Thanavaro," he eventually said, torturing me.

Spit it out, man! For God's sake.

I saw Tikaro's chest heave with an enormous, determined and painful intake of breath before he finally found the voice to tell me.

"Benedict, he's dying."

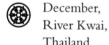 December,
River Kwai,
Thailand

Strange, isn't it, how some of us laugh when told something tragic and that's exactly what I did. I laughed and thought, oh come on. My brother's not dying. He's not. He's a monk in an orange robe at Wat Pah Chatanan. He's not dying. He's not.

He can't.

That's all I remember of the night they told me.

It was the following day that I learned more. Antony has cancer of the stomach. He was diagnosed six months ago but with the treatment he was having, seemed to be coping. He had been having treatment while I was there but had been so convinced he'd be all right, he hadn't wanted to tell me. He didn't come to the River Kwai because he couldn't miss any of the sessions at the hospital in Ubon. All those visits with the Abbot. All those secret glimpses of a life without me, outside the market in Ubon with the Abbot, the argument with Tikaro at Poo Jom Petch. I'd had no idea what it was I'd been witnessing. Tikaro had wanted Antony to tell me.

"He'd wanted to come with you," Tikaro told me. "He thought he would have been well enough but things started to deteriorate."

To think he'd kept all that from me. The poor man. What had he been dealing with?

Urgency entered my thoughts and I needed to act, to do something, to be with him, to see him. I frantically began to find my things and start to pack. I had no plan. I just needed to go. Tikaro stopped me.

"Benedict, slow down," he said as he tried to take my arms.

He realised I was in shock. I began to fight him, angry with him for stopping me from keeping busy, angry with him for telling me about my brother. I flailed my arms at him, lost in a fog of fear and finally, once he'd circled me with his arms and had pulled me towards him, I sobbed into his chest, unable to speak anymore, unable to do anything but be held. He slowly guided me towards a seat and we sat for a long while, no words between us. Tikaro escorted me to my room.

Once my tears began to cease and my eyes could again adjust to the world, the first thing that came into my view was Uncle Erno's casket, still sitting patiently, waiting to be relieved of its fragile cargo. Tikaro, protectively monitoring my every move, saw me looking over at it.

"He knew, y' know," he said.

I didn't understand.

"Your uncle. He knew. About Thanavaro. He knew."

I still didn't get it.

"He knew how ill your brother was," he explained when he saw my uncomprehending face.

"He couldn't have. He died months ago."

"Your brother was diagnosed just before Erno died. He wrote to Erno and told him but asked him not to tell you. Your uncle died before Thanavaro got a response but he told your solicitor to change his will. He wanted to make sure, whatever happened, that you got to see your brother. That's why he asked you to scatter his ashes in Thailand. Your solicitor made all the arrangements."

In that moment, Uncle Erno was with me and I burst into tears. I could feel his presence in the room. Not just his ashes, but him. My kind, fragile, quirky-voiced uncle who'd sent me halfway round the world to scatter his ashes in the very country where he knew my long time unseen brother was probably going to die.

"Why me?" I'd asked Mr Hollingsworth when he'd told me Uncle Erno had requested that I went to Thailand.

"I don't know," he'd replied. "We witness all kinds of requests at these times."

Had everyone known but me?

Erno's casket wouldn't let me go. Not just yet.

"I want to scatter my uncle's ashes. Before we leave. I need

to do it before I leave."

Later, more composed after coffee and able to think, I asked Tikaro, "What happened to you?" Amaro was with us.

"Well," he drawled. "I'd kinda had my fill of life as a monk so I asked the Ajahn if I could leave. He was cool about it, so here I am, with three week's growth of hair."

And he smiled widely at me, teeth just edging his bottom lip.

"But I thought you were there for keeps," I said.

"Don't seem that way, I guess," he replied.

"Yeh," said Amaro, lightly but with an effort in his banter that hadn't been there before. "Life as a Buddhist monk can get a bit rough if you're not into reincarnation."

"Seriously, Tikaro," I laughed, still in shock about my brother and wanting to pretend it wasn't really happening. "You don't believe in rebirth?"

"I just can't get my head round that one," he replied and laughed, a tired, sad laugh, through his short, stubbly beard. "I'm Greg now."

"Greg with hair," I teased. "Lots of hair."

"I guess I'm over compensating a little," he said, stroking his beard of stubble, and we all laughed, a wishful laugh, full of the knowledge of what lay ahead for us all.

 Wat Pah Chatanan,
The Isaan,
N.E. Thailand

What lay ahead of us arrived.

Mr Joo took us to the bridge in his truck that morning after breakfast. It was a brilliantly sunny morning with a crisp,

clear blue sky and I sat up front in the cab with Uncle Erno on my knee.

When we arrived at the bridge and pulled up alongside the railway lines, we found Ajahn Sumeno waiting and smiling. His old kind face looked into mine with a gentleness and grace that went straight to my heart. He bowed to me.

"My child, you have been with me."

"You knew didn't you? About my brother," I asked him and he nodded, seriously.

"It wasn't my place to tell you," he said.

"And about the gold leaf in Uncle Erno's ashes. You knew about that too, didn't you?"

And again, he nodded.

"Your solicitor wrote to us. The gold is from the rings that belonged to your uncle's friends," he told me. "He vowed to scatter these rings with his ashes. Arthur, your solicitor's father, his ring is there and Charlie's."

There was silence as I joined Greg and Amaro who were waiting for me at the start of the bridge. The sun was strong, glancing off the water which was a delicate greeny turquoise, picking up its hue from the clear blue sky overhead. There were a few tourists around but not too many as it was still early and many of them wouldn't arrive until the train pulled in later. I hugged Uncle Erno in front of me as I sat down on the dry grassy bank and rested my cheek on the top of the casket.

A few moments to be. For every beginning there is an ending.

Behind us, over towards the buildings running by the railway, I heard movement. Greg turned to look too and Amaro. Sumeno was stood at the end of the bridge looking

over towards the buildings from where a Thai monk emerged, head down, his orange robe glowing in the sunshine, his bare feet silently and carefully being placed one directly in front of the other.

Behind him appeared another monk, his head bowed like the one in front, his feet following his footsteps, his robe wrapped around his body and over his shoulder.

Then, another monk, followed by another, and another, emerging silently, one by one, gracefully heading towards us. They cut a line over to the railway and headed down the centre of the track towards the bridge. Still they kept emerging one by one, monk after monk after monk until there were forty, fifty, sixty monks creating a moving wall of orange robes heading towards the bridge.

We watched in awestruck silence as they filtered by and I hugged Uncle Erno to my chest.

"Did you know about this?" I asked the boys.

"Not a clue," said Amaro quietly. "Not a clue."

By now the line of holy men stretched halfway across the bridge, their golden robes like a torch flashing its light between the enormous curves of black iron, a beacon shining out from between the girders. One by one I watched them pass as I stood with Amaro and Greg at the start of the bridge. Sumeno joined them and he stopped as he drew level with us. The monks in front walked on, creating space for me, and Sumeno smiled as he gestured for me and Amaro to join him.

"Mr Joo called us when he knew you were coming to scatter the ashes," he told me.

Greg stayed behind but not before he had leaned forward and kissed me gently on the forehead. No one had explained my role in this ceremony but I let myself be carried forward

by the procession, my place given to me by Ajahn Sumeno, Uncle Erno's casket clutched to me.

When I reached the centre of the bridge, the monks halted, the line now stretching from one side of the river to the next. We were all still for a very long, silent moment. I could hear the flow of the water below our feet and there was an incredible reflection of the bridge in the water, its black arches shimmering on the surface, light brush strokes of bright, golden orange shining on the water.

Sumeno held out his hand, gesturing to me to step forward onto the crow's nest in between the two centre arches. As I did, he began to chant in Pali, the other monks joining in until I was surrounded by a wall of their soft, low voices. I could feel the sun warm on my back and as I lifted the box onto the rail, the breeze dropped and the world went silent around me apart from the steady, lulling vibration of the monks chanting. I opened the box and peeled away the seal. Then, holding the bag tightly inside the casket, I tipped it and let the weight of the ash slowly tip forward. As it left the wooden confines of the casket, the breeze lifted, carrying the freed ash and golden flecks into the air, picking them up and taking them out over the river like crushed autumn leaves being lifted into a beckoning sky.

The gold sparkled in the sunshine, rays dancing as they reflected off the edges of the delicate flakes. As the breeze took hold, the joyful spray glinted with bright eyelets of fire spreading into the sky towards the horizon. The monks' chanting continued as the ash drifted up, up and away until finally, without me noticing exactly when, it was no more, given to the river and taken into eternity.

Uncle Erno had gone.

I stepped down from the rail and as I took the casket and

began to gather the polythene in, I found a single gold flake, resting on the lip of the box, resisting flight. I thought of Thanavaro and for a few, fearful moments, my body froze. I knew I would be doing this for him one day soon.

I picked up the delicate gold flake on the tip of my finger and held it up to the breeze. Reluctantly at first, it gradually let its edges be lifted until it too was ready to be released to join the flow of the river. I followed its path as it danced on the breeze, playfully skipping through the air, reflecting the sunshine back as if singing to me, wanting to share its joy. I said goodbye just before it magically vanished into the brilliant blue above.

As the chanting reverberated around the bridge I closed my eyes. I hardly noticed when it stopped. Sumeno waited until I was ready before he eventually turned and the monks at the end of the bridge began to filter away as silently and as gracefully as they had appeared. One by one we made our way off the bridge and I stepped aside as I reached the end, to let each of the remaining monks pass.

Greg was waiting on the bank and he came up to give me a huge hug. I leaned my head into his shoulder but I didn't feel sad, as I'd expected. I'm not sure what it was I felt. But it felt OK. Amaro found us and said he was going to go back to the monastery with the monks.

I ate with Greg that night, in silence, and slept as best I could knowing that this was to be my last night on the River Kwai.

Next morning, Amaro and Greg took me to the station to catch a train back to Bangkok and to the airport where we caught a plane to Ubon in the evening. The same journey I'd made alone, a couple of months before. But this time when I emerged at the top of the escalator, looking down into the

arrival lounge, Antony wasn't there like before. I searched for his face among the many that were looking up at me but none was his.

The minibus was waiting for us at the airport and when we arrived at Chatanan, Greg and Amaro sat me at the table in the kitchen. It was dark, not a person in sight, and even the faint whisper of the forest seemed to have forgotten to keep us company. They made some noodle soup and put it in a flask for me and then took me to the same kuti where I'd spent my first night.

It was lonely when they left, no orchids on the shrine like before, no candles welcoming me home.

They'd explained that Thanavaro now lived in the guest villa. He was more comfortable there. They explained that they had been told that his cancer had spread to his lymphatic system. They explained that he was asleep and that it would be best to wait until morning to see him.

I lay awake in the dark expecting tears but they didn't come. If I cried, that would make it real. While it still wasn't real, there was nothing to cry about, so I begged the tears not to come.

I couldn't sleep so I lit some candles and sat in my kuti, opening the noodle soup, taking a cupful but I wasn't able to drink and I tipped it back. Opposite me, sitting peacefully and calmly as if nothing was happening was the small statue of Buddha that had been placed in my room when I first arrived. It was watching me, smugly. We stared each other out for a long few minutes, his expression unchanging and I felt a fire of resentment grow in my chest. My iPod lay unused on the floor beside me and I picked it up and hurled it at the Buddha. It hit the statue, smashing the iPod to pieces and sending Buddha to the wall. I wanted to scream but I

knew if I started I wouldn't stop, and I didn't think the forest was ready to hear just how loud my scream would be.

Then, I thought of Antony.

Sleep visited for only a restless few hours before dawn and I was woken by harsh daylight piercing the shutters and stabbing my eyes. For a fleeting moment, I wasn't there. None of it was there and I was flying up the highway on a Harley after Antony, chasing rainbows, wearing no helmets. But, mercilessly, the weight of pain that rested on my chest dragged me back to Chatanan and my kuti and now.

I heard someone approaching on the path outside and caught the familiar, barely audible sound of a monk's robe being swept over a shoulder. Antony, I thought, he's come to see me. And then, no, Benedict, no. Get a grip.

When I opened the door to my kuti I found the Abbot of Wat Pah Chatanan and Amaro waiting in the sunshine. My sad welcome party.

"Benedict," said the Abbot. "This must be a very difficult time for you and I offer the support of all our community and our deepest, deepest love. Please, whatever we can do to help, just ask and it is yours."

I managed a faint smile.

"After the meal, I will take you to see your brother. He has a medical attendant looking after him. And please," he said, now pausing to look me directly in the eye, "Stay at Chatanan for as long as you like. Treat it as home."

"I don't think I can eat anything," was all I could find to say.

The Abbot's presence was very warm and comforting. He was someone older, someone with experience in this stuff and his solidity and centredness soothed the shaking that had been going on inside me all night.

"Before we go over to the guest house," he continued, "I'd like to explain about Thanavaro's illness. Is now a good time to do this?"

I nodded and he and Amaro sat on the ground in front of my kuti, resting against some rocks in the dry, arid sunshine. I joined them and we sat in a circle.

"How are you feeling?" he asked.

How was I supposed to answer? I hadn't been aware that I was feeling anything. I looked into this gentle man's concerned face.

"Scared," I heard myself reply and swallowed hard on the lump that was threatening to grow in my throat. The Abbot nodded, and after a few moments continued, in his calm and confident, reassuring tone.

"Thanavaro has cancer. It originated in the stomach and has spread to his lymphatic system. I'm afraid, as is common, it wasn't detected in the early stages and Thanavaro's latest symptoms didn't present themselves until very, very recently. He was having chemotherapy in Ubon where there is a very good hospital but it hasn't stopped the cancer."

He spoke gently and thoughtfully, watching me as I listened, checking for signs of comprehension written in my face.

"He is very ill," he continued. "And very weak."

Amaro sat still beside me, watching the ground. Sadness emanated all around him but he remained stoic, being strong for me.

"Why wasn't it spotted earlier?" I asked.

Surely they could've done something to stop this thing from growing? What were they all playing at? The Abbot breathed in slowly, and then out again before he answered calmly.

"Stomach cancer is very difficult to spot," he explained and added, "Benedict, everything that could have been done, has been done."

I nodded, knowing the anger I was feeling towards him was unjustified, but feeling it nonetheless. It pushed against my temples, burning inside my chest and gripping in my fists. All I could do was hold it in. I also felt a pinprick of anger towards Antony but I pushed it away. I was getting tired of being angry.

"What is he like now?" I wanted to know.

"He's very ill."

"I know that," I insisted, "But what is he like? What does he look like? When you say he's weak, how weak is that?"

The Abbot nodded gently, acknowledging my need to know more and spoke very steadily.

"He can't move much and he is on very strong medication for the pain which makes him drowsy."

"Will he recognise me?"

I needed to know what I was going to be walking in on, needed to know if my brother was still with me or if he'd already left.

"Oh yes, and he can still speak," reassured the Abbot, "You can still hold a conversation with him. He just tires easily."

As he told me this, we heard the light patter of tiny Thai feet on the path that led to my kuti and the rustle of sarongs. From behind the nearby bathroom came Mae Li and the white haired lady from the kitchen, whose name I still hadn't caught. Their usually smiling faces were replaced by sombre, sad ones, but they were still filled with generosity and kindness. As soon as they saw the monks, they stopped and knelt, bowing three times. Both were laden with a large bouquet of bright, sunny flowers which they had been

carrying in their arms but which now rested on their knees as they placed their palms together to Wai towards the monks. The Abbot spoke to them in Thai and they nodded, silently and then both looked at me. Mae Li said something and the Abbot turned towards me.

"They have brought you flowers," he explained, "And thought you may wish to have them placed in your brother's room."

And then Mae Li produced a small bottle from inside the folds of her skirt.

"And Mae Li has brought you some water. She asked one of the monks to chant over it. It's to help your brother."

"Help him?"

The Abbot stalled for a moment but decided to tell me.

"To help him on his journey."

And it finally sank in. You really are dying, aren't you Antony.

"They want you to know too," he continued, "That they will be here for you and that you are part of their family now."

I looked at Mae Li, her eyes connecting with mine and I begged them to shine like before and send their joy rushing through my veins. But her eyes didn't smile. Instead, they were sad and concerned and told me that she knew how difficult this was for me, and that she knew that their ways were different from mine and that I was finding this oh so very, very hard.

I got up and walked over to the two kneeling women. Mae Li held her hand out and I crouched in front of them while they both held my hands and each touched my cheek.

"Thank you," I said in English and tried to smile.

As I got up, I turned to the two monks and told them, "I'd

like to see Antony now."

It's difficult to describe what I felt as we walked over to the guest house that morning. The house loomed in the distance, growing so large that it towered over our small bodies, its darkness and danger so threatening that twice I stopped and nearly turned back. The monks waited for me while I silently fought for strength and we continued along the dusty path, past tall dry grasses which ushered me forward and with the rays of the morning sun behind me.

It was very quiet when we reached the house and I could see through the screens that there was no one downstairs and the shutters in the bedrooms were closed. We entered and the Abbot went upstairs to let the medical attendant know of our arrival.

Silence boomed until Amaro said, "It means so much to Thanavaro that you are here." And I heard the echo from when Thanavaro himself had said those words to me. If only you'd said why, Thanavaro. If only you'd said why.

I could hear the shutters being opened upstairs and the patter of shoeless feet above our heads and it was some minutes before the Abbot appeared again.

"Would you like to come now?" he said.

Upstairs, there was a man in a white tunic waiting for me at the bedroom door, my bedroom door where I'd spent happy nights listening to music, reading War and Peace and waiting for the next beautiful sunrise. He smiled and gave me a Wai, then showed me into the room. It had all changed. There was now a metal bed, not just a mattress on the floor, and there was a clinical looking table in the far corner with all sorts of medical stuff on it. A shrine had been created in the other corner with a statue of the Buddha overlooking proceedings and the room had the stingy, sharp smell of a

hospital. A wind chime hung up against the far window and every so often it chimed optimistically. The shutters had been opened halfway, letting the daylight in but sheltering the room from the heat of the sun's harsh rays.

The bed was on my left as I stood in the door and I knew that Antony was lying there but I didn't want to look. I needed to postpone the blunt pain of reality for a moment longer. I turned towards him.

He lay there, still and pale and linked up to God knows how many drips, tubes and bags. He was awake and he was waiting for me to look at him. I turned and let my eyes fall on his. They lay me bare as I saw my dying brother for the first time and my chest burst with the tears of half a lifetime. I had so wanted to be strong for him at this moment, so wanted not to cry but the tears crowded my being. My feelings poured into the empty space that had once been between us.

I walked over and bent to hug him, my vision blurred and my body heaving with the sobs I'd been holding at bay for so long. As I put my arms round him, feeling his frail, bony torso close to mine, he carefully shifted in his bed and I finally felt his arms encircle me and his head rest between my shoulder and my neck. He clung to me so tightly, breaking all the rules as I sobbed into the pillow and he gripped me so hard that I thought his brittle body would break. I could feel him shaking from inside, a deep, unstoppable, dreadful shudder from within that spoke of unmentionable fear, of a place so dark that it caused faith to falter.

When I drew away from him, I took his fragile, weak hand as I sat down in a chair that the Abbot had pulled up to the side of the bed. Antony's skin looked so grey and old, almost transparent, and I could see the thin, narrow veins

which were still carrying blood around his aching body. Looking up, I saw that he was smiling at me, a smile that defied the condition of his body.

"So, they found you then," he said and I could hardly believe the joy in his weary voice.

"I'm still pissed off you didn't come," I teased, surprised at my own capacity for black humour, and we both laughed.

The Abbot and Amaro tactfully left, saying they would arrange for some food to be brought over for me after the meal. They left the attendant as chaperone and as soon as they departed I felt another layer of inhibition lift and I sobbed some more, unable to say anything.

"I couldn't tell you Benedict. I couldn't do that when we thought there was still hope of me beating it," said Antony. "I didn't want to stop you from carrying out Uncle Erno's wishes, but," and he paused, "I couldn't come with you."

"You should have said something, Antony. I could have coped."

"I know," he said, reticently, closing his eyes and resting for a while, drawing breath, "But I'm not sure I could have coped with telling you."

And he closed his wet eyes, tears crowding the corners of his eyelids, strength abandoning him.

I let Antony rest and watched while he slept. He needed to do that a lot. I sat with the attendant, listening to his breathing, noticing how hard even that had become. He was thin and pale and I knew from that first day that the brother I had known was never coming back. This person was my brother now. This was Thanavaro, the monk.

I stayed with him all day, only leaving for a few minutes to eat something when the Abbot returned. I managed to sleep too, resting in the chair beside Antony's bed, dozing in the

warm, shadowy light. Returning to my kuti at night wasn't easy. I wanted to stay at the villa, sleep in the next room, just to be close to Antony, just to be near, just in case, but it wasn't practical.

As soon as dawn broke, I returned. Antony hadn't woken up and again I sat with the attendant, waiting for the moments when my brother's illness allowed him enough energy to be with me. He woke in stages. First half opening his eyes, still not aware of where he was or that I was with him. He fell asleep again and gradually began to stir about half an hour later. I was hoping for a smile when he finally realised I was there and I wasn't ready for what happened.

He didn't smile. He'd woken from a place I couldn't imagine and I could see that to utter even one word demanded a fortress of energy. His eyes were scared as the first thing he said was,

"I'm dying," and he wept as I got up and held him in my arms, cradling his head, his beautiful head, shiny from loss of hair and stubble-free. He sobbed like a fallen child and I learnt then to just hold him, nothing more, no well-meaning words, no self-comforting, just loving silence.

What is there to say to someone who's dying?

After the sobs had ceased, I tried to lift his mood and began to tell him about my visit to the River Kwai.

"I thought of you while I was there," I said gently. "Sitting by the river, remembering our trip on the Mekong. Thank God I hadn't left," I whispered, knowing how near I had come to leaving Thailand and never seeing my brother ever again.

Antony rested, catching his breath before telling me,

"We knew you hadn't left. Ajahn Sumeno told us you were still at the river. Amaro is not finding all this easy," he

confided, his energy returning for a short while.

"It's hard, Antony."

"How does he think I feel?" he asked, raising his voice and then checking himself and looking over to the Thai attendant who was calmly doing nothing except sitting and waiting over by the shutters. His anger surprised me but it invigorated him temporarily.

"I've felt so lost, Benedict," he said. "The first drug treatment seemed quite hopeful, that was when you were here and then, just before you left, I started to bleed again and they needed to do more tests. I didn't find out how serious it was until you'd gone and then I thought…" He faltered and again closed his eyes, resting before summoning the strength to face his darkness again. "I thought I might never see you again and I asked them to go and look for you."

And then he broke down.

"I'm so sorry, Benedict. I'm so sorry," and he wept into the palms of his hands as he held them to his face and I leant forward and hugged him hard, feeling his brittle bones grate.

I let him rest and then asked,

"Antony, will you answer me something? No one else will tell me."

He nodded.

"How long have you got?"

As he lay there, a cool cotton sheet covering his skeletal torso, he stared me straight in the eye. There were dark shadows under the sockets where sunshine used to play and each time he embarked on the laboured process of blinking, he seemed to lose another ounce of his slowly sapping energy. His skin looked old and the colour was slipping further from him. Even his mole had lost its vigour but his

bald head, his beautiful bald head, was gleaming in the broken sunshine which had crept round the corner of the shutter.

In reply to my question, Antony slowly took my hand in his and said, "Benedict, I've got all the time in the world."

Antony was in a lot of pain. He had a pump which fed medication to him and, when it got really bad, he could squeeze it to get an extra dose. He also had a saline drip and was prone to infections. He caught a chest infection shortly after I arrived and it weakened him a great deal. I visited every day and stayed with him for most of the day, watching him when he slept, giving him space when he meditated, holding his hand when he rested and listening to him when he wanted to talk.

I got into a routine of attending the morning meal with the rest of the Sangha after Antony had asked me to because he was worried I wasn't looking after myself. It was a good idea as it meant I saw the other monks and wasn't too cut off from life in the monastery.

The Abbot caught me one morning.

"You know, if you would like to come with me to meditate, I will teach you."

What is it about Buddhist monks that seems to bestow upon them a sixth sense that told them what I wanted before I'd even recognised it myself? I had wanted to try meditation, to see if I could get a glimpse of my brother's life but I hadn't yet got to the point of asking anyone or doing anything about it.

"If you come with me each day, after half past three, I will explain to you how we meditate."

So I did, every evening for the last few days, sitting in the Outside Sala with the Abbot and a novice, cross-legged for half an hour. Then, as I got used to it, I sat for longer, while

Antony slept.

At first it did nothing, absolutely nothing. What was all the fuss about? I just sat there trying to watch my breath as instructed but instead listened to the creak of my knees and followed my thoughts as they wandered from the inane to the very serious. I thought about stiff limbs and how I now knew what Amaro had meant when he talked of Pansa being three months of achy knees. I thought about the meal we had had that morning and how remarkable it is that the villagers manage to make delicious food from the simplest of things. I thought of my brother lying in bed, unable to eat anything at all. Then, as instructed, I tried to watch my breath again.

Over time, the half-hour went faster and I followed what arrived in my head. Not so much thoughts and images, but sensations. Then something else clicked into place. I can't really describe it other than my mind was able to transfer from the here and now into a place it'd never travelled before. A small door had been opened and I'd allowed myself to walk through into a new arena and a new way to be.

Antony still meditated. He'd spend hours lying still and I'd know not to disturb him until he opened his eyes. I was so grateful to the Abbot for showing me a glimpse of something my brother saw in those last few days.

"Sing to me," Antony said one afternoon.

He was tired, his face drained, his eyes closed.

"What, here?" I asked.

"Where else, stupid," he teased.

"What would you like me to sing?"

And he waited as I picked up on the poignancy of this moment. I realised we were about to go on a journey filled with memories long since buried and Antony was the one who was going to hold my hand and guide me through.

"That one Mum used to sing to us. You know, the one about the stars shining."

Slowly my mind traced the years back to the time he was talking about. Mum, singing us to sleep as we lay in our bunk beds, me on the bottom bunk because I wasn't big enough to climb the ladder, Antony listening from above and Mum sat by me, stroking my hair. Mum, who died of stomach cancer as I stood watching her sideways from next to the bed.

"Antony, I don't think I can."

"'Course you can," he said, knowing where I'd just gone and I felt a faint pressure on my hand as he squeezed my palm.

I don't know from where I found the strength to sing to him but somehow it came to me and I sang quietly as he lay with his eyes closed and a smile on his calm, slowly dying face. The Mamas and Papas from years ago, finding us.

Stars shining bright above you.

Stars fading but I will linger on dear.

Antony wanted to talk a lot about our childhood. He wanted to hear of the times we'd spent playing in the fields behind our house when Mum was still alive, how she'd call us in for tea by clattering a wooden spoon on an old tin tray, how we'd fight over whose turn it was to use the tape recorder. We remembered when we'd each got a brand new bicycle for Christmas and how I fell off mine, splitting my head open so Dad had had to rush me to the doctor for stitches, and the time when Antony had got his first 125cc motorbike and rolled it into the garage wall because he hadn't worked out how to use the foot brake.

Those were the days my friend. We thought they'd never end.

I enjoyed the reminiscing while I could still see the

pleasure it brought Antony but I'm not sure he ever felt the growing ache that I could feel in my heart as our precious time together ticked away.

I still had things to learn from my brother. I learnt that the tradition of monks shaving their eyebrows wasn't, as I'd thought, something to do with sacrificing their identity or following the Buddha's example. It started only three hundred years ago when Burmese spies would disguise themselves as monks and the only way their enemies could tell the real monks from the fake ones, was to shave the monks' eyebrows. Any man found later with half-grown hedgehog eyebrows was deemed to be spy. It had nothing at all to do with anything spiritual.

I learnt that included in the vows my brother had taken when he got ordained was a vow to the Sanga, the community, and that the way of life here would disintegrate if individual people didn't make a commitment to those with whom they shared that life.

I learnt that key to a Buddhist spiritual life is gaining an understanding of our emotional life and that the two are irretrievably linked. The more we get to know our emotions, the closer we can get to our spiritual self. I didn't have to feel bad about feeling angry, resentful or sad anymore, I just needed to accept that I did and try to understand it.

I learnt too that the monks didn't believe that theirs was the only way to live a spiritual life or that it was the best way, just that it was a good way and for now, even if it wasn't perfect, it was as good a path to follow as any.

It made me think of Amaro and what he'd said to me in the early days of being at Wat Pah Chatanan. Here, all anybody is trying to be is a good person. Nothing more, just

good, and I realised I wanted to be a good person, especially now, for my brother.

Antony wanted to prepare a living will. I didn't know what he meant until he explained he wanted to tell everyone his wishes so it was there for us all to see should he become too weak to explain. I slept badly the night he told me, not wanting to wake and have to transcribe such a stark reminder that he was going to die. A reminder from the very person who was doing the dying. But as with most things during those last weeks, a strength found me from somewhere, given in part, I know, by Uncle Erno.

Antony wanted to die here, at Chatanan. He didn't want to go to hospital. He didn't want to be resuscitated at any time and he refused any form of artificial feeding. And he wanted me to scatter his ashes and he told me where. I wrote it all down in long hand and we kept it by his bed.

"I'm frightened, Benedict," he said as I held his hand, "but I'm not supposed to be."

"How are you supposed to be?" I asked him.

The room that day was darkened to try and keep it cool. Temperatures outside had begun to soar so there was no way the shutters could have been opened. The heat from the light would have been too much for Antony. It could be a bit strange sometimes, stuck in a dark room for days when the sun was shining brightly outside. Time no longer had much meaning. Day time, night time, it was all time with Antony and that was all I cared about.

"I'm supposed to accept this as part of life's cycle," he told me. "Death's a part of life, not an end, not even a beginning, just a part of an ongoing process."

"So?"

"So I shouldn't be frightened."

"Antony, there's no right or wrong way to do this."

"No, don't you see? If my faith was strong enough, I wouldn't be frightened. It would take all the fear away."

"Your faith can't ever take away you being human," I said, trying to comfort him but not sure if I was. "You haven't failed just because you're frightened," and I kept hold of his delicate hand as he drifted into silence, his eyes losing focus and finally closing into sleep.

He wasn't the only one who was frightened.

The time he could spend talking lessened with each day. He grew tired more quickly and the pain became much worse. He weakened to the point where he could no longer administer his own pain relief.

Greg came to visit a few times. He was living in the monastery now, having stopped talking of any plans to leave for the time being. He didn't need to mention it but we both knew he was waiting until after my brother had passed away.

"He looks so happy when he's asleep," he said one afternoon when he'd joined us. And then, to me, "He's a good man your brother, a very good man."

Greg had changed. He was the same, lanky, goofy American I'd met when I arrived but once out of his robe he was more comfortable, more confident. His hair had also grown considerably, his eyebrows no longer looked like crewcut hairy caterpillars but he'd shaved the beard off.

"What will you do after," I began to ask but I couldn't finish the sentence.

"When I go back?" he offered, helpfully. "I'm not sure. Visit my folks first, I guess. We've got a heap of catching up to do. I'm thinking of calling in at the San Francisco monastery, up there in the Redwood forests. I'd kinda like to see it and ease myself back into the States. Then I guess I'll

have to fly home and find me a job and, who knows, maybe even a woman?" And he smiled, a relaxed man.

Amaro wasn't such easy company. He was finding it all very difficult and, since Antony had worsened, hadn't been to visit. I met him one afternoon in the Outside Sala.

"I know I should visit," he said. "But I can't. I can't face it."

He looked so stressed, the strain of whatever was going on for him having taken its toll in his once calm, happy face. Gone was his flippancy. Gone were the gesticulating arms and the boyish grin. He was sitting restlessly on the floor of the Sala, unable to get comfortable, shifting from one haunch to another, continually wringing his hands or driving a fist into the floor.

I just sat and, unlike before, let him do all the talking. A complete role reversal.

"I know I should try to be different but I don't seem able. It tests you, all this," he wanted to explain. "Thanavaro shouldn't die. He's young, he's fit, he's full of life," and he looked over at me as if I didn't know what he meant. "He's my friend and I want him here, with me, helping me through my dark days, sitting next to me at the meal."

He paused for a short moment as if only by putting his feelings into words did they begin to make sense.

"D'you know what's hardest of all?" he said, close to tears, his firm, toned face crumbling. "Realising that I'm angry. I'm angry at Thanavaro! I'm angry at him for getting ill!" And he hit the wooden floor. "For chrissakes, how about that, Benedict? And I'm angry at the world and it scares me."

Watching him struggle to come to terms with the reality of his friend and mentor dying strengthened me. I now knew more than ever, that for Antony's sake, I needed to help Amaro.

"I've been angry too, Amaro," I told him. "I've felt all of what you're feeling. Nobody expects you to find this easy but there isn't much time left. Antony is young, yes, but he's no longer fit, no longer full of life like you said. He's dying."

There, I'd said it, and as the words left my mouth, I marvelled at how easy it had become.

"No one can force you to see him," I said, "but I know he'd like it. And, more than that Amaro, I think he's waiting for you."

 December,
Wat Pah Chatanan
Thailand

It's not easy keeping a diary at the moment, not easy knowing that what I'll be writing about is my brother's death. But I still want to. Reading Uncle Erno's scrawled diary, written on stolen bits of paper that would have cost his life if he'd been caught, makes me want to write this. And anyway, soon this may be all I have left of Antony. My brother. Thanavaro. The monk.

The Abbot has visited Thanavaro a few times. Sometimes they meditate together, Thanavaro lying in bed and the Abbot sitting in the lotus position at the far side of the room on the floor. I've watched them a couple of times. There is an incredible peace when they are like this together. An energy that fills the room. The visits have lifted Thanavaro a little and he is stronger. He is more animated and spends less time asleep, is able to talk for a few minutes at a time. He is clearly in a lot of pain but he doesn't let on how bad it really is. He'll simply ask for more medication and lie quietly with his eyes closed until it takes effect. For a few days now, he's

been able to administer the painkillers himself.

The Abbot is such a kind man. I know he's allowed etiquette to be broken with me spending so much time alone with Thanavaro and, sin of sins, holding him. He hasn't even mentioned it. A good job because we would have had to have words.

I haven't let the other rules of the monastery get me down. What's the point? I've got a lot of respect for them, for how the monks live, what they're aiming for, and the kindness embodied in them and the lay people is unarguable.

Thanavaro is very peaceful and strong in himself these days. The fear has gone and instead he is very self-contained and if anything, even though he is the one who is ill, the one about to face a journey we cannot begin to comprehend, it's as if he is the one giving us strength. When you enter his room it feels full of light, an uplifting place to be rather than one which needs those things added. It's as if Thanavaro is looking after us, knowing that very shortly, we will need to borrow some of the strength he has found.

I got a Christmas card from Captain Archie today. The small card shows an innocent picture of snow covered English hillsides with tiny sheep dotting the landscape. There's a robin in the foreground, sitting on the branch of a holly tree. It's such a far away image that I struggle to relate to it. It's nearly Christmas at home. The nights will be dark, the shops full, there'll be carol singers in town and late-night shopping. If I'd still been there, I'd have had my Christmas tree up by now, its fairy lights twinkling, golden baubles dangling and that daft Christmas fairy that Stella gave me three years ago stuck on the top. At work we would have been run off our feet with Christmas parties and I would be

panicking because I hadn't bought all my Christmas presents. A world away.

I placed Captain Archie's card next to Thanavaro's bed.

They don't celebrate Christmas in The Isaan. Why would they?

It does however, coincide this year with a Buddhist festival. A full moon falls on Christmas Eve which means, like every full moon, there'll be an all-night vigil and the villagers and monks will spend the whole night in the Sala, chanting and meditating. Some of the women crash out in the kitchen at about midnight and they have a sleep-over. I think I might join them. I also think I'd like to go on Pindabah on Christmas morning too.

 December,
Wat Pah Chatanan
Thailand

It's Christmas Eve. I met the white haired lady from the kitchen on my way back to the guest house the other day. She's called Mae Hao and she still takes my arm as she smiles and chats away to me in her native dialect. I can catch a few words now, like Pansa, Ajahn and Pindabah. She counted on her fingers how many Pansas the Abbot has been in charge here and then she said a word I've heard a number of times in the last few days.

"Kisamet," she said and pointed to me. "Kisamet," she grinned and nodded.

I nodded in return and said the word back to her.

"Kisamet."

Then she waved over at the Sala, carried on chatting and I assumed she was talking about the vigil which was going

to take place. From the way she circled both her arms in front of her, it looked like there'd be lots of people coming to the 'Kisamet' festival and I thought she was showing me that they'd all be bowing and kneeling, and sleeping, from what she was miming.

"Kisamet," I nodded to her.

She nodded back.

"Pindabah," she added, rapidly going through my entire Thai vocabulary. "Pindabah," and tapped me on the chest, seriously, then waved over towards the village, patting her own chest. She did the whole routine twice.

Pindabah. You. Pindabah. Village. Pindabah. Me.

She was telling me to look out for her when I went through the village during Pindabah in the morning. I knew that was where she lived and then she mimed drinking from a cup and she pointed at me again.

Pindabah. You. Pindabah. Village. Pindabah. Me. Pindabah. Drink.

Mae Hao was inviting me in for a drink tomorrow morning after Pindabah. A Christmas morning drink with the neighbours.

Before we parted she had one, final mime for me to lighten my spirits. This time my clue word was Ajahn, which I kept hearing as she pointed to me. She mimed a monk, who she called Ajahn, hands folded in his lap, eyes closed. The Ajahn was meditating, sitting still and upright. She continued the mime, the Ajahn was still meditating, hands folded in his lap, eyes closed, head beginning to drop forward slowly. The Ajahn was nodding off, and again, Mae Hao mimed. Ajahn, hands folded in his lap, eyes closed, struggling to lift his head, and finally, Ajahn, nodding off in the middle of meditation, head dropping forward until he woke himself

with a startled jerk and had to quickly remember where he was before he composed himself again.

"Ajahn!" I laughed with Mae Hao, convinced I'd got her joke. A monk falling asleep while meditating. I did my own mime to show her I'd understood.

But Mae Hao shook her head vigorously.

"Ajahn Farang!" she shouted.

Thai monks don't fall sleep during meditation, she was telling me. Only the foreign monks do that because they haven't got the stamina and Mae Hao chortled at her own joke, as I felt my own belly shake with the release of another layer of tension and I laughed uninhibitedly with her. Sweet relief from my gruelling days and nights.

As tiny Mae Hao walked away she was still chortling to herself.

"Ajahn Farang," she chuckled while she pointed at me again, shuffling her way down the leaf swept footpath that led to the monastery gates and out towards her village.

"Ajahn, bumph," she laughed, letting her arms and head fall, mimicking the sleeping monk. "Bumph." And she laughed all the way to the gate.

"Is it an ongoing joke?" I asked Thanavaro later when I was with him.

I watched his slow thoughts process, reflected in his puzzled face. Then, recognition. He tried not to laugh too hard because it hurt too much and then, he enlightened me.

"It's me she's talking about," he smiled, slowly. "Yes, it is an ongoing joke they have about the Farang monks not being able to meditate for long stretches but a few months ago, I did it," and he broke off to laugh gently. He breathed a few times before carrying on. "I fell asleep in the middle of a vigil."

"You?"

He nodded slightly, still laughing.

"Not only that, I fell over and went crashing into the metal bowl that I had beside me and sent it flying. It was so loud," he said, tears of laughter at the corner of his eyes as he remembered, stopping quickly to take in more oxygen and to squeeze on his pain relief pump. Eventually he opened his eyes and looked at me, his dark, lively eyes searching mine.

"It was so funny, it hurt," he mocked, with black humour.

We laughed until the hurt was too much, me holding my stomach.

Thanavaro's condition had remained fairly stable for the last two days but he was weakening. He hadn't been eating for a long, long time and he was so thin. Amaro finally plucked up the courage to visit. I tried not to judge him too harshly for leaving it so long.

I was lost in this thought, sitting by the path that leads to the guest villa, when a slow, American voice said,

"What's up, Easy Rider?"

It was Greg, on his way to visit. He crouched down beside me.

"Amaro," I told him. "I'm pissed off with him. It's taken him ages to get round to visiting Thanavaro, as if none of us are finding it difficult," and I hurled a pebble into the tall grass. "It's Thanavaro who needs the help, he's the one who's dying," I continued grumpily. "You'd think Amaro could've got a grip before now."

"Don't be too harsh," said Greg calmly. "At least he's got there." And he sat with me for a while, watching the grass grow.

Later, on the way over to see my brother, I passed Mae Li. She was picking herbs by the side of the path, placing them

carefully on a cloth she'd laid out on the ground.

"Sawat di kha," I called over to her and she nodded the same back to me.

"Kisamet?" she asked, and when she saw that I hadn't quite understood, she pointed over to the main monastery and repeated, "Kisamet." And she pointed back to me.

"Yes, I'll be there," I said, nodding. "For the vigil, I'll be there. Kisamet, Mae Li."

And we both smiled.

"Does it get very busy at Kisamet?" I asked Thanavaro once I reached the guest villa.

"At what?" he replied, quietly.

"At Kisamet, the vigil, tonight."

Thanavaro's shoulders poked out sharply from under the sheet and the skin over his drawn face pulled away over the cheek bones. His eyes sank into his head and he looked grey and wasted. I remembered the men I'd seen in the photos at Ajahn Sumeno's museum.

But he still found the energy to tease me. "So you're going to Kisamet tonight, are you?"

"Yes, with the villagers," I said defensively but he laughed weakly at me again.

"Benedict," he said, touchingly, "I thought you realised. Kisamet isn't the name of our vigil. It's Christmas, that's how they say the English word here. Kisamet. It's their way of pronouncing it." And then, after a pause for breath and pain relief, he added, "They know it's a special time for you. For me and you, and they want you to feel at home."

"Christmas," I said, embarrassed and touched. "Kisamet."

"It just falls on the same night as the full moon festival. It's going to be an important day for all of us," he remarked and gently closed his eyes.

I watched as he went to sleep, his bony chest very gently lifting and falling under the white sheet and after about half an hour, I left.

 December,
Wat Pah Chatanan
Thailand

On the night of Christmas Eve I walked over to the main part of the monastery at around eight in the evening to join the other monks and villagers for the all night, full moon vigil. It was an eerie evening as I approached through the trees with the moon beaming down, a silver white orb in the far away sky casting an elegant shimmer on the path and the leaves. As I neared the main Sala, I could hear the voices of the villagers chanting, a different chant from the monks, less refined but more blatantly joyful and full of giving. The sound filled the forest, moving between the trees, finding a way out and pulling me nearer.

In the Sala, there must have been about a hundred villagers kneeling and sitting on the floor. The monks were sat on the far ledge in silence and as I entered, the volume of the chanting grew until I could feel it vibrate inside my chest. It was beautiful. Mae Li shuffled up to greet me when she saw me arrive, silently taking my arm which she held tightly as we sat down with the other villagers and I listened to their chanting.

Once it finished, the Abbot moved from his spot to take up position on a large chair which had been placed in front of the villagers. He didn't rush but waited until his helpers had sorted cushions, a jug of water and had helped him with his robes. The villagers waited patiently.

Eventually, the Abbot began to talk. He spoke in fluent Thai with a confidence that came from years of living here. He didn't come across as pious or preaching. He joked with them, made them laugh, and occasionally I heard an English word thrown in.

"'Santa Claus,'" said the Abbot a few times, usually followed by lots of giggles from the villagers and a few questions.

The villagers sat, listened and waited while he treated them to over two hours of his lulling, benevolent voice, an intimate audience with the people without whom the monastery couldn't exist. Towards the end of his talk, the Abbot's tone changed to one of sombre reflection and amidst the singing Thai words, I heard him mention Thanavaro's name and then clearly, my own name, Benedict. He was telling all the villagers about what was happening over at the guest villa. Mae Li, beside me, remained still, meditating, concentrating, and all the while she refused to let go her tight, strengthening grip on my arm.

My private world was being shared, and whereas before I'd have retreated at the thought of the pending pain, now I simply felt loved.

The Sala was lit by candlelight, a soft, low glow that was dimmed even further once the talk and the chanting was over. The whole community settled in for the night's meditation with a final shift of position and the pulling of a blanket over their shoulders until finally, there was stillness and a silent peace.

I sat with Mae Li as time ticked away and the hands on my watch moved past midnight and into Christmas Day, the full moon watching over this cradle nestling in The Isaan forest.

At about twelve thirty, with no need for announcement,

some of the women finished meditating and left the Sala, heading for the kitchen. Christopher was already there and had prepared flasks of a hot drink which everyone helped themselves to and then sat down. He brought me over a steaming cup.

"Please, miss. You drink good Thai ginger tea," and, being Christopher, he left before I could say thank you.

I sat with the women as they chatted and I knew that they were trying to welcome me into their group because I kept hearing 'Kisamet' followed by silence. I'd look up and they'd all be staring at me with wide, kind grins.

Mae Li was talking quite a bit and I imagined she was filling them in on Thanavaro's condition. We all finished our drink and one by one the women started to lie down on the floor to get some rest before being woken at three-thirty. I so wanted to nudge up next to them and feel the warmth of a motherly breast. I wanted to lose myself in their generous love and be swallowed up by their kindness, the best Christmas present I could wish for.

But I needed to leave and rest properly. As I got up to go, Mae Li gave me a knowing smile and Mae Hao, who I hadn't noticed, suddenly sat up with a jerk.

"Pindabah," she reminded me. "Pindabah."

Before I went to bed, I called in on Thanavaro. It was Christmas night and not a creature stirred. The attendant bowed his head in acknowledgment of my arrival and through the dim, warm candlelight, I could see that my brother was asleep, his face resting peacefully and childlike, a calm smile on his colourless lips. At that moment, I wished I'd brought him a gift. I would have placed it at the foot of his bed so, when he woke, it would have magically been there in the morning without him knowing. You see,

Thanavaro, Father Christmas does exist after all.

With resigned acceptance, I knew that the one Christmas present I really wanted simply wasn't going to happen. The attendant bowed towards me again as I let the door close silently behind me and left to get a few hours sleep before Pindabah.

My alarm screamed at five o'clock and in my rush to get up, I enjoyed a temporary reprieve from waiting reality. It was Christmas morning and the Abbot was waiting at the Sala when I arrived and he was joined by Amaro, three other monks, Sister Susan and Greg. There was no need for words apart from a greeting from the Abbot and smiles from the others. Amaro walked beside me out of the monastery gates and stayed close as we neared the village and fell into single file. He was in front of me as we walked, with Susan and Greg behind. The dawn began to rise as we entered the hut-lined village and we made our way through the criss-cross of streets.

By the time we reached Mae Hao's house, the sun was belting out bright rays of yellow sunshine. She was kneeling with a basket of rice, waiting for the monks along with her neighbours. The Abbot greeted her and asked her something. Her response had everyone in stitches.

"What's she said?" I asked Greg.

"Mae Hao had an operation on her eyes a while ago," he explained, "and the Abbot was asking her how they were now. She told him, "My eyes are fine, but did you know you have two heads?""

On seeing me, Mae Hao's face lit up and she stretched out her arms in greeting and got to her feet. She told the Abbot something and then took my arm, leading me out of the line of monks and towards a row of dusty wooden buildings. I

turned to see the monks set off, Greg and Susan smiling back at me.

"Have fun," Greg called. "We'll see you later."

Mae Hao's house backed onto a banana grove. There was no downstairs, apart from a small dusty, open kitchen which housed a gas stove and a red motorbike. The main indoor area was upstairs while the outdoor living room consisted of a low, bamboo table which spread over most of the available space in between the pillars. There was a thin, old Thai man squatting on a log over by the trees, stripping away the bark of a twig with a sharp knife. He'd already got through a whole heap of them and had a mountain more to work on. He didn't bother to look up as I came in, just continued slicing at the twigs, slice, slice, slice.

Mae Hao was proud of where she lived. She beamed as she showed me the kitchen, her stove, the rooms upstairs, her chickens, her bananas, her forest. The table served as a seating area too and Mae Hao sprawled herself across it as she spoke, lying down on one side, propped up on her elbow and chatting away to me. She waved her arms, swung herself up and then rested down on her elbow again, pointed at the ceiling, pointed at the kitchen door and then at the man sat by the trees, still stripping bark. He looked up as she called over to him and they exchanged a few words and then she chatted to me, on and on, full of joy, full of pride and full of kindness.

I've no idea what she was saying.

"Santa Claus," she said once, pronouncing it very badly, and she giggled, and continued chattering in her own language. I caught the word 'Ajahn' and gathered she was telling me about the Abbot's talk last night. "Santa Claus," she repeated. "Santa Claus."

I smiled back and listened to her, babbling happily, not a care in the world it seemed, a smile for every occasion. I found it difficult to play along, my brother playing on my mind. I couldn't find the right words to communicate with her, couldn't find those few words we had in common, couldn't find the fun in it anymore, but I could recognise the kindness she was offering and it warmed my heart. After an hour or so of her kind hospitality, I left, bowing a thank you and stealing a huge hug from her.

I don't remember much about walking back to the monastery.

When I got to the guest villa, on my way to visit Thanavaro and wish him Happy Christmas, I could see people through the screens downstairs in the living room. It was the Abbot, Amaro and Greg. They were talking to each other but when they saw me arrive, they all stopped, silent. Their faces were full of fear. Something was up and a knife couldn't have hit my heart more fiercely than the looks on their faces. I sprinted into the house.

"Benedict," said the Abbot, a compassionate, serious look in his brow.

"What is it?" I asked, trying to keep my voice low, my heart racing, beating so fast it hardly let any oxygen in. Come on man, tell me! And I headed towards the staircase and started to climb before he had a chance to reply. Please God. Don't let me have missed him.

"Thanavaro is very weak," the Abbot said, following me. "I think you may be shocked."

Weak but alive. Thanavaro was pitiful, a living skeleton, the flesh fallen away, his eyes collapsed, his face sunk into the pillow. He couldn't lift his head, he was too weak and his mouth wouldn't say the words he tried to speak as he sensed

I'd arrived. I crouched at his bedside to hold him near to me and to put my ear next to his mouth as he struggled to utter my name.

"Quiet, Thanavaro," I whispered. "I'm here now."

I could feel his icy skin against my cheek and the bones of his fingers as I held his hands. He moaned, a loud groan rising inside him unable to be released, and I found the pump to dispense some more pain relief. He calmed a little, drifting.

"But he was fine yesterday," I complained to the Abbot, panic making my voice shake. "He was talking."

"Yes," was all he said.

Amaro and Greg had now entered the room.

"Excuse me, Ajahn," said Amaro, and then bowed respectfully. He walked over and knelt down beside me, next to the bed, putting his arm round me and the back of his hand delicately on Thanavaro's face. His orange robe enveloped me like a cape, a soft, sacred cape. As I let myself lean further into Amaro's forbidden embrace, he pulled me closer and I could feel the warmth of this vibrant, young, alive man trying to shelter me, trying to protect me from harm. He'd found strength for me from somewhere.

Thanavaro lay very still until the pain hit his poor, ravaged body again and he moaned with agony. Sensing the urgency of the moment, I squeezed Amaro's hand tightly as I asked them all,

"Please, can I have a few moments alone with him?"

Once they'd all gone, including the attendant who had been at Thanavaro's bedside day and night for weeks, I became aware of the energy in the room, Thanavaro's energy. It was like a strong, shining light emanating from him, illuminating all around him, filling the room and

glowing brightest of all where he lay. It was a warm and kind energy, offering me strength, offering love to fill the void and I clung to him.

"It's OK," I told him. "I'll be all right," and as I held him for those final few minutes I sensed, deep within me, that I would.

I sensed too, somewhere, the moment when he left. A moment between being there and being no more. It felt fine. He was content, rid of pain, rid of the thing that had been eating his being, rid of his suffering.

I love you, Thanavaro. My brother, the monk.

His energy stayed in the room while I continued to hold him and I let my cheek rest against his. I kissed his forehead and finally I hugged him for the last time.

When I let go, I placed his hands close to his chest and knelt on the floor beside him. I stayed with him while the Abbot returned and sat down on the floor behind me, followed by Amaro, Greg and the attendant. The room vibrated with Thanavaro's lifted energy which stayed with us for a long while until it finally decided to leave and the room was given back to Chatanan.

I got to my knees and I bowed to my brother, three times, low to the floor.

January,
San Francisco International Airport,
USA

We cremated Thanavaro at Chatanan. It was just how old Sumeno had said. They built a big pyre and placed his simple, thin wooden coffin on top. Christopher lit the fire and while the community looked on, I cried as the dry

wood quickly took hold and the coffin disintegrated. I returned later with Greg and Amaro to gather the ashes that were left and they helped me place them in a bag and put them in Uncle Erno's casket.

I rested for a few days at Chatanan, sleeping mostly, crying with Mae Li, calling Michaela to tell her what had happened and telling her when I would be home. I flew back to Bangkok with Greg and we arranged to fly to Los Angeles together.

I said goodbye to Amaro with an easy heart. I knew I would see him again. Didn't know where, didn't know when, but I knew I would.

"You invite me to your ordination, OK?" I ordered and as I watched the moment pass when I wanted to give him a hug, I knelt down at his feet and bowed three times.

The flight to Los Angeles was pleasant enough and gave me time to reflect, to remember and to plan. On arrival I arranged for my rucksack to be forwarded to Manchester and Greg sorted out a cab to take us to our hotel. We stayed a couple of days to sleep, to cry some more and recover from jet lag before heading downtown to hire two red Harley-Davidson Softails and riding up the coast to San Francisco, my brother's ashes in Uncle Erno's casket strapped to my pillion.

The views were incredible as we sailed up the highway with the Pacific Ocean crashing onto the cliffs below us and the wide open road stretching and curving out in front of us, through smart Santa Barbara, past Los Padres, up through the forests of Big Sur and into Monterey. A Superdream of a journey.

"One day," he'd said. "Just you wait, one day."

From Monterey we rode through Santa Cruz and then up

the peninsula, hitting the southern San Francisco city traffic before we headed north for the Golden Gate Bridge. The sun was still shining brightly, fending off the cold air as we paused at the toll booths and, just before setting off through the magnificent twin towers that make-up this bridge of dreams, I took one last glance at the polished wooden casket behind me. Greg looked over at me, squinting behind his sunglasses and he smiled as we set off.

The water under the Golden Gate was turquoise blue as we rode across, the famous city skyline easing away behind as we headed on over towards Marin County.

Greg stayed with me as we parked up on the far side of the bridge and walked over to look out over the bay, back towards the skyscrapers.

"You OK?"

I nodded. There was no way I was not going through with this.

I scattered Antony's ashes into San Francisco Bay from the Golden Gate Bridge on New Year's Day. I sang quietly for him as I did it. Birds singing in the sycamore trees. Mamas and Papas all the way.

Say 'Nighty-night' and kiss me. Just hold me tight and tell me you'll miss me.

We lingered at the bridge for an hour or so, Greg holding me while I stared out at the boats sailing in the bay, letting go, getting ready.

We stayed overnight at the American Theravada Buddhist monastery, an hour's ride north. The Abbot was very gracious and understanding. When we left, we rode the Softails back into San Francisco where we dropped them off at the rental office and took a cab back to the airport.

"You gonna be OK?" Greg asked once more, with gentle,

familiar concern while we waited for his connection to Fort Worth. From there he was heading home to Georgia, to see his family and get reacquainted.

"Yes," I reassured him smiling, knowing there'd be sadness, knowing there'd be grief but knowing I'd be OK.

"Thank you Greg," I said. "Thank you for everything."

His slightly goofy, sweet Jesus face smiled back at me.

"Be sure an' write," he said. "I'll need some relief from my folks."

With another kind smile, a big long hug and a gentle kiss on my cheek, he was gone, on his way home.

I stood for a few minutes watching his back disappear through the line of passengers. Then, I picked up my small bag of belongings, checked the departure time for my flight back to Manchester and looked out for the gate number. I thought of my brother and Uncle Erno as I found a place to sit. I thought of home and the friends I knew would be waiting for me. Michaela, Joe and the rest of the gang.

I checked my watch and found my new iPod, the one I'd bought at the duty free. There were a couple of hours to go before my eleven hour flight home.

Time to sit, to wait and to remember

Always to remember.

The End

Street by Street

C000070292

YORK

TADCASTER

Bishopthorpe, Copmanthorpe, Dunnington, Haxby, Heslington, Nether Poppleton, Skelton, Stamford Bridge, Strensall

2nd edition September 2007
© Automobile Association Developments Limited 2007

Original edition printed February 2003

Enabled by | Ordnance Survey® This product includes map data licensed from Ordnance Survey® with the permission of the Controller of Her Majesty's Stationery Office. © Crown copyright 2007. All rights reserved. Licence number 100021153.

The copyright in all PAF is owned by Royal Mail Group plc.

Published by AA Publishing (a trading name of Automobile Association Developments Limited, whose registered office is Fanum House, Basing View, Basingstoke, Hampshire RG21 4EA. Registered number 1878835).

Produced by the Mapping Services Department of The Automobile Association. (A03166)

A CIP Catalogue record for this book is available from the British Library.

Printed by Oriental Press in Dubai

Ref: ML154z

Key to map pages	ii-iii
Key to map symbols	iv-1
Enlarged map pages	2-3
Main map pages	4-31
Index – towns & villages	32
Index – streets	33-40
Index – featured places	40-41
Acknowledgements	41

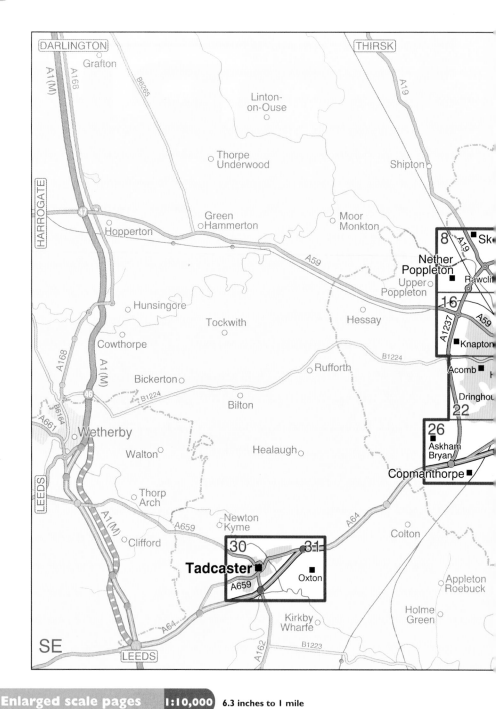

ii

DARLINGTON
Grafton
Linton-
on-Ouse
THIRSK
Thorpe
Underwood
Shipton
HARROGATE
Green
Hammerton
Moor
Monkton
8
Sk
Hopperton
Nether
Poppleton
Rawcli
Upper
Poppleton
16
Hunsingore
Tockwith
Hessay
Knapton
Cowthorpe
Acomb
Bickerton
Rufforth
Dringhou
B1224
22
Bilton
26
Askham
Bryan
Wetherby
Healaugh
Walton
Copmanthorpe
LEEDS
Thorp
Arch
Newton
Kyme
Colton
Clifford
30
31
Appleton
Roebuck
Tadcaster
Oxton
A659
Holme
Green
SE
Kirkby
Wharfe
LEEDS
B1223

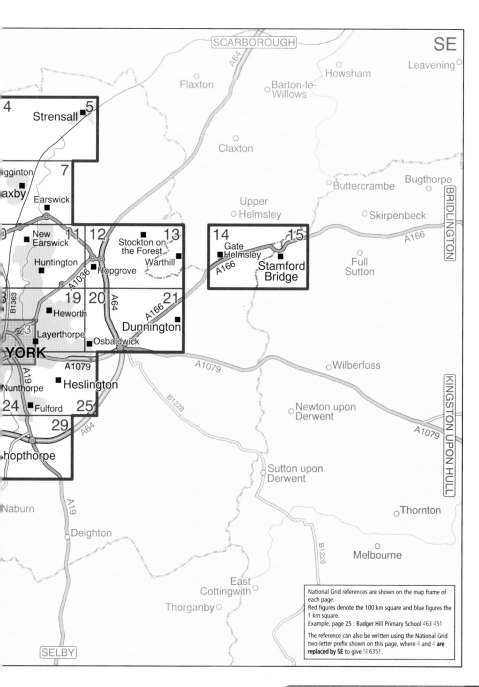

SE

SCARBOROUGH

Leavening

Howsham

Flaxton

Barton-le-Willows

BRIDLINGTON

4

5
Strensall

7

gginton

axby

Earswick

Claxton

Upper
Helmsley

Buttercrambe

Bugthorpe

Skirpenbeck

A166

11 12 13
Stockton on
the Forest
Warthill
Hopgrove
Huntington

New
Earswick

Full
Sutton

14 15
Gate
Helmsley
A166
Stamford
Bridge

A1036

B1363

19 20 21
A166
Dunnington
Heworth
Layerthorpe
Osbaldwick

A64

YORK

A1079

A1079

Wilberfoss

KINGSTON UPON HULL

A19

Nunthorpe

Heslington

24 25
Fulford

29

hopthorpe

A64

Newton upon
Derwent

A1079

Naburn

A19

Deighton

Sutton upon
Derwent

B1228

Thornton

B1228

Melbourne

East
Cottingwith

Thorganby

National Grid references are shown on the map frame of
each page.
Red figures denote the 100 km square and blue figures the
1 km square.
Example, page 25 : Badger Hill Primary School 463 451

The reference can also be written using the National Grid
two-letter prefix shown on this page, where 4 and 4 are
replaced by SE to give SE6351.

SELBY

4.2 inches to 1 mile   **Scale of main map pages 1:15,000**

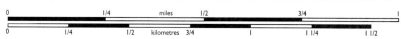

0   1/4   miles   1/2   3/4   1

0   1/4   1/2   kilometres 3/4   1   1 1/4   1 1/2

iv

Junction 9	Motorway & junction	LC	Level crossing
Services	Motorway service area		Tramway
	Primary road single/dual carriageway		Ferry route
Services	Primary road service area		Airport runway
	A road single/dual carriageway		County, administrative boundary
	B road single/dual carriageway		Mounds
	Other road single/dual carriageway	17	Page continuation 1:15,000
	Minor/private road, access may be restricted	3	Page continuation to enlarged scale 1:10,000
← ←	One-way street		River/canal, lake, pier
	Pedestrian area		Aqueduct, lock, weir
	Track or footpath	465 Winter Hill	Peak (with height in metres)
	Road under construction		Beach
	Road tunnel		Woodland
P	Parking		Park
P+	Park & Ride		Cemetery
	Bus/coach station		Built-up area
	Railway & main railway station		Industrial/business building
	Railway & minor railway station		Leisure building
	Underground station		Retail building
	Light railway & station		Other building
	Preserved private railway		

⊓⊓⊓⊓⊓⊓	City wall		♜	Castle
A&E	Hospital with 24-hour A&E department		⌂	Historic house or building
PO	Post Office		Wakehurst Place NT	National Trust property
📖	Public library		Ⓜ	Museum or art gallery
i	Tourist Information Centre		♞	Roman antiquity
i	Seasonal Tourist Information Centre		⚊	Ancient site, battlefield or monument
	Petrol station, 24 hour Major suppliers only		⚒	Industrial interest
✝	Church/chapel		❋	Garden
🚻	Public toilets		◉	Garden Centre Garden Centre Association Member
♿	Toilet with disabled facilities		🌱	Garden Centre Wyevale Garden Centre
PH	Public house AA recommended		🌲	Arboretum
🍴	Restaurant AA inspected		🐂	Farm or animal centre
Madeira Hotel	Hotel AA inspected		🦌	Zoological or wildlife collection
🎭	Theatre or performing arts centre		🐦	Bird collection
🎥	Cinema			Nature reserve
⚑	Golf course		◀🔊	Aquarium
▲	Camping AA inspected		V	Visitor or heritage centre
🚐	Caravan site AA inspected		♈	Country park
▲🚐	Camping & caravan site AA inspected		◠	Cave
🎢	Theme park		✗	Windmill
🏛	Abbey, cathedral or priory		🛢	Distillery, brewery or vineyard

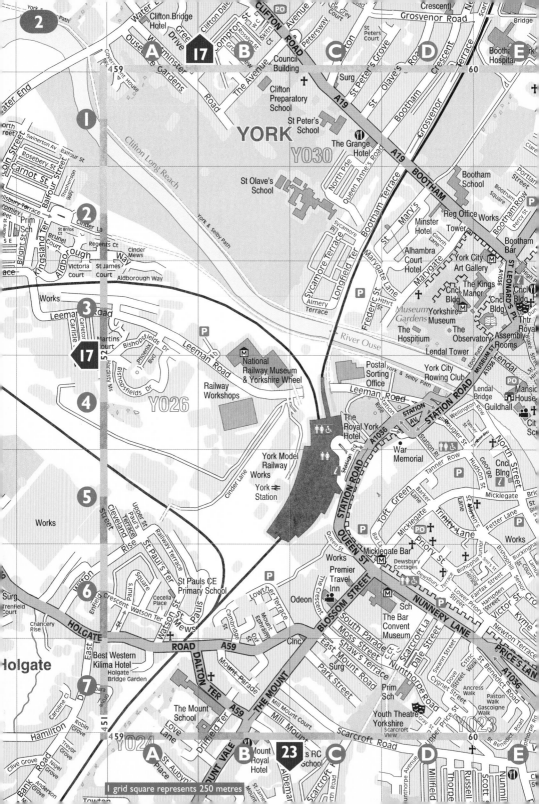

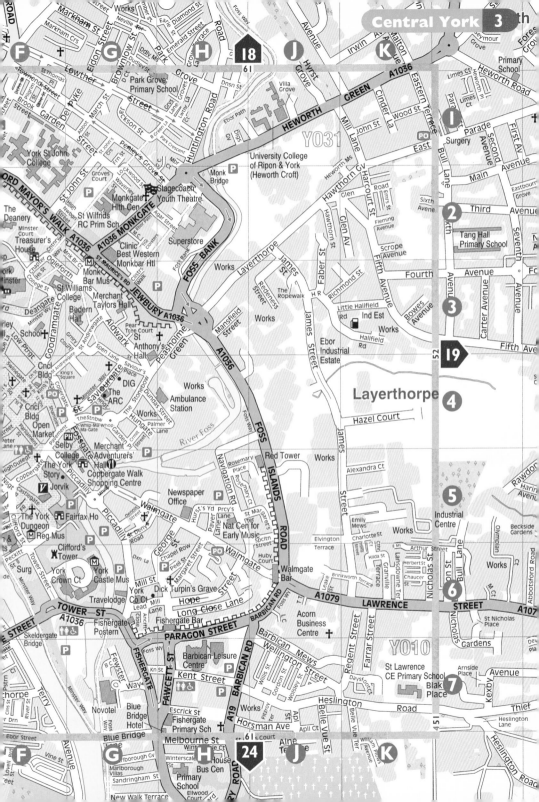

Duncombe Farm

Redwing Farm

Works

Park House Farm

Oak Wood

Duncombe Lane

Centenary Way

E   F   G   H

63   64

Wood House Farm

Centenary Way

Moray Cl

W Cl

Heath Ride

Gns Gdns

Renshaw Gn

Darfield Cl

Jarwick Gn

Chaucer La

Chatsworth Av

Woburn

Redmayne Sq

Lakeside

Heath Ride

Chapman Close

Tudor Way

Crail Cl

Thorn...

I

Ellis Wood

New Lane

Terrington

Blacklee

Northfields

Nrthflds

Nettlewoods

Northfields

Park Gate

Littlethorpe Close

Cou...

Stuart Close

River Foss

Centenary Way

Forest Lane

Hawthorne Ms

Southfields Road

The Village

Works

PO

LC

Brecks Lane

Strensall

York Golf Club

2

Haxby Moor Road

Works

Robert Wilkinson Prim Sch

Strensall New Bridge

Church

West End

La

West End Cl

Moorland Garth

Princes's Road

Orchard Way

Glebe Rd

Harvest Cl

LC

LC

Moor Lane

Lords Moor Lane

Road

3

Leyfield Close

Creaser Close

Westpit Lane

Dr Ellis

Riverside Walk

Lynwood Cl

Frank...

Middlecroft Drive

Low Cft

Middlecroft

Station Sq

York Road

Highlands Av

Oaklands

The Willows

Flaxton Road

Golf Cou...

Centenary Way

Edoi Way

Adlington Cl

Durlston Dr

Durston Dr

Smmns Cl

Melcombe Avenue

Cd Wk

On Gdns

T Court

Pl

Kirklands

WV

H M

The

Oak Tree Way

Oak Tree Cl

Carr Lane

4

Sussex Way

Langton Court

Woodleigh

Chalden Cl

Oakhill Crs

Balfour Way

Pelham Pl

Portsham Pl

Pasture Cl

Wbrin Cl

Scott Moncrieff Road

Foss Bridge

Barley Rise

York Road

Beech

Crncrft

Wheatcrt

Newton Way

Oknapton Cl

Ox

Cumbria Avenue

Humber Drive

Oakbutts Farm

Centenary Way

Ryecroft

Wain...

Brch Tr

St Wilfreds Cl

Wilfreds

Hollis Crescent

Howard Road

Howard Road

Scott Moncrieff Road

5

Homelea

Farriers Chase

Strensall Camp

Strensall Road

Cheshire Avenue

Scott Moncrieff Road

Towthorpe Bridge

Alexandra Road

Strensall Park

63   64

459

E   7   **F**   **Tow** **G** **orpe**   **H**

Towthorpe Road

Towthorpe Common

E F G 5 H

Towthorpe Road

Towthorpe Bridge

Alexandra Road

62 63 59

Strensall Park

Towth

Usher Lane

1

Towthorpe Moor Lane

Usher Park Road

Snadim

NION

Keldale

South Ville

Swarthdale

Scriven Grove

Lansdown Way

Keldale Close

New Forge Court

Chatsworth Drive

Netherwindings

Moor

2

Windmill Way

Old Coppice

Falcon

Mallard Wy

Towthorpe Road

West

Nooks

Thrnhls

Garths End

River Foss

Lane

58

ron Road

Butterfield y School

LC

Linley Av

Folks Cl

The Lndings

Haxby Landing

Hall Farm

Moor Lane

Earswick Grange

Calf Close

Landing Lane

Foss Way

Lock House

3

Works

Centenary Way

L H L

E C

Whitelands

The Garden Village

YO32

y

Landing Lane

Chase

Earswick

Lock House

E Cl

Wisker Lane

Northlands Avenue

Willow Grove

Laurel Cl

4

Earswick Village

Strensall Road

Rowley Court

Stablers Walk

Shilton Close

Garth

Firtree Close

Earswick

457

Foss Way

Centenary Way

5

Connaught Way

Riverside Crs

Strensall Road

A1237

Vesper Wk

Mulberry Ct

Avon Drive

Crinan

Trent Avenue

Witham Dr

Kingsclere

Langley Court

Manor Ct

Price

Broome

Kin Wy

Burne

Broome Way

62 63

E F H G H

Linden Cl

Heron

Drakes Cl

Strensall Road

Chiltern Wy

South Down Road

Gm Cl

N C Wy

North Lane

Dyke

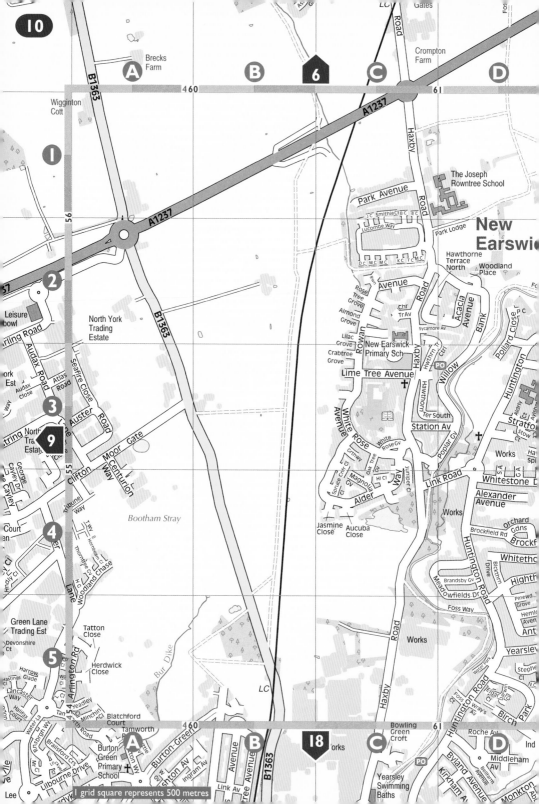

Huntington

White House Farm

Hopgrove Farm

Hopgrove

Monks Cross Shopping Park

Monks Cross Drive

Works

Works

Garth Road

Keith Avenue

Huntington Primary Sch

Green Acres

Lea Way

Bracken Close

Fern Close

Heather Close

Woodland Way

Brecks Lane

North Lane

North Lane

North Moor Road

The Old Village

River Foss

North Moor Road

PO

Surg

Kendrew Close

Glade

Wood Way

Cleveland Way

New Lane

Cheviot Cl

Cmbrn

leton Way

Drive

Jockey Lane

Saddlers Cl

Forge Close

York City Knights RLFC (Huntington Stadium)

Kathryn Av

Julia Av

Julia Avenue Retail Park

Jockey Lane

Martello Wy

P+

Cemetery

Elm Grove

Sherwood Grove

Minster Av

Grove

Dalby Mead

Andrew

Barfield Estate

Barfield Road

Sefton Av

Monk Stray

Rythorpe Grange Farm

Stockton Lane

Tang Hall Beck

Sow Dike

Monks Cross Link

A1237

A1036

A1237

North Lane

56

55

454

62

63

63

62

Avon Drive

Trent Avenue

Witham Dr

Broome Way

Close

South Down Road

Langley Court

Strensall

Heron

Mill Hill Dr

E   F   7   G   H

I

2

3

12

4

5

E   F   19   G   H

Heworth Cricket Club & York Hockey Club

Surg

Surg

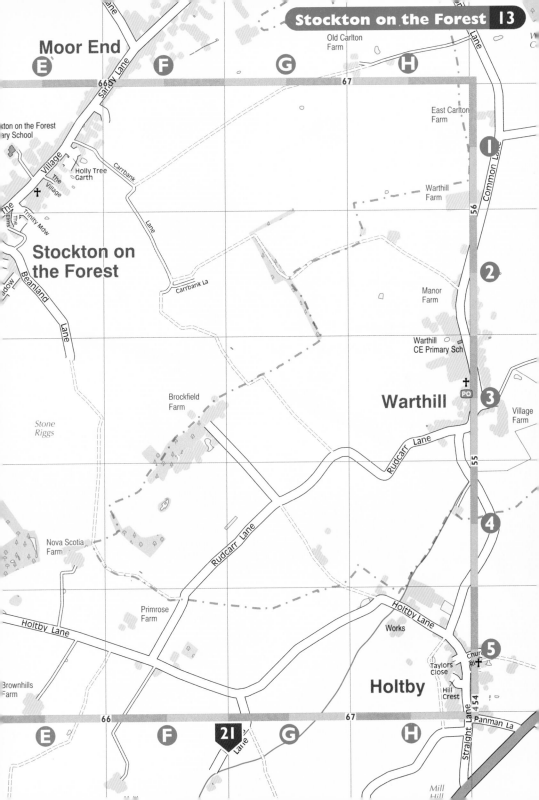

Moor End

E **F** **G** **H**

Old Carlton Farm

66 Salby Lane 67

East Carlton Farm

1

Common Lane

kton on the Forest ary School

Village The Village

Holly Tree Garth

Carrbank

Warthill Farm

56

The Elms Trinity Mdw

Stockton on the Forest

Carrbank Lane

Carrbank La

Manor Farm

2

Beanland Lane

Mop

dow

Warthill CE Primary Sch

Stone Riggs

Brockfield Farm

Warthill

PO

3

Village Farm

Rudcarr Lane

55

Nova Scotia Farm

Rudcarr Lane

4

Primrose Farm

Holtby Lane

Works

Holtby Lane

Holtby Lane

Straight Lane

454

Panman La

Church Riv

5

Taylors Close

Brownhills Farm

Hill Crest

Holtby

E **F** 21 Lane **G** **H**

66 67

Mill Hill

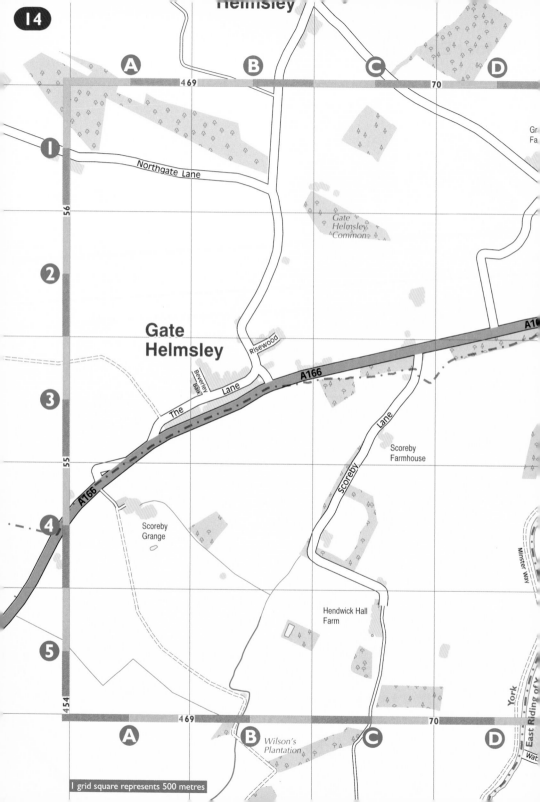

14

Helmsley

A 469 **B** **C** 70 **D**

56

Northgate Lane

I

Gr
Fa

Gate
Helmsley
Common

2

Gate
Helmsley

Risewood

55

The Lane

Beverley Bank

A166

A166

3

A166

A1

Scoreby Lane

Scoreby
Farmhouse

4

A166

Scoreby
Grange

Hendwick Hall
Farm

Minster Way

5

454

York

East Riding of Y

A 469 **B** **C** 70 **D**

Wilson's
Plantation

Wat

1 grid square represents 500 metres

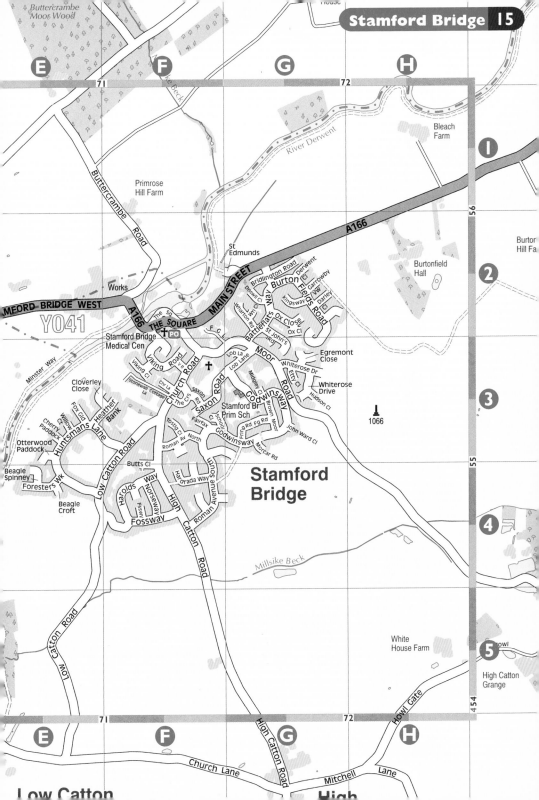

Buttercrambe
Moor Wood

E   F   G   H

71   72   56

Bleach
Farm

River Derwent

Primrose
Hill Farm

A166

Burtor
Hill Fa

Buttercrambe Road

Works

St Edmunds

MEORD BRIDGE WEST

YO41

A166

THE SQUARE
The Sq
PO

Stamford Bridge
Medical Cen

Minster Way

Main Street

Bridlington Road
Burton
Way
Driswil Road
Bridlington Rd
Driswil Cl
Wharton Rd
F.C.L
St John's
Rd

Battleflats
Ox Close
Ox Cl

Fields Road
Derwent
Kingsway Garrowby
Darley

Burtonfield
Hall

Egremont
Close

Viking
Road
Church Road
Viking Cl
Chr La
Stonewall Cottage
La
Saxon
Church Crs

Cloverley
Close

Fox Gld
Willow
Heather
Bank

Cherry
Paddock

Otterwood
Paddock

Huntsmans Lane

Low Catton Road

Butts Cl

Lob La
Lob Lane

Moor
Road

Midgley Cl
Saxon
Road
Fairfax
School Road
Rosta Ct

Stamford Br
Prim Sch

Roman Av North

Cowper
Godwinsway
Brown Moor

Whiterose Dr
Eth Rd
Hudson Cl

Whiterose
Drive

1066

Beagle
Spinney
Foresters Wk

Beagle
Croft

Harolds
Way
Fossway
Noreway
FSSWy

High Catton Road

Harrada Way
Roman Avenue South

Frtg Rd Fg Rd

Godwinsway

Morcar Rd

John Ward Cl

**Stamford
Bridge**

Low Catton Road

Millsike Beck

White
House Farm

owl

High Catton
Grange

55

High Catton Road

Howl Gate

454

E   F   G   H

71   72

Church Lane

Mitchell   Lane

Low Catton   **High**

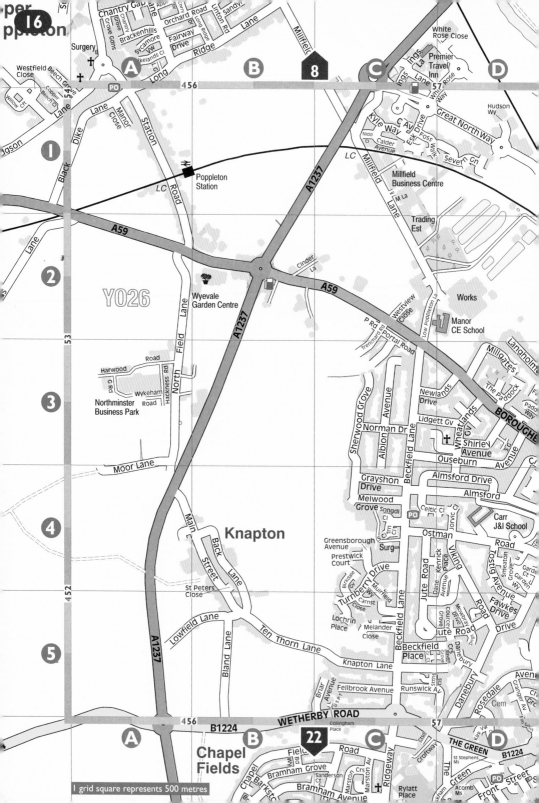

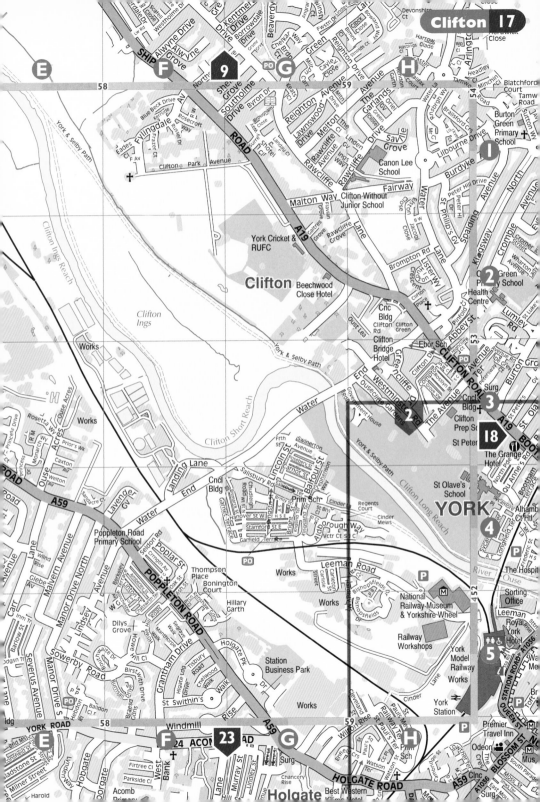

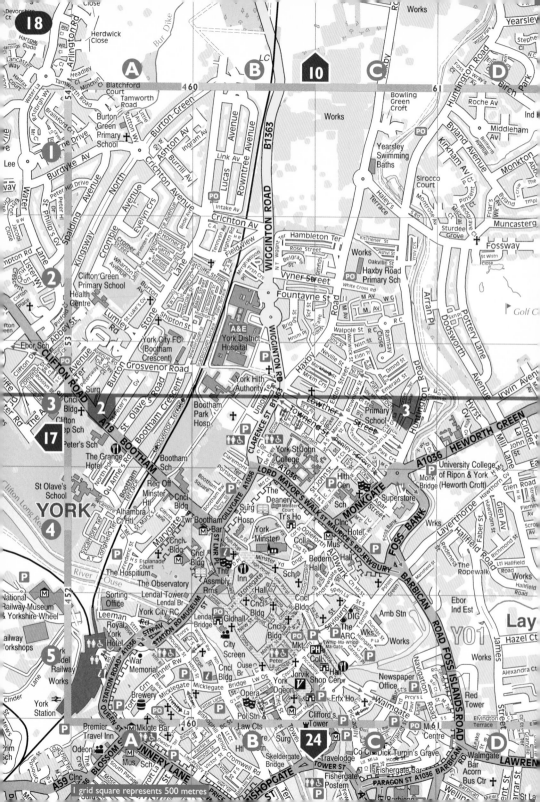

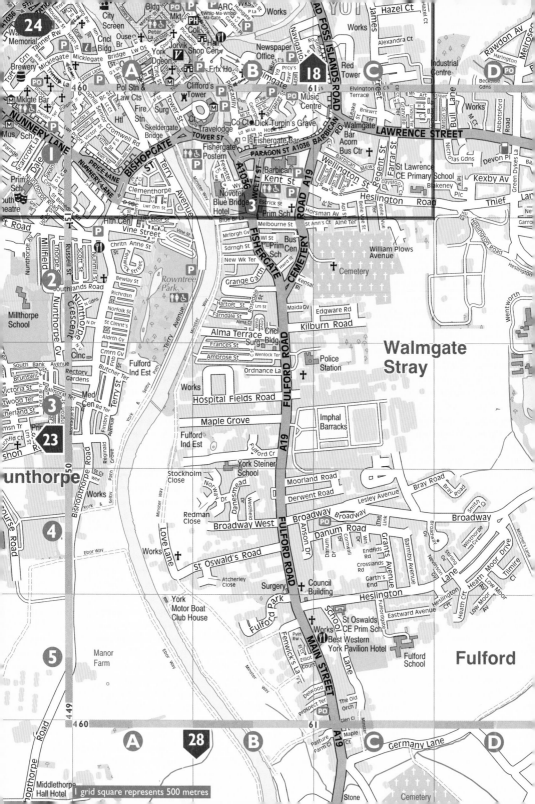

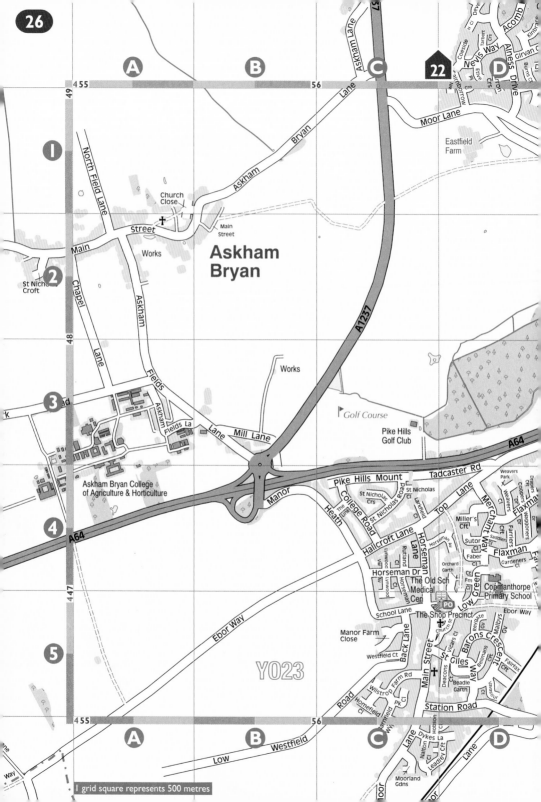

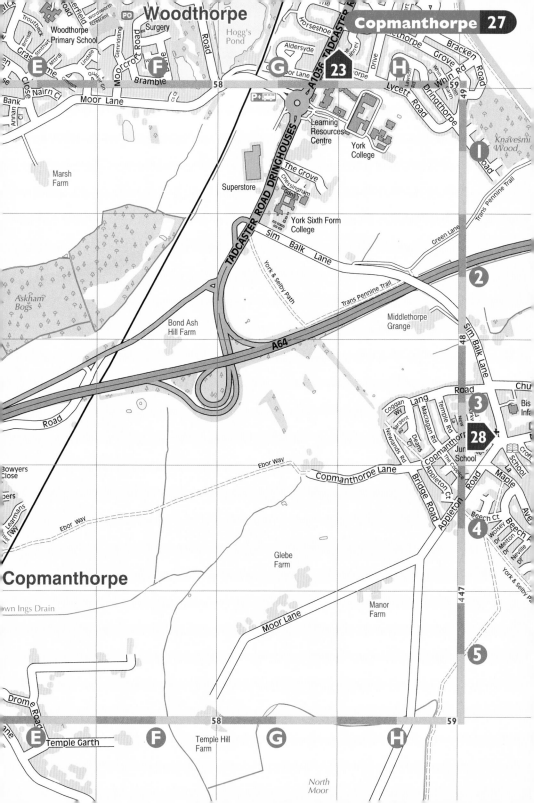

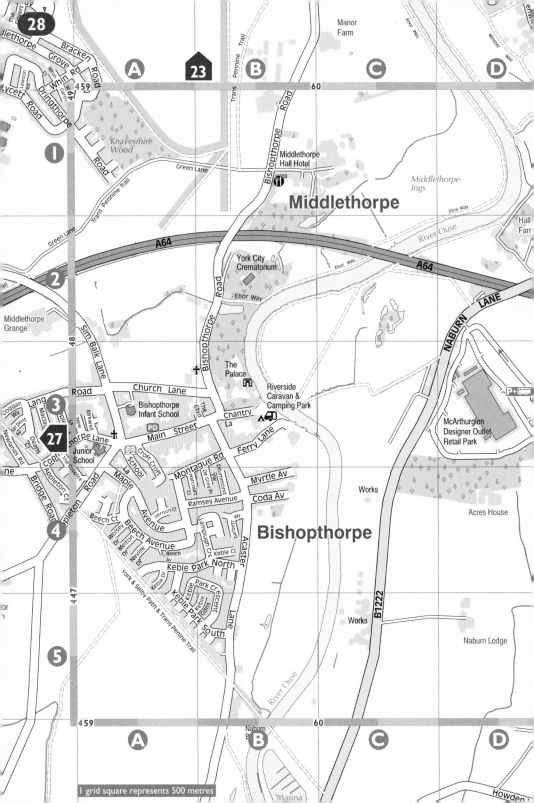

A   B   C   D

4 47   48

1

A659

River Wharfe

KELCBAR HILL

WETHERBY ROAD

Riverside Primary School

TADCASTER

Wighill Lane

Heatherdene

Ingleby Dr

Prospect Dr

Mill Lane

Mla Rosemary Rw

COMMERCIAL

2

Smaws Farm

Kelcbar Close
K Cl
Kelcbar Way
Tower Crs
Westfield Ter
Westfield
Station Rd
A659

St Josephs RC Primary School

Selby College

Surg

3

Inholmes

Inholmes La

Edgerton Close

Edgerton Dr

Edgerton Garth

Edgerton Court

Edgerton Road

Station

Fairfield Road

Tadcaster Sports & Leisure Centre

Tadcaster CC

St Joseph's St

CHAPEL ST

WESTGATE
PO
KIRKGATE
BRIDGE ST

New St

Centre Lane

HIGH STREET

LEEDS ROAD

Ind Est

F Rd

Tadcaster Albion FC

43

ROMAN ROAD

4

A659

Cedar Dr
Aspen
Beech Walk
Fairfield Way
Fairfield

Queen's Gdns

Cemetery

Carnet Lane

Marlborough Av

Marlborough Drive

Dorchester Road

Willow

Broom Rd

Hillcrest Rise

Hillcrest
Hillcrest Ct

Calcaria Crs

West Mt

Golf Links Crs

Golf Links Av

Golf Links Court
The Links

Golf Links Road

Calcaria Rd

Stutton Road

Magnet Sports Club

Tadcaster Ings

A162

A64

Sedge Rise

Woodlands

Wil Vw

Windmill Grove

Avenue

Firtree Crs

PO

5

Windmill
W Rl
W Rl

The Fairways

Hawthorn Av

Hawthorn Croft

Hawthorn Close

4 42

4 47   48

A   B   C   D

A64

Moor Lane

Stutton

Church Lane

Weedling Gate

Cork Beck

A162

Grims
Gran

E   F   G   H

Little Catterton Lane

Catterton Lane

Rolling Bridge

I

Eastfield Close

Bow Bridge View

F Dr
F Dr
Field Drive

Turnpike Rd

Toll Bar Way

44

Auster Bank Vw

Astr Bnk Rd

A64

YORK   ROAD   A659

Astr Bnk Crscnt

Meadow
Dr
Y S

PO

Old Brewery Cdns

2

Tadcaster East Primary School

Oxton Hall

Slice Lane

Oxton Lane

Oxton La
Oxton Drive

LS24

Ouston Lane

Oxton   Lane

3

43

Oxton

4

Ouston Farm

Kettleman Bridge

5

442

E   F   G   H

50   51

Acomb	22 C2	Hall Garth	21 G5	Middlethorpe	28 B1	Stamford Bridge	15
Askham Bryan	26 B2	Haxby	6 D3	Murton	20 D3	Stockton on the Forest	13
Bishopthorpe	28 B4	Heslington	25 E3	Nether Poppleton	8 B4	Strensall	5
Chapel Fields	22 A1	Heworth	19 F3	New Earswick	10 D2	Tadcaster	30
Clifton	17 G2	Holgate	23 F1	Nunthorpe	23 H4	Tang Hall	19
Copmanthorpe	27 E4	Holtby	13 H5	Osbaldwick	20 B5	Walmgate Stray	24
Dringhouses	23 E4	Hopgrove	12 A4	Overton	8 A2	Warthill	13
Dunnington	21 G4	Huntington	11 E3	Oxton	31 G3	West Field	22
Earswick	7 G4	Knapton	16 B4	Rawcliffe	9 F4	Wigginton	6
Fulford	24 D5	Knavesmire	23 G5	Skelton	8 D2	Woodthorpe	22
Gate Helmsley	14 A2	Layerthorpe	3 K4	South Bank	23 G3	York	2

USING THE STREET INDEX

Street names are listed alphabetically. Each street name is followed by its postal town or area locality, the Postcode District, the page number, and the reference to the square in which the name is found.

Standard index entries are shown as follows:

Abbey St *RAW/SKEL* YO30.............**17** H3

Street names and selected addresses not shown on the map due to scale restrictions are shown in the index with an asterisk:

Albert St *FUL/HES* YO10 * **3** H6

GENERAL ABBREVIATIONS

ACC	ACCESS	E	EAST	LDG	LODGE	R	RI
ALY	ALLEY	EMB	EMBANKMENT	LGT	LIGHT	RBT	ROUNDAB
AP	APPROACH	EMBY	EMBASSY	LK	LOCK	RD	RO
AR	ARCADE	ESP	ESPLANADE	LKS	LAKES	RDG	RI
ASS	ASSOCIATION	EST	ESTATE	LNDG	LANDING	REP	REPUE
AV	AVENUE	EX	EXCHANGE	LTL	LITTLE	RES	RESERV
BCH	BEACH	EXPY	EXPRESSWAY	LWR	LOWER	RFC	RUGBY FOOTBALL C
BLDS	BUILDINGS	EXT	EXTENSION	MAG	MAGISTRATE	RI	RI
BND	BEND	F/O	FLYOVER	MAN	MANSIONS	RP	RA
BNK	BANK	FC	FOOTBALL CLUB	MD	MEAD	RW	R
BR	BRIDGE	FK	FORK	MDW	MEADOWS	S	SO
BRK	BROOK	FLD	FIELD	MEM	MEMORIAL	SCH	SCH
BTM	BOTTOM	FLDS	FIELDS	MI	MILL	SE	SOUTH E
BUS	BUSINESS	FLS	FALLS	MKT	MARKET	SER	SERVICE A
BVD	BOULEVARD	FM	FARM	MKTS	MARKETS	SH	SH
BY	BYPASS	FT	FORT	ML	MALL	SHOP	SHOPP
CATH	CATHEDRAL	FTS	FLATS	MNR	MANOR	SKWY	SKY
CEM	CEMETERY	FWY	FREEWAY	MS	MEWS	SMT	SUM
CEN	CENTRE	FY	FERRY	MSN	MISSION	SOC	SOC
CFT	CROFT	GA	GATE	MT	MOUNT	SP	SI
CH	CHURCH	GAL	GALLERY	MTN	MOUNTAIN	SPR	SPR
CHA	CHASE	GDN	GARDEN	MTS	MOUNTAINS	SQ	SQU
CHYD	CHURCHYARD	GDNS	GARDENS	MUS	MUSEUM	ST	STR
CIR	CIRCLE	GLD	GLADE	MWY	MOTORWAY	STN	STAT
CIRC	CIRCUS	GLN	GLEN	N	NORTH	STR	STRE
CL	CLOSE	GN	GREEN	NE	NORTH EAST	STRD	STRA
CLFS	CLIFFS	GND	GROUND	NW	NORTH WEST	SW	SOUTH W
CMP	CAMP	GRA	GRANGE	O/P	OVERPASS	TDG	TRAD
CNR	CORNER	GRG	GARAGE	OFF	OFFICE	TER	TERR
CO	COUNTY	GT	GREAT	ORCH	ORCHARD	THWY	THROUGH
COLL	COLLEGE	GTWY	GATEWAY	OV	OVAL	TNL	TUN
COM	COMMON	GV	GROVE	PAL	PALACE	TOLL	TOLL
COMM	COMMISSION	HGR	HIGHER	PAS	PASSAGE	TPK	TURNP
CON	CONVENT	HL	HILL	PAV	PAVILION	TR	TR
COT	COTTAGE	HLS	HILLS	PDE	PARADE	TRL	TR
COTS	COTTAGES	HO	HOUSE	PH	PUBLIC HOUSE	TWR	TO
CP	CAPE	HOL	HOLLOW	PK	PARK	U/P	UNDERP
CPS	COPSE	HOSP	HOSPITAL	PKWY	PARKWAY	UNI	UNIVERS
CR	CREEK	HRB	HARBOUR	PL	PLACE	UPR	UP
CREM	CREMATORIUM	HTH	HEATH	PLN	PLAIN	V	V
CRS	CRESCENT	HTS	HEIGHTS	PLNS	PLAINS	VA	VAL
CSWY	CAUSEWAY	HVN	HAVEN	PLZ	PLAZA	VIAD	VIAD
CT	COURT	HWY	HIGHWAY	POL	POLICE STATION	VIL	V
CTRL	CENTRAL	IMP	IMPERIAL	PR	PRINCE	VIS	V
CTS	COURTS	IN	INLET	PREC	PRECINCT	VLG	VILL
CTYD	COURTYARD	IND EST	INDUSTRIAL ESTATE	PREP	PREPARATORY	VLS	VIL
CUTT	CUTTINGS	INF	INFIRMARY	PRIM	PRIMARY	VW	VW
CV	COVE	INFO	INFORMATION	PROM	PROMENADE	W	W
CYN	CANYON	INT	INTERCHANGE	PRS	PRINCESS	WD	WC
DEPT	DEPARTMENT	IS	ISLAND	PRT	PORT	WHF	WH
DL	DALE	JCT	JUNCTION	PT	POINT	WKS	WA
DM	DAM	JTY	JETTY	PTH	PATH	WLS	WE
DR	DRIVE	KG	KING	PZ	PIAZZA	WY	V
DRO	DROVE	KNL	KNOLL	QD	QUADRANT	YD	YA
DRY	DRIVEWAY	L	LAKE	QU	QUEEN	YHA	YOUTH HOS
DWGS	DWELLINGS	LA	LANE	QY	QUAY		

POSTCODE TOWNS AND AREA ABBREVIATIONS

ACOMB	Acomb	CYK	Central York	HXB/STR	Haxby/Strensall	RYKW	Rural York w
COP/BISH	Copmanthorpe/	FUL/HES	Fulford/Heslington	RAW/SKEL	Rawcliffe/Skelton	STMFBR	Stamford Bri
	Bishopthorpe	HEWTH	Heworth	RYKS	Rural York south	TAD	Tadcas

A

ey St *RAW/SKEL* YO30 17 H3
otsford Rd *FUL/HES* YO10 24 D1
ot St *HEWTH* YO31 3 G1
otsway *HEWTH* YO31 18 D1
lton Gv *HXB/STR* YO32 6 D2
cia Av *HXB/STR* YO32 10 D2
cia Gv *HXB/STR* YO32 6 D2
ster La *COP/BISH* YO23 28 B5
mb Ct *ACOMB* YO24 * 22 D1
mb Ms *RYKW* YO26 22 C1
mb Rd *ACOMB* YO24 23 E1
mb Wood Cl *ACOMB* YO24 22 C5
mb Wood Dr *ACOMB* YO24 22 B5
rn Wy *ACOMB* YO24 22 D4
laide St *COP/BISH* YO23 23 H2
ngton Cl *HXB/STR* YO32 5 F3
r St *HEWTH* YO31 3 G2
ty Av *ACOMB* YO24 23 F4
ty Gv *ACOMB* YO24 23 F4
ree Ct *ACOMB* YO24 23 F4
any St *RYKW* YO26 17 G4
marle Rd *COP/BISH* YO23 23 H2
rt Cl *HEWTH* YO31 19 E1
ert St *FUL/HES* YO10 * 3 H6
on Av *RYKW* YO26 16 C3
on St *CYK* YO1 2 E6
in Av *FUL/HES* YO10 19 F5
in Wy *FUL/HES* YO10 25 F2
borough Wy *RYKW* YO26 2 A3
erley Ct *HXB/STR* YO32 10 D3
ersyde *ACOMB* YO24 23 E5
er Wy *HXB/STR* YO32 10 C4
eth Gv *COP/BISH* YO23 24 A2
wark *CYK* YO1 3 G3
kander Av *HEWTH* YO31 10 D4
kandra Ct *FUL/HES* YO10 3 K5
kandra Rd *HXB/STR* YO32 5 F5
arth Ri *HEWTH* YO31 19 G2
arth Rd *HEWTH* YO31 19 G2
n St *RAW/SKEL* YO30 18 B2
n Cl *FUL/HES* YO10 19 F5
ndale *ACOMB* YO24 22 D4
rton Dr *RYKW* YO26 8 A4
gton Dr *HEWTH* YO31 19 G3
a Ct *FUL/HES* YO10 24 B2
a Gv *FUL/HES* YO10 24 B2
a Ter *FUL/HES* YO10 24 B2
ery Ter *RAW/SKEL* YO30 2 C3
ond Gv *HXB/STR* YO32 10 C2
sford Dr *RYKW* YO26 16 C4
sford Rd *RYKW* YO26 16 D4
ess Dr *ACOMB* YO24 22 B5
e Ter *FUL/HES* YO10 24 C2
s Gv *FUL/HES* YO10 20 A5
yne Dr *RAW/SKEL* YO30 9 F5
yne Gv *RAW/SKEL* YO30 9 F5
berley St *RYKW* YO26 17 F4
ber St *HEWTH* YO31 18 C3
bleside Av *FUL/HES* YO10 19 G5
brose St *FUL/HES* YO10 24 B3
y Johnson Wy
AW/SKEL YO30 9 H3
ress Wk *COP/BISH* YO23 2 D7
roft Cl *CYK* YO1 3 G6
lerson Gv *ACOMB* YO24 23 F2
rew Dr *HXB/STR* YO32 11 E5
ram Cl *RAW/SKEL* YO30 9 G5
an Cl *ACOMB* YO24 27 E1
e St *COP/BISH* YO23 24 A2
on Dr *FUL/HES* YO10 24 B4
hea Dr *HEWTH* YO31 10 D5
llo Ct *FUL/HES* YO10 3 J7
llo St *FUL/HES* YO10 3 J7
le Blossom Ct *ACOMB* YO24 22 B3
leby Gld *HXB/STR* YO32 6 D4
leby Pl *HEWTH* YO31 19 F4
lecroft Rd *HEWTH* YO31 19 G2
le Garth *RYKW* YO26 8 A5
leton Ct *COP/BISH* YO23 27 H4
leton Rd *COP/BISH* YO23 27 H4
nhall Cl *HXB/STR* YO32 6 C3
yle St *COP/BISH* YO23 23 H3
ngton Rd *RAW/SKEL* YO30 10 A5
nstrong Wy *RAW/SKEL* YO30 9 F3
cliffe Ms *FUL/HES* YO10 * 24 B2
side Pl *FUL/HES* YO10 24 D1
an Pl *HEWTH* YO31 18 C2
hur Pl *RAW/SKEL* YO30 8 C1
hur St *FUL/HES* YO10 3 K6
ndel Gv *ACOMB* YO24 22 C5
ot Rd *HXB/STR* YO32 6 B1
ot Wy *ACOMB* YO24 22 D2
bourne Wy *ACOMB* YO24 22 C4
Cl *HEWTH* YO31 19 G2
dale Rd *RYKS* YO19 21 H4
Ashford Pl *ACOMB* YO24 22 D2
Ash La *HXB/STR* YO32 6 D1
Ashley Park Crs *HEWTH* YO31 19 G3
Ashley Park Rd *HEWTH* YO31 19 G2
Ashmeade Cl *ACOMB* YO24 22 B5
Ash St *RYKW* YO26 17 F5
Ashton Av *RAW/SKEL* YO30 18 B1
Ashville St *HEWTH* YO31 18 C2
Ash Wk *HXB/STR* YO32 5 G3
Ashwood Gld *HXB/STR* YO32 6 C5
Askham Bar *ACOMB* YO24 * 27 G1
Askham Bryan La
COP/BISH YO23 26 C1
Askham Cft *ACOMB* YO24 22 B3
Askham Fields La
COP/BISH YO23 26 B3
Askham Gv *ACOMB* YO24 22 B2
Askham La *COP/BISH* YO23 22 A5
Aspen Cl *RYKS* YO19 21 H3
Aspen Wy *TAD* LS24 30 B3
Asquith Av *HEWTH* YO31 19 F4
Atcherley Cl *FUL/HES* YO10 24 B4
Atlas Rd *RAW/SKEL* YO30 9 H3
Aucuba Cl *HXB/STR* YO32 10 C4
Audax Cl *RAW/SKEL* YO30 9 H3
Audax Rd *RAW/SKEL* YO30 9 H3
Auster Bank Av *TAD* LS24 31 E2
Auster Bank Crs *TAD* LS24 31 E2
Auster Bank Rd *TAD* LS24 31 E1
Auster Bank Vw *TAD* LS24 31 E1
Auster Rd *RAW/SKEL* YO30 9 H3
Avenue Rd *RAW/SKEL* YO30 18 A3
Avenue Ter *RAW/SKEL* YO30 18 A3
The Avenue *HXB/STR* YO32 6 C1
HXB/STR YO32 6 D3
RAW/SKEL YO30 2 B1
Aviator Ct *RAW/SKEL* YO30 9 G3
Avon Dr *HXB/STR* YO32 7 F5
Aylesham Ct *HXB/STR* YO32 10 D3

B

Bachelor Hl *ACOMB* YO24 22 C2
Backhouse St *HEWTH* YO31 3 F1
Back La *COP/BISH* YO23 26 C5
HXB/STR YO32 6 B2
RYKS YO19 21 G2
RYKW YO26 16 B4
Back Swinegate *CYK* YO1 3 F4
Back West Vw *RAW/SKEL* YO30 18 A2
Bad Bargain La *HEWTH* YO31 19 G3
RYKS YO19 12 C5
Badger Paddock *HEWTH* YO31 10 D4
Badger Wood Wk
FUL/HES YO10 25 H2
Baildon Cl *RYKW* YO26 17 E5
Baile Hill Ter *CYK* YO1 2 E7
Baker St *RAW/SKEL* YO30 18 B2
Balfour St *RYKW* YO26 17 G4
Balfour Wy *HXB/STR* YO32 5 F4
Balmoral Ter *COP/BISH* YO23 23 H3
Bankside Cl *RYKW* YO26 8 A4
Bannisdale *ACOMB* YO24 22 C5
Barbara Gv *ACOMB* YO24 23 F1
Barbers Dr *COP/BISH* YO23 26 D4
Barbican Ms *FUL/HES* YO10 3 J6
Barbican Rd *FUL/HES* YO10 3 J7
Barden Ct *RAW/SKEL* YO30 9 G5
Barfield Rd *HEWTH* YO31 19 E1
Barker La *CYK* YO1 2 D5
Barkston Av *RYKW* YO26 22 A1
Barkston Cl *RYKW* YO26 22 A2
Barkston Gv *RYKW* YO26 22 A1
Barkston Rd *RYKW* YO26 22 A1
Bar La *CYK* YO1 2 C5
Barley Ri *HXB/STR* YO32 5 F4
Barley Vw *HXB/STR* YO32 6 C3
Barlow St *RYKW* YO26 17 E5
Barmby Av *FUL/HES* YO10 24 C4
Barmby Cl *RAW/SKEL* YO30 9 G5
Barons Crs *COP/BISH* YO23 26 D5
Barrett Av *ACOMB* YO24 23 F1
Barstow Av *FUL/HES* YO10 24 D1
Bartle Garth *CYK* YO1 * 3 G3
Barton Cl *RAW/SKEL* YO30 9 F4
Bateson Cl *FUL/HES* YO10 25 G3
Battleflats Wy *STMFBR* YO41 15 G3
Baysdale Av *FUL/HES* YO10 25 H1
Beaconsfield Ms *ACOMB* YO24 22 D1
Beaconsfield St *ACOMB* YO24 22 D1
Beadle Garth *COP/BISH* YO23 26 D5
Beagle Cft *STMFBR* YO41 15 E4
Beagle Ridge Dr *ACOMB* YO24 22 C3
Beagle Spinney *STMFBR* YO41 15 E4
Beanland La *HXB/STR* YO32 13 E2
Bean's Wy *HEWTH* YO31 19 G1
Beaufort Cl *FUL/HES* YO10 25 F1
Beaulieu Cl *HXB/STR* YO32 11 E1
Beaverdyke *RAW/SKEL* YO30 9 G5
Beckett Dr *FUL/HES* YO10 20 A5
Beckfield La *RYKW* YO26 16 C5
Beckfield Pl *RYKW* YO26 16 C5
Beckside Gdns *FUL/HES* YO10 19 E5
Beckwith Cl *HEWTH* YO31 19 H2
Bedale Av *FUL/HES* YO10 20 A5
Bede Av *RAW/SKEL* YO30 18 A2
Bedern *CYK* YO1 * 3 G3
Beech Av *ACOMB* YO24 23 F1
COP/BISH YO23 28 A4
Beech Cl *TAD* LS24 31 E3
Beech Ct *COP/BISH* YO23 28 A4
The Beeches *RAW/SKEL* YO30 8 D1
RYKW YO26 8 A4
Beech Gld *HEWTH* YO31 11 E4
Beech Gv *RYKW* YO26 16 D5
Beech Pl *HXB/STR* YO32 5 F4
Beechtree Rd *TAD* LS24 30 B4
Beech Wk *TAD* LS24 30 B3
Beech Wy *RYKW* YO26 8 A5
Beechwood Gld *ACOMB* YO24 22 B3
Beeforth Cl *HXB/STR* YO32 10 C1
Belcombe Wy *RAW/SKEL* YO30 17 H2
Belgrave St *HEWTH* YO31 18 B2
Bell Cl *HXB/STR* YO32 6 C3
Belle Vue St *FUL/HES* YO10 3 J7
Belle Vue Ter *FUL/HES* YO10 3 K7
Bellfarm Av *HEWTH* YO31 18 D1
Bellhouse Wy *ACOMB* YO24 22 C3
Bellmans Cft *COP/BISH* YO23 26 D5
Bellwood Dr *ACOMB* YO24 22 B4
Belmont Cl *RAW/SKEL* YO30 9 G5
Beresford Ter *COP/BISH* YO23 24 A3
Berkeley Ter *RYKW* YO26 17 F4
Beverley Balk *STMFBR* YO41 14 B3
Beverley Gdns *HEWTH* YO31 * 3 J1
Bewlay St *COP/BISH* YO23 24 A2
Bilsdale Cl *RAW/SKEL* YO30 9 F4
Birch La *HXB/STR* YO32 6 D2
Birch Pk *HEWTH* YO31 10 D5
Birch Tree Cl *HXB/STR* YO32 5 F4
Birkdale Gv *RYKW* YO26 16 C4
Birstwith Dr *RYKW* YO26 17 F5
Bishopgate St *COP/BISH* YO23 2 E7
Bishophill Junior *CYK* YO1 2 E6
Bishophill Senior *CYK* YO1 2 E6
Bishops Ct *CYK* YO1 * 2 E6
Bishopsfileds Dr *RYKW* YO26 2 A4
Bishopsway *FUL/HES* YO10 25 G1
Bishopthorpe Rd
COP/BISH YO23 28 B3
Bismarck St *RYKW* YO26 17 G4
Black Dike La *RYKW* YO26 16 A1
Blacklee Cl *HXB/STR* YO32 5 H1
Blackthorn Dr *HEWTH* YO31 10 D4
Blakeley Gv *RAW/SKEL* YO30 9 G3
Blakeney Pl *FUL/HES* YO10 3 K7
Blake St *CYK* YO1 2 E3
Bland La *RYKW* YO26 16 B5
Blatchford Ct *RAW/SKEL* YO30 10 A5
Blenheim Ct *RAW/SKEL* YO30 9 E3
Bleriot Wy *RAW/SKEL* YO30 9 H3
Blossom St *ACOMB* YO24 2 C6
Blue Beck Dr *RAW/SKEL* YO30 17 F1
Blue Bridge La *FUL/HES* YO10 24 B2
Blue Coat *RYKS* YO19 20 D3
Board St *COP/BISH* YO23 24 A2
Bog La *ACOMB* YO24 26 D1
Bollans Ct *CYK* YO1 * 3 G3
Boltby Rd *RAW/SKEL* YO30 9 G4
Bonington Ct *RYKW* YO26 17 F4
Bootham *RAW/SKEL* YO30 2 D2
Bootham Crs *RAW/SKEL* YO30 2 D1
Bootham Park Ct
HEWTH YO31 * 18 B3
Bootham Rw *RAW/SKEL* YO30 2 E2
Bootham Sq *RAW/SKEL* YO30 2 E2
Bootham Ter *RAW/SKEL* YO30 2 C2
Boothwood Rd *RAW/SKEL* YO30 9 G4
Bore Tree Baulk *RYKS* YO19 20 D5
Boroughbridge Rd *RYKW* YO26 16 D3
Borrowdale Dr *RAW/SKEL* YO30 9 G5
Bouthwaite Dr *RYKW* YO26 17 F5
Bow Bridge Vw *TAD* LS24 31 F1
Bowes Av *HEWTH* YO31 3 K3
Bowland Wy *RAW/SKEL* YO30 9 H5
Bowling Green Cft
HEWTH YO31 18 C1
Bowling Green La *HEWTH* YO31 3 G1
Bowness Dr *RAW/SKEL* YO30 9 F5
Bowyers Cl *COP/BISH* YO23 27 E4
Bracken Cl *HXB/STR* YO32 11 E2
Bracken Hl *FUL/HES* YO10 25 G1
Brackenhills *RYKW* YO26 8 A5
Bracken Rd *ACOMB* YO24 23 F5
Bradley Dr *ACOMB* YO24 22 C4
Braeside Gdns *ACOMB* YO24 17 F5
Brailsford Crs *RAW/SKEL* YO30 17 H1
Bramble Dene *ACOMB* YO24 22 D5
Bramham Av *RYKW* YO26 22 A1
Bramham Gv *RYKW* YO26 22 A1
Bramham Rd *RYKW* YO26 22 A2
Bramley Garth *HEWTH* YO31 19 G3
Brandon Gv *HXB/STR* YO32 12 B3
Brandsby Gv *HEWTH* YO31 10 D4
Brandsdale Crs *FUL/HES* YO10 25 H1
Bransholme Dr *RAW/SKEL* YO30 9 H4
Branton Pl *RYKW* YO26 22 A1
Bray Rd *FUL/HES* YO10 24 D4
Breary Cl *ACOMB* YO24 23 F3
Brecks Cl *HXB/STR* YO32 6 C3
Brecksfield *RAW/SKEL* YO30 8 D1
Brecks La *HXB/STR* YO32 5 H2
HXB/STR YO32 11 E2
Brentwood Crs *FUL/HES* YO10 25 G2
Bretgate *CYK* YO1 * 3 J6
Briar Av *RYKW* YO26 16 C5
Briar Dr *HEWTH* YO31 11 E5
Bridge Cl *HXB/STR* YO32 6 C4
Bridge Rd *COP/BISH* YO23 27 H4
Bridge St *CYK* YO1 2 E5
TAD LS24 30 D3
Bridle Wy *RYKW* YO26 22 A1
Bridlington Rd *STMFBR* YO41 15 G2
Briergate *HXB/STR* YO32 6 D4
Briggs St *HEWTH* YO31 18 B2
Bright St *RYKW* YO26 17 G4
Brinkworth Ter *FUL/HES* YO10 3 J6
Broad Acres *HXB/STR* YO32 6 C4
Broad La *COP/BISH* YO23 22 A2
Broad Oak La *HXB/STR* YO32 6 C2
Broadstone Wy *RAW/SKEL* YO30 9 F3
Broadway *FUL/HES* YO10 24 B4
Broadway Gv *FUL/HES* YO10 24 C4
Broadway West *FUL/HES* YO10 24 B4
Brockfield Park Dr
HEWTH YO31 10 D4
Brockfield Rd *HEWTH* YO31 10 D4
Bromley St *RYKW* YO26 17 G4
Brompton Rd *RAW/SKEL* YO30 17 H2
Brooklands *FUL/HES* YO10 20 A5
Brook St *HEWTH* YO31 3 F1
Broome Cl *HXB/STR* YO32 11 E1
Broome Rd *HXB/STR* YO32 11 F1
Broome Wy *HXB/STR* YO32 11 F1
Broom Rd *TAD* LS24 30 B4
Brougham Cl *RAW/SKEL* YO30 17 G1
Broughton Wy *FUL/HES* YO10 19 G5
Browney Cft *FUL/HES* YO10 3 G7
Brownlow St *HEWTH* YO31 3 G1
Brown Moor *STMFBR* YO41 15 G3
Brunel Ct *RYKW* YO26 17 G4
Brunswick St *COP/BISH* YO23 23 H3
Buckingham Ct *CYK* YO1 * 2 D6
Buckingham St *CYK* YO1 2 E6
Buckingham Ter *CYK* YO1 * 2 E6
Bull La *FUL/HES* YO10 24 D1
HEWTH YO31 19 E3
Burdyke Av *RAW/SKEL* YO30 17 H1
Burlington Av *FUL/HES* YO10 19 E5
Burnholme Av *HEWTH* YO31 19 G3
Burnholme Dr *HEWTH* YO31 19 F3
Burnholme Gv *HEWTH* YO31 19 F4
Burniston Gv *FUL/HES* YO10 19 F5
Burnsall Dr *RYKW* YO26 17 F5
Burns Ct *ACOMB* YO24 22 B5
Burrill Av *RAW/SKEL* YO30 18 A1
Burrill Dr *HXB/STR* YO32 6 B2
Burton Av *RAW/SKEL* YO30 18 A2
Burton Fields Rd *STMFBR* YO41 15 G2
Burton Gn *RAW/SKEL* YO30 18 A1
Burton Stone La
RAW/SKEL YO30 18 A3
Burtree Av *RAW/SKEL* YO30 8 C2
Butcher Ter *COP/BISH* YO23 24 A3
Buttercrambe Rd
STMFBR YO41 15 E1
Buttermere Dr *RAW/SKEL* YO30 9 F5
Butters Cl *HXB/STR* YO32 6 B2
Butt Hl *HXB/STR* YO32 6 B2
Butts Cl *STMFBR* YO41 15 F4
Byland Av *HEWTH* YO31 18 D1
Byron Dr *RAW/SKEL* YO30 17 G1

C

Caedmon Cl *HEWTH* YO31 19 F2
Caesar Ct *COP/BISH* YO23 2 D7
Cairnborrow *ACOMB* YO24 22 B5
Caithness Cl *RAW/SKEL* YO30 9 F3
Calcaria Ct *ACOMB* YO24 23 F4
Calcaria Crs *TAD* LS24 30 B4
Calcaria Rd *TAD* LS24 30 B4
Caldbeck Cl *RAW/SKEL* YO30 9 H5

Calder Av *RYKW* YO26 16 C1
Calf Cl *HXB/STR* YO32 6 D3
Calvert Cl *HXB/STR* YO32 6 C4
Cambrian Cl *HXB/STR* YO32 11 E3
Cambridge Ms *ACOMB* YO24 * 2 B6
Cambridge St *ACOMB* YO24 2 B6
Cameron Gv *COP/BISH* YO23 24 A3
Cameron Walker Ct
COP/BISH YO23 * 24 A2
Campbell Av *ACOMB* YO24 23 E2
Campleshon Rd
COP/BISH YO23 23 H3
Canham Gv *FUL/HES* YO10 25 H1
Canterbury Cl *HXB/STR* YO32 6 B1
Carey St *FUL/HES* YO10 24 B3
Carleton St *RYKW* YO26 17 G4
Carlisle St *RYKW* YO26 17 G4
Carl St *COP/BISH* YO23 24 A2
Carlton Av *FUL/HES* YO10 25 F1
Carmelite St *CYK* YO1 3 G4
Carmires Av *HXB/STR* YO32 7 E2
Carnot St *RYKW* YO26 17 G4
Carnoustie Cl *RYKW* YO26 16 C5
Caroline Cl *ACOMB* YO24 23 F1
Carrbank La *RYKS* YO19 13 F2
Carrfield *ACOMB* YO24 22 C4
Carrick Gdns *ACOMB* YO24 23 E1
Carrington Av *RYKW* YO26 17 F4
Carr La *RYKW* YO26 17 E5
Carrnock Ct *HXB/STR* YO32 11 E5
Carron Crs *ACOMB* YO24 22 B5
Carter Av *HEWTH* YO31 19 E4
Castle Cl *HXB/STR* YO32 6 A1
Castlegate *CYK* YO1 3 F5
Catherine Ct *FUL/HES* YO10 3 K6
Catterton La *TAD* LS24 31 H1
Cavendish Gv *FUL/HES* YO10 25 H1
Caxton Av *RYKW* YO26 17 E4
Cayley Cl *RAW/SKEL* YO30 9 G5
Cayley Ct *RAW/SKEL* YO30 * 9 H4
Cecelia Pl *ACOMB* YO24 2 A6
Cecilia Pl *ACOMB* YO24 * 2 A6
Cedar Dr *TAD* LS24 30 B3
Cedar Gld *RYKS* YO19 21 G4
Cedar Gv *HEWTH* YO31 19 G2
Cedarwood Cl *ACOMB* YO24 22 B3
Celtic Cl *RYKW* YO26 16 C4
Cemetery Rd *FUL/HES* YO10 24 B2
Centenary Wy *CYK* YO1 3 F2
HXB/STR YO32 7 F5
HXB/STR YO32 11 E1
Centre La *TAD* LS24 30 D3
Centurion Wy *RAW/SKEL* YO30 10 A3
Chaldon Cl *HXB/STR* YO32 5 F4
Chalfonts *ACOMB* YO24 23 F3
Chaloner's Crs *ACOMB* YO24 22 D5
Chaloner's Rd *ACOMB* YO24 22 D4
Chancery Ct *ACOMB* YO24 22 C1
Chancery Ri *ACOMB* YO24 23 F1
Chantry Cl *ACOMB* YO24 22 C5
Chantry Gap *RYKW* YO26 8 A5
Chantry Gv *RYKW* YO26 8 A5
Chantry La *COP/BISH* YO23 28 B3
Chapel Fields Rd *RYKW* YO26 22 B1
Chapel Rw *CYK* YO1 3 H6
Chapel St *TAD* LS24 30 C3
Chapmans Ct *ACOMB* YO24 27 F1
Chapter House St *CYK* YO1 3 F3
Charles Moor *HEWTH* YO31 19 E2
Charlotte St *FUL/HES* YO10 3 K5
Charlton St *COP/BISH* YO23 24 A2
Chase Side Ct *ACOMB* YO24 23 E4
Chatsworth Av *HXB/STR* YO32 5 H1
Chatsworth Dr *HXB/STR* YO32 7 F2
Chatsworth Ter *RYKW* YO26 17 F5
Chaucer La *HXB/STR* YO32 5 H1
Chaucer St *FUL/HES* YO10 3 K6
Chaumont Wy *HXB/STR* YO32 12 D2
Chelkar Wy *RAW/SKEL* YO30 9 G5
Chelwood Wk *RYKW* YO26 17 F5
Cherry Garth *HEWTH* YO31 19 G4
Cherry Gv *RYKW* YO26 8 A5
Cherry Hill La *COP/BISH* YO23 * 3 F7
Cherry La *ACOMB* YO24 23 F4
Cherry Orch *HXB/STR* YO32 * 6 D3
Cherry Paddock *HXB/STR* YO32 6 D3
STMFBR YO41 15 E3
Cherry St *COP/BISH* YO23 3 F7
Cherry Tree Av *HXB/STR* YO32 10 C2
Cherry Wood Crs *RYKS* YO19 29 F2
Cheshire Av *HXB/STR* YO32 5 F5
Cheshire Cl *RAW/SKEL* YO30 9 F4
Chesney Flds *ACOMB* YO24 22 D3
Chessingham Gdns
ACOMB YO24 27 G1
Chessingham Pk *RYKS* YO19 21 H5
Chestnut Av *HEWTH* YO31 19 E2
Chestnut Gv *RYKW* YO26 16 D5
The Chestnuts *HXB/STR* YO32 6 C3
Cheviot Cl *HXB/STR* YO32 11 E3
Chiltern Wy *HXB/STR* YO32 11 E1
Chipstead Wk *HXB/STR* YO32 5 F3
Chudleigh Rd *RYKW* YO26 17 G4
Church Balk *RYKS* YO19 21 G3
Church Cl *COP/BISH* YO23 26 A1
Churchfield Dr *HXB/STR* YO32 6 C2
Church La *COP/BISH* YO23 28 A3
CYK YO1 3 F5
HXB/STR YO32 5 F2
HXB/STR YO32 6 C2
HXB/STR YO32 10 D1
RAW/SKEL YO30 8 C1
RYKS YO19 21 G3
RYKW YO26 8 B4
STMFBR YO41 15 F3
Church Ms *RYKW* YO26 22 C1
Church Ri *RYKS* YO19 13 H5
Church Rd *FUL/HES* YO10 19 H5
STMFBR YO41 15 F3
Church St *COP/BISH* YO23 26 C5
CYK YO1 3 F4
RYKS YO19 21 G3
Cinder La *ACOMB* YO24 2 B5
HEWTH YO31 3 K1
RYKW YO26 16 B2
RYKW YO26 17 G4
Cinder Ms *RYKW* YO26 2 A2
City Mills *CYK* YO1 * 3 F6
Claremont Ter *HEWTH* YO31 2 E1
Clarence St *HEWTH* YO31 3 F1
Clarks Ter *HEWTH* YO31 * 19 E3
Claygate *HEWTH* YO31 19 G3
Clay Pl *ACOMB* YO24 22 D3
Clementhorpe *COP/BISH* YO23 2 E7
Clement St *COP/BISH* YO23 2 E7
Cleveland St *ACOMB* YO24 2 A5
Cleveland Wy *HXB/STR* YO32 11 E3
Clifford St *CYK* YO1 3 F5
Clifton Dl *RAW/SKEL* YO30 17 H3
Clifton Gn *RAW/SKEL* YO30 17 H2
Clifton Moor Ga *RAW/SKEL* YO30 9 H4
Clifton Park Av *RAW/SKEL* YO30 17 F1
Clifton Pl *RAW/SKEL* YO30 17 H2
Clifton Rd *RAW/SKEL* YO30 17 H3
Clive Gv *ACOMB* YO24 23 F2
The Cloisters *HEWTH* YO31 3 G2
Cloisters Wk *HEWTH* YO31 3 G3
Cloister Wk *HEWTH* YO31 * 3 G3
The Close *RAW/SKEL* YO30 17 G1
Cloverley Cl *STMFBR* YO41 15 E3
Cobble Court Ms *ACOMB* YO24 * 2 C7
Cobham Wy *RAW/SKEL* YO30 9 F4
Coda Av *COP/BISH* YO23 28 B4
Coeside *ACOMB* YO24 22 B5
Coggan Cl *COP/BISH* YO23 * 23 H2
Coggan Wy *COP/BISH* YO23 27 H3
Coledale Cl *RAW/SKEL* YO30 9 G5
Colenso St *COP/BISH* YO23 3 F7
Cole St *HEWTH* YO31 3 F1
Colliergate *CYK* YO1 3 F4
College Rd *COP/BISH* YO23 26 C4
College St *CYK* YO1 3 F3
Collingham Pl *RYKW* YO26 * 16 C5
Collingwood Av *ACOMB* YO24 23 F2
Coltons Cottages
RAW/SKEL YO30 * 18 A2
Commercial St *TAD* LS24 30 D3
Common La *FUL/HES* YO10 25 G4
Common Rd *RYKS* YO19 21 H4
Compton St *RAW/SKEL* YO30 17 H3
Concorde Pk *RAW/SKEL* YO30 9 H3
Coneycroft *RYKS* YO19 21 H3
Coney St *CYK* YO1 2 E4
Conifer Cl *HXB/STR* YO32 10 C4
Coningham Av *RAW/SKEL* YO30 9 F4
Coniston Cl *RAW/SKEL* YO30 9 F5
Coniston Dr *FUL/HES* YO10 19 G5
Connaught Ct *FUL/HES* YO10 * 24 B4
Connaught Wy *HXB/STR* YO32 7 F5
Constantine Av *FUL/HES* YO10 19 F5
Conway Cl *RAW/SKEL* YO30 9 F3
Coopers Dr *COP/BISH* YO23 26 D4
Copmanthorpe La
COP/BISH YO23 27 H4
Copperbeech Cl *RYKS* YO19 21 G3
The Copper Beeches
RYKS YO19 21 G3
Coppergate *CYK* YO1 3 F5
Coppergate Wk *CYK* YO1 * 3 F5
Coppice Cl *HXB/STR* YO32 6 D1
The Coppice *COP/BISH* YO23 27 H3
Copwood Gv *HXB/STR* YO32 6 C3
Corban Wy *HXB/STR* YO32 6 B2
Corlett Ct *ACOMB* YO24 22 C4
Cornborough Av *HEWTH* YO31 19 E3
Corncroft *HXB/STR* YO32 5 F4
Corner Cl *HXB/STR* YO32 6 A2
Cornlands Rd *ACOMB* YO24 22 C2
Cornwall Dr *FUL/HES* YO10 24 C4
Cornwood Wy *HXB/STR* YO32 6 C3
Cosmo Av *HEWTH* YO31 19 E4
Cotswold Wy *HXB/STR* YO32 11 F1
Cottage Ms *HEWTH* YO31 * 19 F3
Count De Burgh Ter
COP/BISH YO23 23 H3
Courcey Gv *RYKW* YO26 16 D5
The Courtyard *COP/BISH* YO23 28 B3
The Covert *ACOMB* YO24 23 F5
Coxlea Gv *HEWTH* YO31 19 G3
Crabtree Gv *HXB/STR* YO32 10 C3
Cranbrook Av *RYKW* YO26 16 D4
Cranbrook Rd *RYKW* YO26 16 D3
Cranfield Pl *ACOMB* YO24 22 C4
Crawley Wy *HEWTH* YO31 19 G3
Creaser Cl *HXB/STR* YO32 5 F3
The Crescent *ACOMB* YO24 2 C6
STMFBR YO41 15 F3
Crichton Av *RAW/SKEL* YO30 18 B2
Crinan Ct *HXB/STR* YO32 7 F5
Croft Ct *COP/BISH* YO23 28 A3
Croft Farm Cl *COP/BISH* YO23 26 D4
Croftside *RYKW* YO26 22 B1
The Croft *HXB/STR* YO32 5 G4
Croftway *RYKW* YO26 22 B1
Crombie Av *RAW/SKEL* YO30 18 A2
Cromer St *RAW/SKEL* YO30 18 A2
Cromwell Rd *CYK* YO1 2 E6
Crookland La *HXB/STR* YO32 6 D1
Crossfield Crs *RYKS* YO19 29 E1
Crosslands Rd *FUL/HES* YO10 24 C4
Cross La *RYKS* YO19 29 F2
Crossmoor La *HXB/STR* YO32 4 B4
Cross St *ACOMB* YO24 22 C1
Crossways *FUL/HES* YO10 25 G2
The Crossway *HEWTH* YO31 18 D1
Crummock *ACOMB* YO24 22 C5
Cumberland Cl *HXB/STR* YO32 5 G4
Cumberland St *CYK* YO1 3 F5
Cumbrian Av *HXB/STR* YO32 5 G4
Curlew Glebe *RYKS* YO19 21 G4
Curzon Ter *COP/BISH* YO23 23 H3
Custance Wk *COP/BISH* YO23 2 D7
Cycle St *FUL/HES* YO10 25 E1
Cygnet St *COP/BISH* YO23 2 D7
Cyprus Gv *HXB/STR* YO32 6 D1

D

Dalby Md *HEWTH* YO31 11 E5
Dale Dike Gv *RAW/SKEL* YO30 9 G4
Dale's La *HEWTH* YO31 19 E3
Dale St *COP/BISH* YO23 2 D7
Dalguise Gv *HEWTH* YO31 3 H1
Dalmally Cl *ACOMB* YO24 26 D1
Dalton Ter *ACOMB* YO24 2 B7
Dane Av *RYKW* YO26 16 D5
Danebury Crs *RYKW* YO26 16 D5
Danebury Dr *RYKW* YO26 16 D5
Danes Cft *FUL/HES* YO10 * 24 B4
Danesfort Av *ACOMB* YO24 22 D2
Danesgate *RYKW* YO26 16 D5
Danesmead *FUL/HES* YO10 24 B4
Daneswell Cl *STMFBR* YO41 15 G2
Danum Dr *FUL/HES* YO10 24 C4
Danum Rd *FUL/HES* YO10 24 C4
Darbie Cl *HXB/STR* YO32 10 C2
Darfield Cl *HXB/STR* YO32 5 H1
Darley Cl *STMFBR* YO41 15 G2
Darnborough St
COP/BISH YO23 2 E7
Darnbrook Wk *HEWTH* YO31 19 G4
Darwin Cl *HEWTH* YO31 10 D5
Davygate *CYK* YO1 2 E4
Daysfoot Ct *FUL/HES* YO10 3 K7
Deacons Ct *COP/BISH* YO23 26 D5
Dealtry Av *HXB/STR* YO32 6 C3
Deangate *CYK* YO1 3 F3
Deanhead Gv *RAW/SKEL* YO30 9 F4
Deans Cl *COP/BISH* YO23 27 H3
Dee Cl *ACOMB* YO24 22 B5
Deepdale *ACOMB* YO24 22 D4
Deer Hill Gv *RAW/SKEL* YO30 9 G3
Deerstone Wy *RYKS* YO19 21 H4
De Grey Ct *RAW/SKEL* YO30 18 A3
De Grey Pl *COP/BISH* YO23 28 B4
De Grey St *HEWTH* YO31 3 F1
De Grey Ter *HEWTH* YO31 3 F1
Deighton Grove La *RYKS* YO19 29 G5
Delamere Cl *HXB/STR* YO32 6 B1
The Dell *RAW/SKEL* YO30 8 C1
Del Pyke *HEWTH* YO31 3 F1
Delwood *FUL/HES* YO10 24 B5
Dennison St *HEWTH* YO31 3 H1
Dennis St *CYK* YO1 3 G5
Deramore Dr *FUL/HES* YO10 25 H1
Deramore Dr West
FUL/HES YO10 2
Derwent Av *FUL/HES* YO10 1
Derwent Cl *STMFBR* YO41 1
Derwent Est *RYKS* YO19 2
Derwent La *RYKS* YO19 2
Derwent Rd *FUL/HES* YO10 2
Deveron Wy *ACOMB* YO24 2
Devon Pl *FUL/HES* YO10 2
Devonshire Ct *RAW/SKEL* YO30
Dewsbury Cottages
ACOMB YO24
Dewsbury Ter *CYK* YO1
Diamond St *HEWTH* YO31 1
Dickens Cl *HXB/STR* YO32 1
Dickson Rd *ACOMB* YO24 2
Didsbury Cl *RAW/SKEL* YO30
Dijon Av *ACOMB* YO24 2
Dikelands Cl *RYKW* YO26
Dikelands La *RYKW* YO26
Dilys Gv *RYKW* YO26 1
Disraeli Cl *HXB/STR* YO32 1
Dixon La *CYK* YO1
Dodgson Ter *RYKW* YO26 1
Dodsworth Av *HEWTH* YO31 1
Doe Pk *RAW/SKEL* YO30
Don Av *ACOMB* YO24 2
Dorchester Rd *TAD* LS24 3
Doriam Av *HEWTH* YO31 1
Doriam Dr *HEWTH* YO31 1
Dove St *COP/BISH* YO23
Drakes Cl *HXB/STR* YO32 1
Drake St *COP/BISH* YO23
Drapers Cft *COP/BISH* YO23 2
Driffield Ter *ACOMB* YO24 2
Dringfield Cl *ACOMB* YO24 2
Dringthorpe Rd *ACOMB* YO24 2
Drome Rd *COP/BISH* YO23 2
Drummond Vw *COP/BISH* YO23 2
Dudley Ct *HEWTH* YO31
Dudley Ms *HEWTH* YO31 1
Dudley St *HEWTH* YO31 1
Dukes Ct *RYKW* YO26 1
Dukes Whf *COP/BISH* YO23 *
Duncombe Dr *HXB/STR* YO32
Duncombe Pl *CYK* YO1
Dundas St *CYK* YO1
Durlston Dr *HXB/STR* YO32

E

Eades Cl *RAW/SKEL* YO30 1
Earle St *HEWTH* YO31 1
Earlsborough Ter
RAW/SKEL YO30 *
Earswick Cha *HXB/STR* YO32
Earswick Village *HXB/STR* YO32
Eason Rd *ACOMB* YO24 2
Eason Vw *ACOMB* YO24 2
Eastbourne Gv *HEWTH* YO31 1
East Cottages
RAW/SKEL YO30 * 1
Eastern Ter *HEWTH* YO31
Eastfield Av *HXB/STR* YO32
Eastfield Cl *TAD* LS24 3
Eastfield Ct *FUL/HES* YO10 2
Eastfield Crs *FUL/HES* YO10 2
Eastholme Dr *RAW/SKEL* YO30
Easthorpe Dr *RYKW* YO26
East Moor Gdns *RYKS* YO19 2
East Mount Rd *ACOMB* YO24
East Pde *HEWTH* YO31
Eastward Av *FUL/HES* YO10 2
East Wy *HEWTH* YO31 1
Eaton Ct *ACOMB* YO24 2
Ebor Pth *CYK* YO1
Ebor St *COP/BISH* YO23
Ebor Wy *COP/BISH* YO23 2
HXB/STR YO32
HXB/STR YO32
RYKW YO26
Ebsay Dr *RAW/SKEL* YO30
Eccles Cl *RAW/SKEL* YO30
Eden Cl *ACOMB* YO24 2
Edgerton Cl *TAD* LS24 3
Edgerton Ct *TAD* LS24 3
Edgerton Dr *TAD* LS24 3
Edgerton Garth *TAD* LS24 3
Edgware Rd *FUL/HES* YO10 2
Egremont Cl *STMFBR* YO41 1
Eighth Av *HEWTH* YO31 1
Elder Gv *HXB/STR* YO32
Eldon St *HEWTH* YO31
Eldon Ter *HEWTH* YO31 1
Eldwick Cl *RAW/SKEL* YO30
Elgar Cl *HEWTH* YO31 1
Elliot Ct *FUL/HES* YO10 2

vood Ct FUL/HES YO10 * 24 B2
a Gv RAW/SKEL YO30 9 F4
End HXB/STR YO32 6 D1
field Av HEWTH YO31 19 E1
field Ter HEWTH YO31 19 E2
Gv HEWTH YO31 11 E4
lands Gv HEWTH YO31 19 E1
park Vw HEWTH YO31 19 F1
park Wy HEWTH YO31 19 F1
Elms HXB/STR YO32 13 E2
Tree Av RYKW YO26 8 A4
tree Gdns RYKW YO26 16 D5
on Cl RAW/SKEL YO30 17 H1
ington Ter FUL/HES YO10 3 J5
vick Gv FUL/HES YO10 19 H5
bleton Dr RAW/SKEL YO30 9 G5
erald St HEWTH YO31 18 C3
ily Ms FUL/HES YO10 3 K6
merson St HEWTH YO31 3 K2
closure Gdns FUL/HES YO10 25 F3
dfields Rd FUL/HES YO10 24 C4
field Crs ACOMB YO24 23 F1
nerdale Av HEWTH YO31 19 G4
rick St FUL/HES YO10 3 H7
dale Av FUL/HES YO10 25 G1
Dr RYKW YO26 16 C1
lanade Ct RAW/SKEL YO30 * 2 C3
ve Pl ACOMB YO24 22 B5
n Dr HXB/STR YO32 6 B1
y Av FUL/HES YO10 19 F5
y Cl STMFBR YO41 15 G3
a Av RAW/SKEL YO30 9 E4
elyn Crs RAW/SKEL YO30 18 A2

F

ber Cl COP/BISH YO23 26 D4
ber St HEWTH YO31 3 J3
rfax STMFBR YO41 15 F3
rfax Cft COP/BISH YO23 26 D5
rfax St CYK YO1 2 D6
rfield Rd TAD LS24 30 C3
rfields Dr RAW/SKEL YO30 8 C1
rfield Wy TAD LS24 30 C3
rway RAW/SKEL YO30 17 H1
rway Dr RYKW YO26 8 A5
Fairways TAD LS24 30 C5
con Cl HXB/STR YO32 7 E2
coner St ACOMB YO24 23 F1
kland St CYK YO1 2 E6
sgrave Crs RAW/SKEL YO30 18 B2
field RYKW YO26 16 D3
field La RYKS YO19 21 G1
mers Wy COP/BISH YO23 26 D4
mlands Rd ACOMB YO24 22 D4
mstead Ri HXB/STR YO32 6 D4
ndale Av FUL/HES YO10 20 A5
ndale Cl HXB/STR YO32 7 E1
ndale St FUL/HES YO10 24 B2
rar St FUL/HES YO10 3 K7
riers Cha HXB/STR YO32 5 F5
riers Cft COP/BISH YO23 26 D4
vcett St FUL/HES YO10 3 H7
vkes Dr RYKW YO26 16 D5
sgate CYK YO1 3 F4
brook Av RYKW YO26 16 C5
wick's La FUL/HES YO10 24 B5
wick St COP/BISH YO23 24 A2
guson Wy HXB/STR YO32 11 E5
n Cl HXB/STR YO32 11 F2
n St HEWTH YO31 3 G1
nway FUL/HES YO10 25 G1
ry La COP/BISH YO23 28 B3
rymans Wk RYKW YO26 8 A3
ter La CYK YO1 2 E5
ersham Crs HEWTH YO31 18 B2
wster Wy FUL/HES YO10 3 G7
wston Dr RAW/SKEL YO30 9 G5
d Ct HEWTH YO31 * 19 F3
d Dr TAD LS24 31 F1
d La FUL/HES YO10 25 G2
d Vw RAW/SKEL YO30 18 B2
h Av HEWTH YO31 3 K2
y Ter RAW/SKEL YO30 18 B2
sbury Av COP/BISH YO23 24 A3
sbury St COP/BISH YO23 24 A3
bank Cl HXB/STR YO32 5 F3
Heath Cl ACOMB YO24 22 C3
Garth La STMFBR YO41 15 F2
t Av HEWTH YO31 19 E3
ree Cl ACOMB YO24 23 E1
XB/STR YO32 7 F4
ree Crs TAD LS24 30 B4
vood Whin HEWTH YO31 11 E3
nergate FUL/HES YO10 3 G7
roy Ter FUL/HES YO10 3 J7
vian Gv RAW/SKEL YO30 17 G1
Flaxman Av FUL/HES YO10 19 F5
Flaxman Cft COP/BISH YO23 26 D4
Flaxton Rd HXB/STR YO32 5 H3
Fleming Av HEWTH YO31 3 K2
Fletcher Ct HXB/STR YO32 6 C2
Fletcher's Cft COP/BISH YO23 27 E4
Florence Gv RAW/SKEL YO30 9 E4
Fold Wk HXB/STR YO32 5 H1
Folks Cl HXB/STR YO32 7 E2
Folly Br RAW/SKEL YO30 8 B2
Fordlands Crs RYKS YO19 29 E1
Fordlands Rd RYKS YO19 29 E1
Forest Cl HXB/STR YO32 6 B3
Forester's Wk ACOMB YO24 22 B3
STMFBR YO41 15 E4
Forestgate HXB/STR YO32 6 C4
Forest Gv HEWTH YO31 19 E3
Forest La RYKS YO19 29 H3
Forest Wy HEWTH YO31 19 E3
Forge Cl HXB/STR YO32 11 E4
Forth St RYKW YO26 17 G3
Foss Bank HEWTH YO31 3 H3
Foss Br HXB/STR YO32 5 E3
Foss Ct HEWTH YO31 10 D5
Fossgate CYK YO1 3 G4
Foss Islands Rd HEWTH YO31 3 J5
Fossland Vw HXB/STR YO32 5 F3
Foss Wk RYKW YO26 16 C1
Foss Wy FUL/HES YO10 3 G7
Fossway HEWTH YO31 18 D2
STMFBR YO41 15 F4
Foston Gv HEWTH YO31 19 E1
Fountayne St HEWTH YO31 18 C2
Fourth Av HEWTH YO31 3 K3
Fox Covert HEWTH YO31 11 E4
Foxcroft HXB/STR YO32 6 C5
Fox Garth RYKW YO26 8 B3
Fox Gld STMFBR YO41 15 E3
Foxthorn Paddock
FUL/HES YO10 25 H1
Foxton Cl ACOMB YO24 22 C4
Foxwood La ACOMB YO24 22 A3
Frances St FUL/HES YO10 24 B3
Frazer Ct RAW/SKEL YO30 17 F1
Frederic St RAW/SKEL YO30 2 C3
Friargate CYK YO1 3 F5
Friar's Wk HEWTH YO31 18 D1
Front St ACOMB YO24 22 C1
Fryors Cl RYKS YO19 20 D4
Fulford Cross FUL/HES YO10 24 B3
Fulfordgate FUL/HES YO10 24 C5
Fulford Pk FUL/HES YO10 24 B5
Fulford Rd FUL/HES YO10 24 B4
Furlong Rd STMFBR YO41 15 G3
Furness Dr RAW/SKEL YO30 9 F5
Furnwood HXB/STR YO32 6 D4
Fylingdale Av RAW/SKEL YO30 17 F1

G

Gainsborough Cl HXB/STR YO32 5 H1
Gale Farm Ct ACOMB YO24 22 C1
Gale La ACOMB YO24 22 C2
Galligap La FUL/HES YO10 19 H5
The Gallops ACOMB YO24 22 B4
Galmanhoe La RAW/SKEL YO30 2 D2
Galtres Av HEWTH YO31 19 G2
Galtres Gv RAW/SKEL YO30 17 G2
Galtres Rd HEWTH YO31 19 G2
Ganton Pl ACOMB YO24 23 E5
Garbett Wy COP/BISH YO23 28 B4
Garburn Gv RAW/SKEL YO30 9 F5
Garbutt Gv RYKW YO26 17 E4
Garden Ct RYKW YO26 16 D4
Gardeners Cl COP/BISH YO23 26 D4
Garden Flats La RYKS YO19 21 H3
Garden Pl CYK YO1 3 G4
Garden St HEWTH YO31 3 F1
The Garden Village
HXB/STR YO32 7 G3
Garden Wy RYKW YO26 16 D4
Garfield Ter RYKW YO26 17 G4
The Garlands RAW/SKEL YO30 17 H1
Garland St RYKW YO26 17 F5
Garnet Ter RYKW YO26 17 F4
Garroway Wy FUL/HES YO10 25 F4
Garrowby Vw STMFBR YO41 15 G2
Garrow Hl FUL/HES YO10 24 D2
Garrow Hill Av FUL/HES YO10 25 E1
Garth Rd HXB/STR YO32 11 F2
Garth's End FUL/HES YO10 24 C4
HXB/STR YO32 7 F2
Garth Ter RAW/SKEL YO30 18 A2
Garthway HXB/STR YO32 10 C3
Gascoigne Wk COP/BISH YO23 2 E7
Gateland Cl HXB/STR YO32 6 C4
Gay Mdw HXB/STR YO32 13 E2
Geldof Rd HXB/STR YO32 11 E5
George Caley Dr RAW/SKEL YO30 9 H3
George Cayley Dr
RAW/SKEL YO30 9 H3
George Ct HEWTH YO31 3 H2
George Hudson St CYK YO1 2 D5
George St CYK YO1 3 H6
Gerard Av HEWTH YO31 19 F3
Germany La FUL/HES YO10 29 E1
Giles Av HEWTH YO31 19 F4
Gillamoor Av HEWTH YO31 19 G4
Gillingwood Rd RAW/SKEL YO30 9 G4
Gillygate HEWTH YO31 2 E2
Girvan Cl ACOMB YO24 22 B5
Givendale Gv FUL/HES YO10 19 H5
The Glade HEWTH YO31 19 G2
Gladstone St ACOMB YO24 22 D1
HEWTH YO31 18 D3
Glaisby Ct HEWTH YO31 19 F3
Glaisdale Rd RYKW YO26 16 A3
Glebe Av RYKW YO26 17 E4
Glebe Cl HXB/STR YO32 5 G3
Glebe Wy HXB/STR YO32 6 C2
Glen Av HEWTH YO31 3 J2
Glen Cl FUL/HES YO10 29 E1
Glencoe St RAW/SKEL YO30 18 A2
Glenridding ACOMB YO24 22 D5
Glen Rd HEWTH YO31 3 K2
Godwinsway STMFBR YO41 15 G3
Golf Links Av TAD LS24 30 B4
Golf Links Ct TAD LS24 30 C4
Golf Links Crs TAD LS24 30 B4
Goodramgate CYK YO1 3 F4
Goodricke Wy FUL/HES YO10 25 E3
Goodwood Gv ACOMB YO24 23 F3
Gordon St FUL/HES YO10 3 J7
Gormire Av HEWTH YO31 10 D4
Gorse Hl RYKS YO19 21 H3
Gorse Paddock HEWTH YO31 11 E4
Gouthwaith Cl RAW/SKEL YO30 9 G4
Government House Rd
RAW/SKEL YO30 * 2 A1
Gower Rd ACOMB YO24 23 E4
Grampian Cl HXB/STR YO32 11 E1
Granary Ct CYK YO1 3 G3
Grange Av TAD LS24 31 E2
Grange Cl RAW/SKEL YO30 8 C1
Grange Crs TAD LS24 30 D2
Grange Garth FUL/HES YO10 24 B2
Grange La COP/BISH YO23 22 A2
Granger Av RYKW YO26 16 D5
Grange Rd TAD LS24 31 E2
Grange St FUL/HES YO10 * 24 C2
Grantham Dr RYKW YO26 17 F5
Grants Av FUL/HES YO10 24 C4
Granville Ter FUL/HES YO10 3 K6
Grape La CYK YO1 3 F4
Grasmere Dr FUL/HES YO10 19 G5
Grasmere Gv RAW/SKEL YO30 9 G5
Grassholme ACOMB YO24 22 C5
Grayshon Dr RYKW YO26 16 C4
Gray St COP/BISH YO23 2 D7
Great North Wy RYKW YO26 16 D1
Greenacres HXB/STR YO32 11 E2
Greencliffe Dr RAW/SKEL YO30 17 H3
Green Cl RAW/SKEL YO30 17 H1
Greencroft Ct RYKS YO19 21 H4
Greencroft La RYKS YO19 21 H4
Green Dike HXB/STR YO32 6 B3
Green Dykes La FUL/HES YO10 24 D1
Greenfield Park Dr
HEWTH YO31 19 F1
Greenfields HEWTH YO31 18 C2
Green La ACOMB YO24 22 D2
COP/BISH YO23 27 H2
HXB/STR YO32 6 A1
RAW/SKEL YO30 9 G5
Green Mdw HEWTH YO31 19 F2
Greensborough Av RYKW YO26 16 C4
Greenshaw Dr HXB/STR YO32 6 C2
Greenside RYKS YO19 21 H4
Greenside Cl RYKS YO19 21 H4
Greenside Wk RYKS YO19 21 H4
Green Sward HEWTH YO31 19 F2
The Green RYKS YO19 21 H4
RYKW YO26 22 C1
Green Wy HXB/STR YO32 11 E2
The Greenway HXB/STR YO32 6 C4
Greenwood Gv ACOMB YO24 22 C4
Gregory Cl RAW/SKEL YO30 8 D1
Grenwich Cl RAW/SKEL YO30 9 F3
Gresley Ct RYKW YO26 16 C5
Greystoke Rd RAW/SKEL YO30 9 G5
Greystone Ct HXB/STR YO32 6 C5
Grimwith Garth
RAW/SKEL YO30 * 9 G4
Grosvenor Rd RAW/SKEL YO30 18 B3
Grosvenor Ter RAW/SKEL YO30 2 D1
Grove Gdns RYKW YO26 8 A5
Groves Ct HEWTH YO31 3 G2
Groves La HEWTH YO31 3 H1
Grove Terrace La HEWTH YO31 18 C3
The Grove ACOMB YO24 27 G1
Grove Vw RAW/SKEL YO30 17 H3

H

Hackness Rd RYKW YO26 16 A3
Hadrian Av FUL/HES YO10 25 F1
Haley's Ter HEWTH YO31 18 C1
Halifax Ct RAW/SKEL YO30 9 H5
Halladale Cl ACOMB YO24 22 B5
Hallard Wy HXB/STR YO32 5 G3
Hallcroft La COP/BISH YO23 26 C4
Hallfield Rd HEWTH YO31 3 K3
Hall Pk FUL/HES YO10 25 F3
Hall Ri HXB/STR YO32 6 D2
Hambleton Av FUL/HES YO10 19 H5
Hambleton Ter HEWTH YO31 18 B2
Hambleton Vw HXB/STR YO32 6 B1
Hambleton Wy HXB/STR YO32 11 E3
Hamilton Dr ACOMB YO24 23 E2
Hamilton Dr East ACOMB YO24 23 F2
Hamilton Dr West ACOMB YO24 22 D2
Hamilton Wy ACOMB YO24 23 E2
Hammerton Cl RYKW YO26 22 B1
Hampden St CYK YO1 2 E6
Handley Cl RAW/SKEL YO30 9 H4
Hanover St East RYKW YO26 17 G4
Hanover St West RYKW YO26 17 G4
Hansom Pl HEWTH YO31 18 B2
Harcourt Cl COP/BISH YO23 28 A4
Harcourt St HEWTH YO31 3 K2
Harden Cl RAW/SKEL YO30 9 G4
Hardisty Ms RYKW YO26 17 G4
Hardrada Wy STMFBR YO41 15 F4
Harewood Cl HXB/STR YO32 6 B1
RAW/SKEL YO30 9 E4
Harewood Wy FUL/HES YO10 25 E2
Harington Av FUL/HES YO10 19 E5
Harlow Cl ACOMB YO24 23 F2
Harlow Ct HXB/STR YO32 5 F4
Harlow Rd ACOMB YO24 23 F2
Harold Ct ACOMB YO24 22 D1
Harolds Wy STMFBR YO41 15 F4
Harrison St HEWTH YO31 19 E3
Harrow Gld RAW/SKEL YO30 9 H5
Hartoft St FUL/HES YO10 24 B2
Harvest Cl HXB/STR YO32 5 G3
Harwood Rd RYKW YO26 16 A3
Hassacarr La RYKS YO19 21 H5
Hastings Cl RAW/SKEL YO30 9 H5
Hatfield Cl RAW/SKEL YO30 9 F3
Hatters Cl COP/BISH YO23 26 D4
Haughton Rd RAW/SKEL YO30 18 B2
Hawkshead Cl ACOMB YO24 22 B4
Hawthorn Av HXB/STR YO32 6 D2
TAD LS24 30 B5
Hawthorn Cl TAD LS24 30 C5
Hawthorn Cft TAD LS24 30 B5
Hawthorne Cl RYKW YO26 8 A4
Hawthorne Ms HXB/STR YO32 5 G3
Hawthorn Gv HEWTH YO31 3 J2
Hawthorn Spinney
HEWTH YO31 10 D3
Hawthorn St HEWTH YO31 3 J2
Hawthorn Ter Central
HXB/STR YO32 10 C3
Hawthorn Ter North
HXB/STR YO32 10 D2
Hawthorn Ter South
HXB/STR YO32 10 C3
Haxby Moor Rd HXB/STR YO32 4 D3
Haxby Rd HEWTH YO31 18 B3
Hazel Cl HXB/STR YO32 10 C4
Hazel Ct FUL/HES YO10 3 K4
Hazel Garth HEWTH YO31 19 G3
Hazelmere Ct HXB/STR YO32 10 D3
Hazelnut Gv RAW/SKEL YO30 10 A4
Hazelwood Av FUL/HES YO10 20 A5
Headland Cl HXB/STR YO32 6 C2
Headley Cl RAW/SKEL YO30 9 H5
Healey Gv HEWTH YO31 19 E1
Heath Cl ACOMB YO24 23 F2
Heath Cft FUL/HES YO10 24 D5
Heather Bank FUL/HES YO10 19 H5
STMFBR YO41 15 F3
Heather Cl HXB/STR YO32 11 F2
Heather Cft HEWTH YO31 10 D4
Heatherdene TAD LS24 30 D2
Heathfield Rd FUL/HES YO10 25 E1
Heath Moor Dr FUL/HES YO10 24 D4
Heath Ride HXB/STR YO32 5 H1
Hebdon Ri ACOMB YO24 22 D1
Helmsdale ACOMB YO24 26 D1
Helmsley Gv HXB/STR YO32 6 A2

Hemlock Av *HEWTH* YO31 10 D5
Hempland Av *HEWTH* YO31 19 E3
Hempland Dr *HEWTH* YO31 19 F2
Hempland La *HEWTH* YO31 19 F3
Hendon Garth *RAW/SKEL* YO30 9 H5
Herbert St *FUL/HES* YO10 3 K6
Herberts Wy *HEWTH* YO31 19 E2
Herdsman Dr *COP/BISH* YO23 27 E4
Herdsman Rd *ACOMB* YO24 22 D4
Herdwick Cl *RAW/SKEL* YO30 10 A5
Herman Wk *ACOMB* YO24 22 C4
Heron Av *ACOMB* YO24 22 C4
Heron Ri *HXB/STR* YO32 11 E1
Hesketh Bank *FUL/HES* YO10 25 H1
Heslin Cl *HXB/STR* YO32 6 C3
Heslington Ct *FUL/HES* YO10 25 F3
Heslington Cft *FUL/HES* YO10 24 D5
Heslington La *FUL/HES* YO10 24 C5
Heslington Rd *FUL/HES* YO10 3 J7
Hessay Pl *RYKW* YO26 22 A1
Hetherton St *RAW/SKEL* YO30 2 C3
Hewley Av *FUL/HES* YO10 19 E5
Heworth *HEWTH* YO31 19 E3
Heworth Gn *HEWTH* YO31 3 J1
Heworth Hall Dr *HEWTH* YO31 19 F3
Heworth Ms *HEWTH* YO31 3 J2
Heworth Pl *HEWTH* YO31 19 E3
Heworth Rd *HEWTH* YO31 19 E3
Heworth Village *HEWTH* YO31 * 19 E3
High Catton Rd *STMFBR* YO41 15 F4
Highcliffe Ct *RAW/SKEL* YO30 17 H3
High Fld *FUL/HES* YO10 20 A5
Highgrove Cl *RAW/SKEL* YO30 9 F3
Highlands Av *HXB/STR* YO32 5 G3
Highmoor Cl *ACOMB* YO24 22 D4
Highmoor Rd *ACOMB* YO24 22 D4
High Newbiggin St *HEWTH* YO31 3 G2
High Oaks *HEWTH* YO31 19 G2
High Ousegate *CYK* YO1 3 F5
High Petergate *CYK* YO1 2 E3
High St *TAD* LS24 30 C3
Highthorn Rd *HEWTH* YO31 10 D4
Hilbeck Gv *HEWTH* YO31 19 G3
Hilbra Av *HXB/STR* YO32 6 D5
Hilda St *FUL/HES* YO10 3 K6
Hillary Garth *RYKW* YO26 17 F5
Hill Crest *RYKS* YO19 13 H5
Hillcrest *TAD* LS24 30 B4
Hillcrest Av *RYKW* YO26 8 B4
Hillcrest Ct *TAD* LS24 30 B4
Hill Crest Gdns *ACOMB* YO24 23 F3
Hillsborough Ter
RAW/SKEL YO30 18 B2
Hill St *ACOMB* YO24 23 E1
Hill Vw *HEWTH* YO31 19 H2
Hinton Av *ACOMB* YO24 22 C4
Hobgate *ACOMB* YO24 22 D1
Hob Moor Dr *ACOMB* YO24 23 E2
Hobmoor Ter *ACOMB* YO24 23 F3
Holburns Cft *FUL/HES* YO10 25 F3
Holgate Bridge Gdn
ACOMB YO24 2 A7
Holgate Lodge Dr *RYKW* YO26 17 F5
Holgate Park Dr *RYKW* YO26 17 G5
Holgate Rd *ACOMB* YO24 23 F1
Hollis Crs *HXB/STR* YO32 5 G4
Holly Bank Gv *ACOMB* YO24 23 F2
Holly Bank Rd *ACOMB* YO24 23 F2
Hollyrood Dr *RAW/SKEL* YO30 9 F3
Holly Ter *FUL/HES* YO10 * 24 A3
Holly Tree Cft *RYKS* YO19 21 H3
Holly Tree Garth *HXB/STR* YO32 13 E1
Holly Tree La *HXB/STR* YO32 6 D3
RYKS YO19 21 H3
Holmefield La *FUL/HES* YO10 25 E3
Holroyd Av *HEWTH* YO31 19 F4
Holtby La *HXB/STR* YO32 12 C4
RYKS YO19 13 E5
Homefield Cl *COP/BISH* YO23 26 C5
Homelea *HXB/STR* YO32 5 F4
Homestead Cl *HXB/STR* YO32 11 E5
Hope St *FUL/HES* YO10 3 H6
Hopgrove La *HXB/STR* YO32 12 B4
Hopgrove La North
HXB/STR YO32 11 H3
Hopgrove La South
HXB/STR YO32 12 A3
Hornbeam Cl *RAW/SKEL* YO30 10 A4
Horner St *RAW/SKEL* YO30 18 A2
Hornsey Garth *HXB/STR* YO32 6 C2
Horseman Av *COP/BISH* YO23 26 C4
Horseman Cl *COP/BISH* YO23 26 C4
Horseman Dr *COP/BISH* YO23 26 C4
Horseman La *COP/BISH* YO23 26 C4
The Horseshoe *ACOMB* YO24 23 E5
Horsfield Wy *RYKS* YO19 21 H3
Horsman Av *FUL/HES* YO10 3 H7
Hospital Fields Rd
FUL/HES YO10 24 B3
Hotham Av *RYKW* YO26 22 B2
Hothams Ct *CYK* YO1 * 3 G5
Houndsway *ACOMB* YO24 22 B4
Howard Dr *RAW/SKEL* YO30 9 E4
Howard Link *RAW/SKEL* YO30 9 F4
Howard Rd *HXB/STR* YO32 5 H4
Howard St *FUL/HES* YO10 24 B2
Howe Hill Cl *RYKW* YO26 17 F5
Howe Hill Rd *RYKW* YO26 17 F5
Howe St *ACOMB* YO24 22 D1
Hubert St *COP/BISH* YO23 23 H3
Huby Ct *CYK* YO1 3 J6
Hudson Cl *STMFBR* YO41 15 G3
TAD LS24 30 D1
Hudson Crs *RAW/SKEL* YO30 17 H2
Hudson St *RAW/SKEL* YO30 18 B2
Hudson Vw *TAD* LS24 30 D2
Hudson Wy *RYKW* YO26 16 D1
TAD LS24 30 D1
Hull Rd *FUL/HES* YO10 25 G1
RYKS YO19 21 F5
Humber Dr *HXB/STR* YO32 5 G4
Hungate *CYK* YO1 3 G4
Hunt Ct *CYK* YO1 * 3 G3
Hunters Cl *HXB/STR* YO32 6 C3
RYKS YO19 21 F4
Hunters Wy *ACOMB* YO24 23 F5
Hunters Wood Wy *RYKS* YO19 21 G4
Huntington Ms *HEWTH* YO31 * 18 C2
Huntington Rd *HEWTH* YO31 3 H1
HXB/STR YO32 10 D3
Huntsmans La *STMFBR* YO41 15 E3
Huntsman's Wk *ACOMB* YO24 22 C3
Hurricane Wy *RAW/SKEL* YO30 9 F3
Hurst's Yd *CYK* YO1 3 H5
Hutton Cl *RYKW* YO26 8 B4
Hyrst Gv *HEWTH* YO31 18 D3

I

Ikin Wy *HXB/STR* YO32 7 F5
Ilton Garth *RAW/SKEL* YO30 9 H4
Ingleborough Av
FUL/HES YO10 19 G5
Ingleby Dr *TAD* LS24 30 D2
Ingleton Wk *HEWTH* YO31 19 F4
Ingram Av *RAW/SKEL* YO30 18 B1
Ings La *RYKW* YO26 8 C5
Ings Vw *RAW/SKEL* YO30 9 E4
Ings Wy *RAW/SKEL* YO30 17 G1
Inholmes La *TAD* LS24 30 B3
Inman Ter *RYKW* YO26 17 E5
Innovation Cl *FUL/HES* YO10 25 F2
Innovation Wy *FUL/HES* YO10 25 F2
Intake Av *RAW/SKEL* YO30 18 B1
Intake La *RYKS* YO19 21 H4
Invicta Ct *ACOMB* YO24 22 B4
Irwin Av *HEWTH* YO31 18 D3
Iver Cl *RYKW* YO26 16 D4

J

Jackson St *HEWTH* YO31 3 G1
Jacobi Cl *RAW/SKEL* YO30 17 H2
James Backhouse Pl
ACOMB YO24 23 E1
James Nicholson Link
RAW/SKEL YO30 9 H4
James St *FUL/HES* YO10 3 J4
James Wy *FUL/HES* YO10 25 E3
Jamieson Ter *COP/BISH* YO23 23 H3
Jasmine Cl *HXB/STR* YO32 10 C4
Jaywick Cl *HXB/STR* YO32 5 G1
Jedwell Cl *HXB/STR* YO32 10 C1
Jennifer Gv *ACOMB* YO24 23 F2
Jervis Rd *ACOMB* YO24 23 E4
Jewbury *CYK* YO1 3 G3
Jockey La *HXB/STR* YO32 11 G5
John Saville Ct *CYK* YO1 * 3 G3
John St *HEWTH* YO31 3 K1
John Ward Cl *STMFBR* YO41 15 G3
Jorvic Cl *RYKW* YO26 16 D4
Julia Av *HXB/STR* YO32 11 G4
Juniper Cl *HXB/STR* YO32 10 C3
Jute Rd *RYKW* YO26 16 C5

K

Kathryn Av *HXB/STR* YO32 11 F4
Keats Cl *RAW/SKEL* YO30 9 G5
Keble Cl *COP/BISH* YO23 28 B4
Keble Dr *COP/BISH* YO23 28 A4
Keble Gdns *COP/BISH* YO23 28 B5
Keble Park Crs *COP/BISH* YO23 28 A5
Keble Pk North *COP/BISH* YO23 28 B4
Keble Pk South *COP/BISH* YO23 28 B5
Keith Av *HXB/STR* YO32 11 F2
Kelcbar Cl *TAD* LS24 30 B2
Kelcbar Hl *TAD* LS24 30 A2
Kelcbar Wy *TAD* LS24 30 B2
Keldale *HXB/STR* YO32 7 E1
Kempton Cl *ACOMB* YO24 22 D3
Kendal Cl *RYKS* YO19 21 H3
Kendrew Cl *HXB/STR* YO32 11 E3
Kenlay Cl *HXB/STR* YO32 10 C2
Kennedy Dr *HXB/STR* YO32 6 D2
Kenrick Pl *RYKW* YO26 16 D4
Kensal Ri *FUL/HES* YO10 24 B2
Kensington Ct *ACOMB* YO24 23 F4
Kensington Rd *RAW/SKEL* YO30 9 E4
Kensington St *COP/BISH* YO23 23 H3
Kentmere Dr *RAW/SKEL* YO30 9 G5
Kent St *FUL/HES* YO10 3 H7
Kerrside *RAW/SKEL* YO30 17 F1
Kerver La *RYKS* YO19 21 H3
Kestrel Wood Wy *HEWTH* YO31 11 E4
Keswick Wy *HXB/STR* YO32 11 E1
Kettleman Br *TAD* LS24 31 E5
Kettlestring La *RAW/SKEL* YO30 9 H3
Kexby Av *FUL/HES* YO10 24 D1
Key Wy *RYKS* YO19 29 F2
Kilburn Rd *FUL/HES* YO10 24 B2
Kimberlows Wood Hl
FUL/HES YO10 25 G1
Kinbrace Dr *ACOMB* YO24 22 B5
Kings Acre *HEWTH* YO31 19 G3
Kingsclere *HXB/STR* YO32 7 F5
Kings Ct *CYK* YO1 3 F4
Kingsland Ter *RYKW* YO26 17 G4
Kings Moor Rd *HXB/STR* YO32 12 D2
King's Sq *CYK* YO1 3 F4
Kings Staith *CYK* YO1 3 F5
Kingsthorpe *ACOMB* YO24 22 D2
King St *CYK* YO1 3 F5
Kingsway *STMFBR* YO41 15 G2
Kingsway North
RAW/SKEL YO30 18 A2
Kingsway West *ACOMB* YO24 22 D3
Kingswood Gv *ACOMB* YO24 22 D2
Kir Crs *ACOMB* YO24 22 C1
Kirkcroft *HXB/STR* YO32 6 C3
Kirkdale Rd *FUL/HES* YO10 20 A5
Kirkgate *TAD* LS24 30 D3
Kirkham Av *HEWTH* YO31 18 D1
Kirklands *HXB/STR* YO32 5 G4
Kirkstone Dr *HEWTH* YO31 19 F3
Kirk Vw *RYKW* YO26 22 C1
Kirkwell *COP/BISH* YO23 28 A3
Kitchener St *HEWTH* YO31 18 C2
Kitemere Pl *ACOMB* YO24 22 B4
Knapton Cl *HXB/STR* YO32 5 G4
Knapton La *RYKW* YO26 16 C5
Knavesmire Crs *COP/BISH* YO23 23 H3
Knavesmire Rd *ACOMB* YO24 23 G2
The Knoll *ACOMB* YO24 22 B3
Kyle Wy *RYKW* YO26 16 C1
Kyme St *CYK* YO1 2 E6

L

Laburnum Garth *HEWTH* YO31 19 E1
Lady Hamilton Gdns
ACOMB YO24 22 D2
Lady Rd *RAW/SKEL* YO30 18 A2
Ladysmith Ms *HXB/STR* YO32 5 F3
Lakeside Ct *ACOMB* YO24 * 23 F4
Lakeside Gdns *HXB/STR* YO32 5 H1
Lambert Ct *CYK* YO1 2 E6
Lamel St *FUL/HES* YO10 25 E1
Lamplugh Crs *COP/BISH* YO23 28 B4
Lancar Cl *HXB/STR* YO32 6 A2
Lancaster Vls *RYKW* YO26 * 8 A5
Lancaster Wy *RAW/SKEL* YO30 9 H5
Landalewood Rd
RAW/SKEL YO30 9 G4
Landau Cl *RAW/SKEL* YO30 17 G1
Landing La *HXB/STR* YO32 7 E4
RYKW YO26 17 F4
The Landings *HXB/STR* YO32 7 E2
The Lane *STMFBR* YO41 14 A3
Lang Av *FUL/HES* YO10 19 F5
Langdale Av *HEWTH* YO31 19 G3
Langholme Dr *RYKW* YO26 16 D3
Langley Ct *HXB/STR* YO32 11 E1
Lang Rd *COP/BISH* YO23 27 H3
HXB/STR YO32 7 F5
Langsett Gv *RAW/SKEL* YO30 9 G3
Langton Ct *HXB/STR* YO32 5 F4
Lansdowne Ter *FUL/HES* YO10 3 K6
Lansdown Wy *HXB/STR* YO32 7 E2
Lanshaw Cft *RAW/SKEL* YO30 9
Larchfield *HEWTH* YO31 19
Larch Wy *HXB/STR* YO32 6
Larkfield Cl *COP/BISH* YO23 26
Lastingham Ter
FUL/HES YO10 * 24
Laurel Cl *HXB/STR* YO32 7
Lavender Gv *RYKW* YO26 17
Lawnswood Dr *RAW/SKEL* YO30 17
Lawnway *HEWTH* YO31 19
Lawrence Ct *FUL/HES* YO10 3
Lawrence St *FUL/HES* YO10 3
Lawson Rd *ACOMB* YO24 23
Layerthorpe *CYK* YO1 3
Lead Mill La *CYK* YO1 3
Leake St *FUL/HES* YO10 3
Learmans Wy *COP/BISH* YO23 27
Lea Wy *HXB/STR* YO32 11
Leeds Rd *TAD* LS24 30
Leeman Rd *RYKW* YO26 2
Leeside *ACOMB* YO24 23
Leicester Wy *CYK* YO1 * 3
Leighton Cft *RAW/SKEL* YO30 9
Lendal *CYK* YO1 2
Lendal Br *CYK* YO1 2
Lerecroft Rd *ACOMB* YO24 22
Lesley Av *FUL/HES* YO10 24
Leven Rd *ACOMB* YO24 22
Levisham St *FUL/HES* YO10 24
The Leyes *FUL/HES* YO10 19
Leyfield Cl *HXB/STR* YO32 5
Leyland Rd *HEWTH* YO31 19
Lichfield Ct *COP/BISH* YO23 23
Lidgett Gv *RYKW* YO26 16
Lilac Av *FUL/HES* YO10 25
Lilac Gv *HXB/STR* YO32 10
Lilbourne Dr *RAW/SKEL* YO30 17
Lilling Av *HEWTH* YO31 18
Lime Av *HEWTH* YO31 19
Limegarth *RYKW* YO26 8
The Limes *HXB/STR* YO32 12
Lime Tree Av *HXB/STR* YO32 10
Lime Tree Ms *RYKS* YO19 21
Lincoln St *RYKW* YO26 17
Lindale *ACOMB* YO24 22
Linden Cl *HXB/STR* YO32 11
Linden Gv *RAW/SKEL* YO30 17
Lindley Rd *RAW/SKEL* YO30 9
Lindley St *ACOMB* YO24 23
Lindley Wood Gv
RAW/SKEL YO30 9
Lindsey Av *RYKW* YO26 17
Lingcroft La *RYKS* YO19 29
Lingfield Crs *ACOMB* YO24 23
Link Av *RAW/SKEL* YO30 18
Link Rd *HXB/STR* YO32 10
Link Road Ct *FUL/HES* YO10 20
The Links *TAD* LS24 30
The Link *COP/BISH* YO23 26
FUL/HES YO10 24
Linley Av *HXB/STR* YO32 7
Linnet Wy *ACOMB* YO24 22
Linton Rd *RYKW* YO26 8
Linton St *RYKW* YO26 17
Lister Ct *RYKW* YO26 * 17
Lister Wy *RAW/SKEL* YO30 17
Little Av *RAW/SKEL* YO30 18
Little Catterton La *TAD* LS24 31
Littlefield Cl *RYKW* YO26 8
Little Garth *RYKW* YO26 8
Little Hallfield Rd *HEWTH* YO31 3
Little La *HXB/STR* YO32 6
Little Mdw *HXB/STR* YO32 6
Little Shambles *CYK* YO1 3
Little Stonegate *CYK* YO1 2
Littlethorpe Cl *HXB/STR* YO32 5
Livingstone St *RYKW* YO26 17
Lloyd Cl *FUL/HES* YO10 25
Lob La *STMFBR* YO41 15
Lochrin Pl *RYKW* YO26 16
Lockey Cft *HXB/STR* YO32 6
Lock House La *HXB/STR* YO32 7
Lockwood St *HEWTH* YO31 3
Lockyer Cl *RAW/SKEL* YO30 17
Long Close La *FUL/HES* YO10 3
Longcroft *HXB/STR* YO32 6
Longfield Ter *RAW/SKEL* YO30 2
Long Furrow *HXB/STR* YO32 6
Long Ridge Dr *RYKW* YO26 8
Longridge Gdns *RYKW* YO26 8
Long Ridge La *RYKW* YO26 8
Longwood Link *RAW/SKEL* YO30 9
Longwood Rd *RAW/SKEL* YO30 9
Lord Mayor's Wk *HEWTH* YO31 3
Lords Moor La *HXB/STR* YO32 5
Loriners Dr *COP/BISH* YO23 26
Lorne St *COP/BISH* YO23 23
Love La *ACOMB* YO24 2
FUL/HES YO10 24

vell St COP/BISH YO23 24 A2
w Catton Rd STMFBR YO41 15 F4
w Cft HXB/STR YO32 5 F3
wer Darnborough St
COP/BISH YO23 3 F7
wer Ebor St COP/BISH YO23 24 A2
wer Friargate CYK YO1 3 F5
wer Priory St CYK YO1 2 D6
weswater Rd RAW/SKEL YO30 9 F5
wfield Dr HXB/STR YO32 6 D1
wfield La RYKW YO26 16 A5
wfields Dr ACOMB YO24 22 C2
w Gn COP/BISH YO23 26 D5
wick ACOMB YO24 22 C5
w La FUL/HES YO10 25 G3
w Mill Cl FUL/HES YO10 25 H1
w Moor Av FUL/HES YO10 24 D5
wn Hl ACOMB YO24 22 C2
w Ousegate CYK YO1 2 E5
w Petergate CYK YO1 3 F3
w Poppleton La RYKW YO26 16 C2
wther Ct HEWTH YO31 3 H1
wther Ms HEWTH YO31 * 18 B3
wther St HEWTH YO31 18 B3
wther Ter ACOMB YO24 2 B6
kley Cl RAW/SKEL YO30 9 G4
cas Av RAW/SKEL YO30 18 B1
combe Wy HXB/STR YO32 10 C2
nley Rd RAW/SKEL YO30 18 A2
nd Cl HXB/STR YO32 6 C3
nds Ct CYK YO1 * 3 F4
ndy Cl RAW/SKEL YO30 9 H5
ett Rd ACOMB YO24 23 F5
lham Ct ACOMB YO24 22 C4
dale Av FUL/HES YO10 25 G1
den Wy ACOMB YO24 22 D1
wood Av COP/BISH YO23 26 C4
wood Cl HXB/STR YO32 5 F3
wood Vw COP/BISH YO23 26 C4
ander Cl RAW/SKEL YO30 9 H3

M

clagan Rd COP/BISH YO23 27 H3
gnolia Gv HXB/STR YO32 10 C4
ida Gv FUL/HES YO10 24 B2
in Av HEWTH YO31 19 E4
in St COP/BISH YO23 26 B2
OP/BISH YO23 26 C5
OP/BISH YO23 28 A3
UL/HES YO10 24 B5
UL/HES YO10 25 F4
YKW YO26 8 A4
YKW YO26 16 A4
TMFBR YO41 15 G2
lbys Gv COP/BISH YO23 26 D5
lham Gv HEWTH YO31 19 G4
llard Wy HXB/STR YO32 7 E2
llory Cl HXB/STR YO32 10 C2
lton Av HEWTH YO31 18 D3
lton Rd HEWTH YO31 19 E2
lton Wy RAW/SKEL YO30 17 G1
lvern Av RYKW YO26 17 E5
lvern Cl HXB/STR YO32 11 F1
ncroft HXB/STR YO32 6 C3
nley Cl HXB/STR YO32 10 C2
e Manor Beeches RYKS YO19 21 G3
nor Cl RYKW YO26 16 A1
nor Ct FUL/HES YO10 24 D1
HXB/STR YO32 11 E1
nor Dr RYKS YO19 21 G4
nor Dr North RYKW YO26 17 E5
nor Dr South RYKW YO26 17 E5
nor Farm Cl COP/BISH YO23 26 C5
nor Garth HXB/STR YO32 6 C3
nor Heath COP/BISH YO23 26 B4
nor La RAW/SKEL YO30 9 E4
nor Park Cl RAW/SKEL YO30 9 F4
nor Park Gv RAW/SKEL YO30 9 F4
nor Park Rd RAW/SKEL YO30 9 E4
nor Rd TAD LS24 30 D2
nor Wy RAW/SKEL YO30 9 F4
nsfield St HEWTH YO31 3 H3
nthorpe Wk RYKW YO26 17 F5
ple Av COP/BISH YO23 28 A4
ple Ct FUL/HES YO10 29 E1
ple Gv FUL/HES YO10 24 B3
plehurst Av HEWTH YO31 18 C2
plewood Paddock
ACOMB YO24 22 C3
rch St HEWTH YO31 3 G1
rgaret Philipson Ct CYK YO1 * 3 G3
rgaret St FUL/HES YO10 3 H6
rket St CYK YO1 3 F4
rkham Crs HEWTH YO31 18 C3
rkham St HEWTH YO31 18 B3
rlborough Av TAD LS24 30 B4
Marlborough Cl RAW/SKEL YO30 9 E3
Marlborough Dr TAD LS24 30 B4
Marlborough Gv FUL/HES YO10 24 B2
Marlborough Vls
FUL/HES YO10 * 24 B2
Marmiam Dr HXB/STR YO32 12 D2
Marston Av RYKW YO26 22 B1
Marston Crs RYKW YO26 22 B1
Martello Wy HXB/STR YO32 11 F5
Marten Cl RAW/SKEL YO30 17 H1
Martin Cheeseman Ct
ACOMB YO24 22 C4
Martins Ct RYKW YO26 17 H4
Marygate RAW/SKEL YO30 2 D3
Marygate La RAW/SKEL YO30 2 C2
Matmer Ct FUL/HES YO10 * 24 D1
Mattison Wy ACOMB YO24 23 E2
Mayfield Gv ACOMB YO24 23 F4
Maythorn Rd HEWTH YO31 10 D5
Meadlands HEWTH YO31 19 G3
Meadowbeck Cl FUL/HES YO10 19 G5
Meadow Ct ACOMB YO24 23 E4
Meadowfields Dr HEWTH YO31 10 C4
Meadow Garth TAD LS24 31 E2
Meadow La HXB/STR YO32 6 D3
The Meadows RAW/SKEL YO30 8 C1
Meadow Wy HEWTH YO31 19 E2
HXB/STR YO32 11 E2
TAD LS24 31 E2
Meam Cl FUL/HES YO10 20 B5
Melander Cl RYKW YO26 16 C5
Melander Gdns HXB/STR YO32 6 D4
Melbourne Ct FUL/HES YO10 * 24 B2
Melbourne St FUL/HES YO10 24 B2
Melcombe Av HXB/STR YO32 5 F3
Melrose Cl HEWTH YO31 19 E4
Melrosegate FUL/HES YO10 19 E5
Melroses Yd CYK YO1 * 3 H5
Melton Av RAW/SKEL YO30 17 G1
Melton Dr COP/BISH YO23 28 A4
RAW/SKEL YO30 17 G1
Melwood Gv RYKW YO26 16 C4
Mendip Cl HXB/STR YO32 11 E1
Merchantgate CYK YO1 3 G5
Merchant Wy COP/BISH YO23 26 D4
Merlin Covert HEWTH YO31 11 E3
Metcalfe La RYKS YO19 19 H4
The Mews RAW/SKEL YO30 * 17 H3
Micklegate CYK YO1 2 E5
Middle Banks HXB/STR YO32 6 B2
Middlecroft Dr HXB/STR YO32 5 F3
Middlecroft Gv HXB/STR YO32 5 F3
Middleham Av HEWTH YO31 18 D1
Middlethorpe Dr ACOMB YO24 23 F5
Middlethorpe Gv ACOMB YO24 23 F5
Middleton Rd ACOMB YO24 22 D2
Midgley Cl STMFBR YO41 15 G3
Midway Av RYKW YO26 8 B5
Mildred Gv ACOMB YO24 23 F2
Milford Wy HXB/STR YO32 6 D4
Millennium Ct HEWTH YO31 * 3 J3
Millers Cft COP/BISH YO23 26 D4
Millfield Av FUL/HES YO10 24 D1
Millfield Gdns RYKW YO26 8 B4
Millfield La FUL/HES YO10 25 E1
RYKW YO26 8 B4
Millfield Rd COP/BISH YO23 23 H2
Millgates RYKW YO26 16 D3
Mill Hill Dr HXB/STR YO32 11 E2
Mill La COP/BISH YO23 26 B3
HEWTH YO31 3 K1
HXB/STR YO32 6 A2
TAD LS24 30 D2
Mill Mt ACOMB YO24 2 B7
Mill Mount Ct ACOMB YO24 2 B7
Mill St CYK YO1 3 G6
Milner St ACOMB YO24 22 D1
Milson Gv FUL/HES YO10 25 E1
Milton Carr RAW/SKEL YO30 9 G5
Milton St FUL/HES YO10 24 D1
Minchin Cl RAW/SKEL YO30 10 A5
Minister Wy CYK YO1 3 G4
FUL/HES YO10 24 B5
Minster Av HEWTH YO31 11 E4
Minster Cl HXB/STR YO32 6 C3
Minster Ct CYK YO1 3 F2
Minster Gates CYK YO1 * 3 F3
Minster Vw HXB/STR YO32 6 C3
Minster Wy CYK YO1 3 F3
FUL/HES YO10 24 B2
STMFBR YO41 14 D4
Minster Yd CYK YO1 2 E3
Minter Cl ACOMB YO24 22 B3
Mistral Ct HEWTH YO31 18 D1
Mitchel's La FUL/HES YO10 24 D4
Miterdale ACOMB YO24 22 C5
Milford Ms HXB/STR YO32 6 D4
Moat Fld FUL/HES YO10 19 H5
Moatside Ct HEWTH YO31 2 E2
Moins Ct FUL/HES YO10 25 H1
Moiser Cl HXB/STR YO32 10 C2
Monarch Wy RYKW YO26 17 E3
Monk Av HEWTH YO31 19 E2
Monk Bar Ct CYK YO1 3 G3
Monk Br HEWTH YO31 3 H2
Monkbridge Ct HEWTH YO31 3 H1
Monkgate HEWTH YO31 3 G2
Monkgate Cloisters
HEWTH YO31 3 G2
Monks Cross Dr HXB/STR YO32 11 G4
Monks Cross Link
HXB/STR YO32 11 G2
Monkton Rd HEWTH YO31 18 D1
Montague Rd COP/BISH YO23 28 A4
Montague St COP/BISH YO23 24 A3
Montague Wk RYKW YO26 8 A4
Montrose Av HEWTH YO31 18 C1
Moorcroft Rd ACOMB YO24 22 D5
Moore Av FUL/HES YO10 19 G5
Moorgarth Av ACOMB YO24 23 F2
Moorgate ACOMB YO24 22 D1
Moor Gv ACOMB YO24 23 E4
Moorland Garth HXB/STR YO32 5 F2
Moorland Rd FUL/HES YO10 24 B4
Moor La ACOMB YO24 26 C1
COP/BISH YO23 27 G5
HXB/STR YO32 4 A3
HXB/STR YO32 5 G3
HXB/STR YO32 7 G2
RYKS YO19 20 C1
RYKW YO26 16 A4
Moorlea Av ACOMB YO24 23 E4
Moor Rd STMFBR YO41 15 G3
Moor Wy HXB/STR YO32 11 F2
Morcar Rd STMFBR YO41 15 G3
Morehall Cl RAW/SKEL YO30 9 G4
Morrell Ct ACOMB YO24 22 B4
Morrell Wy FUL/HES YO10 25 E2
Morritt Cl HEWTH YO31 19 E1
Moss St COP/BISH YO23 2 C6
Mount Ephraim ACOMB YO24 2 B6
Mount Pde ACOMB YO24 2 B7
Mount Ter ACOMB YO24 * 2 B7
The Mount ACOMB YO24 2 B7
Mount V ACOMB YO24 23 G2
Mount Vale Dr ACOMB YO24 23 G2
Mowbray Dr RYKW YO26 16 D5
Muirfield Wy RYKW YO26 16 C4
Mulberry Ct HXB/STR YO32 7 F5
Mulberry Dr HXB/STR YO32 6 D1
Mulwith Cl HEWTH YO31 19 F3
Muncastergate HEWTH YO31 18 D2
Murray St ACOMB YO24 23 F1
Murrough Wilson Pl
HEWTH YO31 18 B2
Murton Garth RYKS YO19 20 C3
Murton La RYKS YO19 20 D4
Murton Wy RYKS YO19 20 A5
Museum St CYK YO1 2 E4
Myrtle Av COP/BISH YO23 28 B4

N

Naburn La RYKS YO19 28 D3
Nairn Cl ACOMB YO24 27 E1
Navigation Rd CYK YO1 3 H5
Nelson's La ACOMB YO24 23 F3
Nelson St HEWTH YO31 18 C3
Nessgate CYK YO1 3 F5
Nether Wy RYKW YO26 8 A4
Netherwindings HXB/STR YO32 7 F2
Netherwoods HXB/STR YO32 5 G1
Neville Dr COP/BISH YO23 28 A4
Neville St HEWTH YO31 18 C3
Neville Ter HEWTH YO31 18 C3
Nevinson Gv FUL/HES YO10 24 C4
Nevis Wy ACOMB YO24 22 B5
Newborough St
RAW/SKEL YO30 18 A3
Newbury Av ACOMB YO24 22 D3
Newby Ter HEWTH YO31 18 B2
Newdale HXB/STR YO32 7 E1
New Forge Ct HXB/STR YO32 7 F2
Newgate CYK YO1 * 3 F4
Newland Park Cl FUL/HES YO10 25 E1
Newland Park Dr
FUL/HES YO10 24 D2
Newlands Dr RYKW YO26 16 C3
Newlands Rd COP/BISH YO23 27 H3
New La ACOMB YO24 23 E1
COP/BISH YO23 27 H3
HXB/STR YO32 5 G1
HXB/STR YO32 11 E5
New St CYK YO1 2 E4
TAD LS24 30 D3
Newton Ter CYK YO1 2 E6
Newton Wy HXB/STR YO32 5 G4
New Walk Ter FUL/HES YO10 24 B2
Nicholas Gdns FUL/HES YO10 24 D1
Nicholas St FUL/HES YO10 24 D1
Nidd Cl RYKW YO26 16 C1
Nidd Gv ACOMB YO24 23 E5
Nigel Gv ACOMB YO24 23 F2
Nightingale Cl HXB/STR YO32 10 D5
Ninth Av HEWTH YO31 19 E4
Norfolk St COP/BISH YO23 24 A2
Norman Dr RYKW YO26 16 C3
Norman St FUL/HES YO10 25 E1
Norseway STMFBR YO41 15 F4
Northcote Av ACOMB YO24 23 E1
Northcroft HXB/STR YO32 7 E2
North Field La COP/BISH YO23 26 A1
RYKW YO26 16 A3
Northfields HXB/STR YO32 5 H1
Northlands Av HXB/STR YO32 7 F4
North La ACOMB YO24 23 E4
HXB/STR YO32 6 D2
HXB/STR YO32 11 F1
North Moor HXB/STR YO32 11 F2
Northmoor Cl HXB/STR YO32 11 E1
North Moor Gdns
HXB/STR YO32 11 E1
North Moor Rd HXB/STR YO32 11 E2
Northolme Dr RAW/SKEL YO30 9 F5
North Pde RAW/SKEL YO30 2 C2
North St CYK YO1 2 E4
Norway Dr FUL/HES YO10 24 B4
Nunmill St COP/BISH YO23 24 A2
Nunnery La COP/BISH YO23 2 D6
Nunthorpe Av COP/BISH YO23 23 H2
Nunthorpe Crs COP/BISH YO23 23 H2
Nunthorpe Dr COP/BISH YO23 24 A2
Nunthorpe Gdns
COP/BISH YO23 24 A2
Nunthorpe Gv COP/BISH YO23 23 H2
Nunthorpe Rd ACOMB YO24 2 D7
Nunthorpe Vw COP/BISH YO23 24 A3
Nursery Ct RYKW YO26 8 B4
Nursery Dr ACOMB YO24 23 E1
Nursery Gdns FUL/HES YO10 25 G1
Nursery Rd RYKW YO26 8 B4

O

Oakdale Rd RAW/SKEL YO30 9 G4
Oaken Gv HXB/STR YO32 6 C1
Oak Gld HEWTH YO31 11 E4
Oakhill Crs HXB/STR YO32 5 F4
Oakland Av HEWTH YO31 19 E2
Oakland Dr HEWTH YO31 19 F3
Oaklands HXB/STR YO32 5 G3
Oak Ri ACOMB YO24 22 C1
Oak St RYKW YO26 17 F4
Oak Tree Cl HXB/STR YO32 5 G3
Oak Tree Gv HXB/STR YO32 10 C4
Oak Tree La HXB/STR YO32 6 C4
Oak Tree Wy HXB/STR YO32 5 G3
Oakville St HEWTH YO31 18 C2
Ogleforth CYK YO1 3 F2
Old Brewery Gdns TAD LS24 31 E2
Old Coppice HXB/STR YO32 7 F2
Old Dike Lands HXB/STR YO32 6 C4
The Old Hwy HXB/STR YO32 5 G4
Oldman Ct ACOMB YO24 22 C4
Old Moor La ACOMB YO24 23 E5
Old Orch HXB/STR YO32 6 D3
The Old Orch FUL/HES YO10 24 C5
Old School Cl FUL/HES YO10 19 G5
Old School Ct RYKW YO26 8 A5
Old Station Yd RYKS YO19 * 21 H5
The Old Village HXB/STR YO32 11 E1
The Old Woodyard
STMFBR YO41 * 15 F3
Orchard Cottages RYKS YO19 21 H3
Orchard Gdns HEWTH YO31 10 D4
Orchard Garth COP/BISH YO23 26 D4
Orchard Paddock HXB/STR YO32 6 D3
Orchard Rd RYKW YO26 8 A5
The Orchard FUL/HES YO10 25 E3
Orchard Vw RAW/SKEL YO30 8 C1
Orchard Wy ACOMB YO24 23 E4
HXB/STR YO32 5 G2
Ordnance La FUL/HES YO10 24 B3
Oriel Gv RAW/SKEL YO30 17 H1
Orrin Cl ACOMB YO24 22 C5
Osbaldwick La FUL/HES YO10 19 H5
Osbaldwick Link Rd
FUL/HES YO10 20 A5
Osbaldwick Village
FUL/HES YO10 19 H5
Osbourne Dr RAW/SKEL YO30 9 F3
Osmington Gdns HXB/STR YO32 5 F3
Osprey Cl ACOMB YO24 22 B4

Ostler's Cl COP/BISH YO23 27 E4
Ostman Rd RYKW YO26 16 C4
Otterwood Bank
ACOMB YO24 * 22 B3
Otterwood La ACOMB YO24 22 B3
Otterwood Paddock
STMFBR YO41 15 E3
Ouse Acres RYKW YO26 17 E4
Ouse Br CYK YO1 2 E5
Ouseburn Av RYKW YO26 16 D3
Ousecliffe Gdns
RAW/SKEL YO30 17 H3
Oust Lea RAW/SKEL YO30 17 G2
Ouston Cl TAD LS24 31 E3
Ouston La TAD LS24 31 E3
Outgang La HEWTH YO31 20 A3
Overdale Cl ACOMB YO24 22 D4
Ovington Ter COP/BISH YO23 23 H3
Owlwood Ct RYKS YO19 21 G4
Owlwood La RYKS YO19 21 G4
Owston Av FUL/HES YO10 25 E1
Ox Calder Cl RYKS YO19 21 H4
Ox Carr La HXB/STR YO32 5 G4
Ox Cl STMFBR YO41 15 G2
Oxford St ACOMB YO24 2 B7
Oxton Dr TAD LS24 31 E3
Oxton La TAD LS24 31 E3

P

Paddock Cha FUL/HES YO10 * 25 F3
Paddock Cl COP/BISH YO23 26 C5
HXB/STR YO32 11 E2
The Paddock RYKW YO26 16 D3
Paddock Wy RYKW YO26 16 D3
Palmer La CYK YO1 3 G4
Parade Ct HEWTH YO31 19 E3
Paragon St FUL/HES YO10 3 H7
Park Av HXB/STR YO32 10 C1
Park Cl RAW/SKEL YO30 8 C2
Park Crs HEWTH YO31 3 H1
Parker Av RYKW YO26 22 B2
Park Ga HXB/STR YO32 5 H1
Park Gv HEWTH YO31 18 C3
Parkland Dr TAD LS24 31 E2
Parkland Wy HXB/STR YO32 6 D3
Park La ACOMB YO24 23 F1
Park Ldg HXB/STR YO32 10 C2
Parkside Cl ACOMB YO24 23 E1
Park St ACOMB YO24 2 C7
Parliament St CYK YO1 3 F4
Paston Wk COP/BISH YO23 2 E7
Pasture Cl HXB/STR YO32 5 G4
RAW/SKEL YO30 8 C1
Pasture Farm Cl FUL/HES YO10 28 D1
Pasture La HEWTH YO31 19 G1
The Pastures ACOMB YO24 23 E4
Pately Pl RYKW YO26 17 E5
Patrick Pool CYK YO1 3 F4
Patterdale Dr RAW/SKEL YO30 9 F5
Pavement CYK YO1 3 F4
Paver La CYK YO1 3 H5
Pavilion Rw FUL/HES YO10 24 B5
Pear Tree Av RYKW YO26 8 A4
Pear Tree Cl HXB/STR YO32 11 E2
Pear Tree Ct CYK YO1 3 G3
Pear Tree La RYKS YO19 21 G4
Peasholme Gn CYK YO1 3 H4
Peckitt St CYK YO1 3 F6
Peel Cl FUL/HES YO10 25 E3
Peel St CYK YO1 3 H6
Pelham Pl HXB/STR YO32 5 F4
Pembroke St RAW/SKEL YO30 18 B2
Penleys Ct HEWTH YO31 * 3 G1
Penley's Grove St HEWTH YO31 3 G1
Pennine Cl HXB/STR YO32 11 E2
Penny Lane Ct CYK YO1 * 3 G3
Pentire Cl RAW/SKEL YO30 9 H5
Pentland Dr HXB/STR YO32 10 D3
Penyghent Av HEWTH YO31 19 F4
Peppercorn Cl RYKW YO26 17 F5
Percy's La CYK YO1 3 H5
Percy St HEWTH YO31 2 E2
Petercroft Cl RYKS YO19 21 H3
Petercroft La RYKS YO19 21 H3
Peter Hill Dr RAW/SKEL YO30 17 H1
Peter La CYK YO1 3 F4
Petersway RAW/SKEL YO30 18 A3
Pheasant Dr ACOMB YO24 22 B5
Philadelphia Ter
COP/BISH YO23 23 H2
Phoenix Bvd RYKW YO26 2 A4
Piccadilly CYK YO1 3 G5
Pike Hills Mt COP/BISH YO23 26 C4
Pilgrim St HEWTH YO31 3 F1
Pinelands HXB/STR YO32 6 D4
Pinelands Wy FUL/HES YO10 25 G1
Pinewood Gv HEWTH YO31 10 D5
Pinewood Hl FUL/HES YO10 25 G1
Pinfold Ct RAW/SKEL YO30 17 H2
Pinsent Ct HEWTH YO31 18 D1
Plantation Dr RYKW YO26 16 D3
Plantation Gv RYKW YO26 16 D3
Plantation Wy HXB/STR YO32 6 B2
Ploughlands HXB/STR YO32 6 C4
Ploughman's Cl COP/BISH YO23 27 E4
Ploughmans' La HXB/STR YO32 6 C4
Plumer Av HEWTH YO31 19 F4
Pollard Cl HXB/STR YO32 10 D3
Poplar Gv HXB/STR YO32 10 D3
Poplar St RYKW YO26 17 F4
Poppleton Hall Gdn RYKW YO26 8 B3
Poppleton Rd RYKW YO26 17 F4
Portal Rd RYKW YO26 16 C2
Portisham Pl HXB/STR YO32 5 G4
Portland St HEWTH YO31 2 E2
Postern Cl COP/BISH YO23 3 F7
Potters Dr COP/BISH YO23 26 D4
Pottery La HEWTH YO31 18 D2
Precentor's Ct CYK YO1 2 E3
Prestwick Ct RYKW YO26 16 C4
Price's La COP/BISH YO23 2 E7
Primrose Vls RAW/SKEL YO30 18 A2
Princess Dr RYKW YO26 17 E3
Princess Rd HXB/STR YO32 5 G2
Prior's Wk RYKW YO26 17 E3
Priory St CYK YO1 2 D5
Priory Wood Wy HEWTH YO31 11 E4
Prospect Ct TAD LS24 30 D2
Prospect Dr TAD LS24 30 D2
Prospect Ter CYK YO1 2 D6
FUL/HES YO10 24 B5
Pulleyn Dr ACOMB YO24 23 F3

Q

Quaker Gn ACOMB YO24 22 C5
Quant Ms FUL/HES YO10 25 F1
Queen Anne's Rd
RAW/SKEL YO30 2 C2
Queen's Gdns TAD LS24 30 C4
Queens Staith Ms CYK YO1 * 2 E6
Queen's Staith Rd CYK YO1 2 E5
Queen St ACOMB YO24 2 C6
Queenswood Gv ACOMB YO24 22 D2
Queen Victoria St
COP/BISH YO23 23 H3

R

Racecourse Rd COP/BISH YO23 23 H4
Radley Ct HXB/STR YO32 5 F4
Railway Ter ACOMB YO24 2 A6
Railway Vw ACOMB YO24 23 E4
Rainsborough Wy
RAW/SKEL YO30 17 H1
Ramsay Cl HEWTH YO31 18 C2
Ramsey Av COP/BISH YO23 28 A4
Ratcliffe Ct RAW/SKEL YO30 8 D1
Ratcliffe St RAW/SKEL YO30 18 A2
Raven Gv RYKW YO26 16 D5
Rawcliffe Av RAW/SKEL YO30 17 G1
Rawcliffe Cl RAW/SKEL YO30 9 F4
Rawcliffe Cft RAW/SKEL YO30 9 E4
Rawcliffe Dr RAW/SKEL YO30 17 G1
Rawcliffe Gv RAW/SKEL YO30 17 G2
Rawcliffe La RAW/SKEL YO30 17 G1
Rawcliffe Wy RAW/SKEL YO30 9 F4
Rawdon Av FUL/HES YO10 19 E5
Ray Dike Cl HXB/STR YO32 6 C4
Raynard Ct ACOMB YO24 * 22 C4
Rectory Gdns COP/BISH YO23 23 H3
Redbarn Dr FUL/HES YO10 25 H1
Redcoat Wy ACOMB YO24 22 B4
Redeness St HEWTH YO31 3 J3
Redgrave Cl HEWTH YO31 18 D1
Redman Cl FUL/HES YO10 24 A4
Redmayne Sq HXB/STR YO32 5 H1
Redmires Cl RAW/SKEL YO30 9 H5
Redthorn Dr HEWTH YO31 11 E5
Redwood Dr HXB/STR YO32 6 C2
The Reeves ACOMB YO24 22 C3
Regency Ms ACOMB YO24 23 F4
Regents Ct RYKW YO26 17 H4
Regents Ms RYKW YO26 17 E3
Regent St FUL/HES YO10 3 K7
Reginald Gv COP/BISH YO23 24 A3
Reighton Av RAW/SKEL YO30 17 G1
Reighton Dr RAW/SKEL YO30 9 G5
Renfrew Gn HXB/STR YO32 5 H1
Renshaw Gdns RYKW YO26 17 F5
Reygate Gv COP/BISH YO23 26 D5
Ribstone Gv HEWTH YO31 19 G3
Richardson St COP/BISH YO23 24 A2
Richmond St HEWTH YO31 3 J3
Ridgeway RYKW YO26 22 B1
Ringstone Rd RAW/SKEL YO30 9 G3
Ripley Gv HXB/STR YO32 6 C1
Risewood STMFBR YO41 14 B3
Rishworth Gv RAW/SKEL YO30 9 G5
Rivelin Wy RAW/SKEL YO30 9 G4
Riversdale HXB/STR YO32 7 F1
Riverside Crs HXB/STR YO32 7 F5
Riverside Gdns RYKW YO26 8 A4
Riverside Wk HXB/STR YO32 5 F3
RYKW YO26 8 A4
River St COP/BISH YO23 3 F7
Riversvale Dr RYKW YO26 8 A4
Robin Gv ACOMB YO24 23 F2
Robinson Dr ACOMB YO24 22 B2
Roche Av HEWTH YO31 18 D1
Rockcliff Ct TAD LS24 30 D2
Rockingham Av HEWTH YO31 19 F5
Rogers Ct ACOMB YO24 22 C4
Rolling Br TAD LS24 31 H1
Rolston Av HEWTH YO31 10 D4
Roman Av North STMFBR YO41 15 F3
Roman Av South STMFBR YO41 15 F4
Roman Cl TAD LS24 30 D2
Ropers Ct COP/BISH YO23 27 E4
The Ropewalk HEWTH YO31 3 J3
Roseberry Gv RAW/SKEL YO30 9 G3
Rosebery St RYKW YO26 17 G3
Rosecomb Wy HXB/STR YO32 6 D4
Rosecroft Wy RAW/SKEL YO30 17 F1
Rosedale Av RYKW YO26 16 D5
Rosedale St FUL/HES YO10 24 B2
Rosemary Ct CYK YO1 3 H5
TAD LS24 30 D2
Rosemary Pl CYK YO1 3 H5
Rosemary Rw TAD LS24 30 D2
Rose St HEWTH YO31 18 B2
Rose Tree Gv HXB/STR YO32 10 C2
Rosetta Wy RYKW YO26 17 E3
Rosslyn St RAW/SKEL YO30 17 H3
Rougier St CYK YO1 2 D4
Round Hl Link RAW/SKEL YO30 9 G4
Rowan Av HXB/STR YO32 10 C3
Rowan Pl HXB/STR YO32 10 C2
Rowley Ct HXB/STR YO32 7 F4
The Rowmans RAW/SKEL YO30 8 D2
Rowntree Av RAW/SKEL YO30 18 B1
Rowntree Whf CYK YO1 * 3 H5
Royal Cha ACOMB YO24 23 F4
Royston Cl HXB/STR YO32 5 H1
Ruby St COP/BISH YO23 23 H3
Rudcarr La RYKS YO19 13 F4
Ruddings Cl HXB/STR YO32 6 D3
Runswick Av RYKW YO26 16 C5
Rushwood Cl HXB/STR YO32 7 E2
Russel Dr RAW/SKEL YO30 17 F1
Russell St COP/BISH YO23 23 H2
Russet Dr HEWTH YO31 19 G4
Rutland Cl COP/BISH YO23 26 C4
Ryburn Cl RAW/SKEL YO30 9 G4
Rydal Av HEWTH YO31 19 F3
Rye Cl HXB/STR YO32 6 C3
Ryecroft HXB/STR YO32 5 F4
Ryecroft Av ACOMB YO24 22 C5
Ryecroft Cl HEWTH YO31 19 H1
Ryehill Cl HXB/STR YO32 10 C1
Ryemoor Rd HXB/STR YO32 6 C3
Rylatt Pl RYKW YO26 22 B1

S

Sadberge Ct FUL/HES YO10 25 G1
Saddlers Cl COP/BISH YO23 26 D4
HXB/STR YO32 11 E4
Sails Dr FUL/HES YO10 25 F1
St Aelreds Cl HEWTH YO31 19 E5
St Andrewgate CYK YO1 3 G3
St Andrew Pl CYK YO1 * 3 F4
St Andrews Ct CYK YO1 * 3 G3
St Ann's Ct FUL/HES YO10 24 B2
St Aubyn's Pl ACOMB YO24 23 G2
St Barnabas Cl RYKW YO26 17 G4
St Barnabas Ct RYKW YO26 * 17 G4
St Benedict Rd COP/BISH YO23 2 E7
St Benidict Rd COP/BISH YO23 2 E7
St Catherines Cl RAW/SKEL YO30 8 D1
St Catherines Pl ACOMB YO24 * 2 B7
St Chads Whf COP/BISH YO23 24 A4
St Clement's Gv COP/BISH YO23 24 A3
St Denys' Rd CYK YO1 3 G5
St Edmunds STMFBR YO41 15 G2
St Edward's Cl ACOMB YO24 23 F4
St George's Pl ACOMB YO24 23 F2
St Giles Ct HEWTH YO31 * 2 E2
St Giles Rd RAW/SKEL YO30 8
St Giles Wy COP/BISH YO23 26
St Helen's Rd ACOMB YO24 23
St Helen's Sq CYK YO1 2
St Hilda's Ms FUL/HES YO10 19
St James Cl RAW/SKEL YO30 9
St James Ct RYKW YO26 * 2
St James Mt COP/BISH YO23 23
St James Pl ACOMB YO24 22
St John's Crs HEWTH YO31 3
St John's Rd STMFBR YO41 15
St John St HEWTH YO31 3
St Josephs Ct ACOMB YO24 22
St Joseph's St TAD LS24 30
St Leonard's Pl RAW/SKEL YO30 2
St Luke's Gv RAW/SKEL YO30 18
St Margaret's Ter CYK YO1 3
St Mark's Gv RAW/SKEL YO30 9
St Martin's La CYK YO1 2
St Mary's RAW/SKEL YO30 2
St Mary's Cl HXB/STR YO32 5
HXB/STR YO32 6
St Mary's Gv FUL/HES YO10 19
St Marys Ms HXB/STR YO32 * 6
St Marys Sq CYK YO1 * 3
St Marys Ter RAW/SKEL YO30 * 2
St Maurice's Rd HEWTH YO31 3
St Michaels Ct ACOMB YO24 22
St Nicholas Av RYKS YO19 29
St Nicholas Cl COP/BISH YO23 26
St Nicholas Crs COP/BISH YO23 26
St Nicholas Pl FUL/HES YO10 * 24
St Nicholas Rd COP/BISH YO23 26
St Nicholas Wy HXB/STR YO32 6
St Olave's Rd RAW/SKEL YO30 2
St Oswald's Rd FUL/HES YO10 24
St Pauls Ms ACOMB YO24 2
St Paul's Sq ACOMB YO24 2
St Paul's Ter ACOMB YO24 2
St Peters Cl RYKW YO26 16
St Peters Ct RAW/SKEL YO30 * 18
St Peter's Gv RAW/SKEL YO30 2
St Philip's Gv RAW/SKEL YO30 17
St Sampson's Sq CYK YO1 3
St Saviourgate CYK YO1 3
St Saviour's Pl CYK YO1 3
St Stephens Ms RYKW YO26 22
St Stephen's Rd ACOMB YO24 22
St Stephen's Sq ACOMB YO24 22
St Swithin's Wk RYKW YO26 17
St Thomas' Pl HEWTH YO31 3
St Thomas's Cl FUL/HES YO10 19
St Wilfrid's Cl HXB/STR YO32 5
St Wilfrid's Rd HXB/STR YO32 5
St Wulstan Cl HEWTH YO31 18
Salisbury Rd RYKW YO26 17
Salisbury Ter RYKW YO26 17
Salmond Rd ACOMB YO24 22
Sandacre Ct RYKW YO26 17
Sandcroft Cl ACOMB YO24 22
Sandcroft Rd ACOMB YO24 22
Sanderson Ct RYKW YO26 22
Sandfield Ter TAD LS24 31
Sandholme HXB/STR YO32 7
Sandmartin Ct ACOMB YO24 22
Sandown Cl ACOMB YO24 23
Sandringham Cl HXB/STR YO32 6
Sandringham St FUL/HES YO10 24
Sandstock Rd HEWTH YO31 19
Sandy Gap HXB/STR YO32 6
Sandyland HXB/STR YO32 6
Sandy La HXB/STR YO32 6
HXB/STR YO32 13
Sandyridge RYKW YO26 8
Sargent Av COP/BISH YO23 27
Saville Gv RAW/SKEL YO30 17
Sawyer's Crs COP/BISH YO23 26
Sawyers Wk RYKS YO19 21
Saxford Wy HXB/STR YO32 6
Saxon Pl HEWTH YO31 18
Saxon Rd STMFBR YO41 15
Scafell Cl RAW/SKEL YO30 9
Scaife Gdns HEWTH YO31 18
Scaife Ms HEWTH YO31 * 18
Scaife St HEWTH YO31 18
Scarborough Ter
RAW/SKEL YO30 18
Scarcroft Hl ACOMB YO24 23
Scarcroft La COP/BISH YO23 2
Scarcroft Rd ACOMB YO24 2
COP/BISH YO23 * 24
Scarcroft Vw COP/BISH YO23 2
Scaudercroft RYKS YO19 21
Scawton Av HEWTH YO31 10
School Cl STMFBR YO41 15
School La COP/BISH YO23 26
COP/BISH YO23 28
FUL/HES YO10 24
FUL/HES YO10 25

ıool St ACOMB YO24 ....22 D1
ɔreby La STMFBR YO41..............14 C4
ɔtt Moncrieff Rd
ɦXB/STR YO32..............................5 H4
ɔtt St COP/BISH YO23................24 A2
iven Gv HXB/STR YO32 ....7 E2
ʼope Av HEWTH YO31....................3 K2
afire Cl RAW/SKEL YO30................9 H3
aton Cl FUL/HES YO10................19 H5
cond Av HEWTH YO31..................19 E3
dge Ri TAD LS24..........................30 A4
fton Av HEWTH YO31 ....19 E1
grave Wk RYKW YO26..................17 F5
by Rd RYKS YO19 ....29 E2
don Rd RYKW YO26......................17 F4
venth Av HEWTH YO31.................19 E4
vern Gn RYKW YO26 ....16 D1
verus Av ACOMB YO24 ....17 E5
verus St ACOMB YO24.................22 D1
ymour Gv HEWTH YO31 ....19 E3
allowdale Gv FUL/HES YO10.....19 H5
ambles CYK YO1............................3 F4
aw's Ter ACOMB YO24....................2 C7
elley Dr HXB/STR YO32 ....5 F3
elley Gv RAW/SKEL YO30 ....17 F1
erbourne Gv HXB/STR YO32.........5 G3
erringham Dr ACOMB YO24......22 D4
erwood Gv HEWTH YO31...........11 E5
RYKW YO26....................................16 C3
ilton Garth Cl HXB/STR YO32 ....7 F4
pton Rd RAW/SKEL YO30............8 D2
pton St RAW/SKEL YO30............18 B2
rley Av RYKW YO26.....................16 D3
atel Cl RAW/SKEL YO30..............17 G1
verdale Ct ACOMB YO24............22 D5
ver St CYK YO1..............................3 F4
 Balk La COP/BISH YO23 ....27 G2
mons Cl HXB/STR YO32 ....5 F3
occo Ct HEWTH YO31..................18 C1
well Gv RYKW YO26....................16 D4
ward St FUL/HES YO10................25 E1
th Av HEWTH YO31 ....3 K2
eldergate CYK YO1 ....2 E6
eldergate Br COP/BISH YO23.......3 F6
elton Br RYKW YO26.......................8 B3
elton Ct RAW/SKEL YO30 ....17 H3
ewsby Gv HEWTH YO31 ....11 E5
ddaw ACOMB YO24.....................22 C5
ssor Rd ACOMB YO24 ....22 B3
e La TAD LS24..............................31 H3
gsby Gv ACOMB YO24 ....23 E4
ales' St CYK YO1 ....2 E6
ary La RYKS YO19 ....20 D3
eaton Gv RYKW YO26..................16 D4
ith Cl FUL/HES YO10....................24 D4
ithie Cl HXB/STR YO32 ....10 C1
merset Cl RAW/SKEL YO30 ....9 F3
merset Rd HEWTH YO31.............18 C1
uth Bank Av COP/BISH YO23 ......23 H3
uth Down Rd HXB/STR YO32....11 E1
uth Esp CYK YO1 ....3 F6
uthfield Crs ACOMB YO24...........23 E4
uthfields Rd HXB/STR YO32 ....5 G2
uthlands HXB/STR YO32..............6 C1
uthlands Rd COP/BISH YO23 ....23 H2
uth La HXB/STR YO32...................6 D2
utholme Dr RAW/SKEL YO30.....17 G1
uth Pde ACOMB YO24 ....2 C6
uth Pk ACOMB YO24 * 22 C3
verby Rd RYKW YO26..................17 E5
alding Av RAW/SKEL YO30.........17 H2
eculation St CYK YO1....................3 J5
encer St COP/BISH YO23 ....2 E7
en La CYK YO1 ....3 G3
y Bank ACOMB YO24....................27 E1
ndle Cl ACOMB YO24 ....22 C4
 Spinney ACOMB YO24 ....23 F5
ingbank Av RYKS YO19...............21 G3
ingfield Cl HEWTH YO31...........19 G2
ingfield Rd RYKW YO26................8 A4
ingfield Wy HEWTH YO31 ....19 G2
inghill Ct TAD LS24 ....30 D2
ing La FUL/HES YO10...................25 E3
ingwood HXB/STR YO32 ....6 D4
ingwood Gv RYKW YO26.............16 D3
uce Cl HXB/STR YO32.................10 C4
urriergate CYK YO1 ....3 F5
 Square STMFBR YO41 ....15 F2
AD LS24 ....31 E2
bler Cl HXB/STR YO32 ....6 A2
blers Wk HXB/STR YO32 ....7 F4
 Stables FUL/HES YO10 * 24 B3
ndale Cl RAW/SKEL YO30.............9 F4
thes Cl RYKW YO26.....................16 D5
mford Br West
TMFBR YO41 ....15 E2
mford St East RYKW YO26.......17 G4
mford St West RYKW YO26 *...17 F4
nley Av HXB/STR YO32 ....6 D4
Stanley St HEWTH YO31................18 C2
Starkey Crs HEWTH YO31.............19 F4
Station Av CYK YO1..........................2 D4
HXB/STR YO32..............................10 C3
Station Est TAD LS24 *...................30 C3
Station Ri CYK YO1...........................2 D4
Station Rd ACOMB YO24..................2 C5
COP/BISH YO23..............................26 C5
HXB/STR YO32.................................7 E2
RYKW YO26......................................16 A1
TAD LS24..30 C3
Station Sq HXB/STR YO32...............5 G3
Steeple Cl HXB/STR YO32................6 B2
Stephenson Cl HXB/STR YO32 ......10 D5
Stephenson Wy RYKW YO26 ....17 G4
Sterne Av HEWTH YO31.................19 F4
Stirling Gv FUL/HES YO10 ....24 D4
Stirling Rd RAW/SKEL YO30 ....9 H3
Stirrup Cl ACOMB YO24 ....22 B4
Stockhill Cl RYKS YO19..................21 G3
Stockholm Cl FUL/HES YO10.........24 A4
Stockton La HEWTH YO31 ....19 F2
The Stonebow CYK YO1 ....3 G4
Stone Br FUL/HES YO10 ....29 E1
Stonegate CYK YO1 ....2 E4
Stonegate Wk CYK YO1 *.................2 E3
Stonelands Ct
RAW/SKEL YO30 ....9 H5
Stone Riggs HXB/STR YO32 ....12 D2
Stonethwaite ACOMB YO24 ....22 C5
Stonewall Cottage La
STMFBR YO41 ....15 F3
Stoop Cl HXB/STR YO32 ....6 C3
Stow Ct HXB/STR YO32 ....10 D3
Straight La RYKS YO19 ....21 H1
Stratford Wy HXB/STR YO32.........10 D3
HXB/STR YO32...............................11 E3
Stray Garth HEWTH YO31 ....19 E2
Straylands Gv HEWTH YO31 ....19 E1
Stray Rd HEWTH YO31....................19 G3
Strensall New Br
HXB/STR YO32...................................5 E2
Strensall Pk HXB/STR YO32 ....7 H1
Strensall Rd HXB/STR YO32...........11 E1
Stripe La RAW/SKEL YO30 ....8 C1
Stuart Rd ACOMB YO24...................22 D3
Stubden Gv RAW/SKEL YO30............9 G4
Sturdee Gv HEWTH YO31 ....18 D2
Summerfield Rd ACOMB YO24......22 C5
Sunningdale Cl RYKW YO26...........16 C4
Sunnydale HXB/STR YO32 ....6 D4
Surrey Wy RAW/SKEL YO30 ....17 G1
Surtees St RAW/SKEL YO30.............18 A2
Sussex Cl FUL/HES YO10 ....25 G2
Sussex Rd FUL/HES YO10................25 G2
Sussex Wy HXB/STR YO32 ....5 F4
Sutherland St COP/BISH YO23 ......23 H3
Sutor Cl COP/BISH YO23................26 D4
Sutton Wy RAW/SKEL YO30............18 A1
Swale Av ACOMB YO24....................23 E4
Swann St COP/BISH YO23................2 D7
Swards Wy FUL/HES YO10..............25 E2
Swarthdale HXB/STR YO32...............7 E1
Swinegate CYK YO1 ....3 F4
Swinegate Ct East CYK YO1 *..........3 F3
Swinerton Av RYKW YO26 ....17 G3
Swinsty Ct RAW/SKEL YO30..............9 G5
Sycamore Av HXB/STR YO32..........10 C2
Sycamore Cl HXB/STR YO32 ....6 D4
RAW/SKEL YO30 ....8 D1
Sycamore Pl RAW/SKEL YO30 ....2 C2
Sycamore Ter RAW/SKEL YO30 ....2 C3
Sycamore Vw RYKW YO26.................8 A5
Sykes Cl RAW/SKEL YO30 *.............18 A3

T

Tadcaster Rd ACOMB YO24.............23 G3
COP/BISH YO23................................26 D3
Tadcaster Rd Dringhouses
ACOMB YO24 ....23 E5
Tamworth Rd RAW/SKEL YO30 ....9 H5
Tang Hall La FUL/HES YO10 ....19 G5
Tanner Rw CYK YO1 ....2 D5
Tanner St CYK YO1 ....2 D4
The Tannery FUL/HES YO10..............3 J6
Tarbert Crs ACOMB YO24 ....22 B5
Tatton Cl RAW/SKEL YO30...............10 A5
Taylors Cl RYKS YO19......................13 H5
Teal Dr ACOMB YO24.......................22 C4
Teck St COP/BISH YO23 * 24 A2
Tedder Rd ACOMB YO24..................22 B3
Telford Ter COP/BISH YO23 ....23 H2
Templars Ct COP/BISH YO23 *........26 C5
Temple Av FUL/HES YO10 ....19 G5
Templemead HEWTH YO31..............18 D1
Temple Rd COP/BISH YO23.............27 H3
Tennent Rd ACOMB YO24 ....22 B2
Tennyson Av RAW/SKEL YO30.......18 B2
Ten Thorn La RYKW YO26 ....16 B5
Terrington Cl HXB/STR YO32 ....5 G1
Terry Av COP/BISH YO23 ....3 F7
FUL/HES YO10...................................24 A3
Terry St COP/BISH YO23.................24 A3
Thanet Rd ACOMB YO24..................22 D3
Thatchers Cft COP/BISH YO23 ......26 D4
Theresa Cl HXB/STR YO32..............11 E5
Thief La FUL/HES YO10...................24 D1
FUL/HES YO10...................................25 E1
Third Av HEWTH YO31....................19 E4
Thirkleby Wy FUL/HES YO10..........19 H5
Thirlmere Dr HEWTH YO31 ....19 F3
Thomas St FUL/HES YO10.................3 K6
Thompson Pl RYKW YO26...............17 F4
Thoresby Rd ACOMB YO24 ....22 B3
Thornbeck RYKS YO19.....................21 G5
Thorncroft RYKS YO19 ....21 H3
Thornfield Av HEWTH YO31...........19 E1
Thornfield Dr HEWTH YO31...........10 D4
Thornhills HXB/STR YO32.................7 F2
Thorn Nook HEWTH YO31..............19 E1
Thornton Moor Cl
RAW/SKEL YO30 ....9 G4
Thorntree Gv
RAW/SKEL YO30 ....10 A4
Thornwood Covert
ACOMB YO24 ....22 C3
Thorpe St COP/BISH YO23 ....23 H2
Tilmire Cl FUL/HES YO10 ....24 D4
Tisbury Rd RYKW YO26 ....17 F5
Tithe Cl ACOMB YO24......................22 B3
Toby Ct HXB/STR YO32 ....5 F3
Toft Gn CYK YO1 ....2 D5
Toll Bar Wy TAD LS24......................31 F1
Top La COP/BISH YO23 ....26 C4
Toremill Cl HXB/STR YO32..............10 C2
Torridon Pl ACOMB YO24................22 B5
Tostig Av RYKW YO26 ....16 D4
Tostig Cl STMFBR YO41...................15 F3
Tower Crs TAD LS24.........................30 B2
Tower Pl CYK YO1 *..........................3 F6
Tower St CYK YO1 ....3 F6
Town End Gdns HXB/STR YO32 ......6 B1
Towthorpe Br HXB/STR YO32 ....5 E5
Towthorpe Moor La
HXB/STR YO32...................................7 H1
Towthorpe Rd HXB/STR YO32.........7 E2
Towton Av ACOMB YO24.................23 F2
Trafalgar St COP/BISH YO23..........23 H3
Tranby Av RYKS YO19.....................20 A5
Trans Pennine Trail
COP/BISH YO23................................27 H2
Trenchard Rd RYKW YO26 ....16 C3
Trenfield Ct ACOMB YO24 * 23 F1
Trent Av HXB/STR YO32 ....7 F5
Trentholme Dr ACOMB YO24..........23 G2
Trent Wy ACOMB YO24...................22 D5
Trevor Gv ACOMB YO24...................23 F2
Tribune Wy RAW/SKEL YO30 ....9 H4
Trinity Ct CYK YO1 *..........................2 D5
Trinity La CYK YO1.............................2 D5
Trinity Mdw HXB/STR YO32............13 E1
Troon Cl RYKW YO26.......................16 C4
Troutbeck ACOMB YO24.................22 C5
Troutsdale Av RAW/SKEL YO30........9 F4
Tudor Rd ACOMB YO24....................22 D2
Tuke Av FUL/HES YO10...................19 G5
Turks Head Ct CYK YO1 *..................3 F3
Turnberry Dr RYKW YO26 ....16 C5
Turner's Cft FUL/HES YO10............25 F4
Turnmire Rd ACOMB YO24.............23 E4
Turnpike Rd TAD LS24 ....31 F1
Turpin Ct CYK YO1 *..........................3 G6
Twin Pike Wy HXB/STR YO32 ....6 B2
Tyneham Wy HXB/STR YO32 ....5 G3

U

Ullswater ACOMB YO24...................22 C5
Undercroft RYKS YO19.....................21 H3
Union Ter HEWTH YO31 ....3 F1
University Rd FUL/HES YO10..........25 E2
Uppercroft HXB/STR YO32 ....6 C2
Upper Hanover St
RYKW YO26 *.....................................17 G4
Upper Newborough St
RAW/SKEL YO30 ....18 B2
Upper Price St
COP/BISH YO23................................23 H2
Upper St Paul's Ter
ACOMB YO24 ....2 A5
RYKW YO26.......................................16 C5
Usher La HXB/STR YO32....................7 E2
Usher Park Rd HXB/STR YO32..........7 E1

V

The Vale RAW/SKEL YO30..................8 C1
Vanbrugh Dr FUL/HES YO10..........25 G1
Vanbrugh Wy FUL/HES YO10.........25 E2
Varvills Ct CYK YO1 * 2 D5
Vavasour Ct COP/BISH YO23..........26 D5
Vernon Cl COP/BISH YO23 ....28 A4
Vernon Rd RAW/SKEL YO30...............9 F4
Vesper Dr ACOMB YO24 ....22 B2
Vesper Wk HXB/STR YO32 ....7 F5
Vicarage Gdns FUL/HES YO10........19 H5
Vicars Cl COP/BISH YO23................26 D5
Victoria Ct RYKW YO26...................17 G4
Victoria Wy HXB/STR YO32.............10 D5
Victor St CYK YO1..............................2 E6
Viking Cl STMFBR YO41 ....15 F3
Viking Rd RYKW YO26 ....16 D4
STMFBR YO41....................................15 F3
Village Garth HXB/STR YO32............6 C1
Village St RAW/SKEL YO30 ....9 F3
The Village HXB/STR YO32...............5 G2
HXB/STR YO32.....................................6 C1
HXB/STR YO32...................................13 E2
Villa Gv HEWTH YO31.........................3 J1
Vincent Wy ACOMB YO24 ....22 C4
Vine St COP/BISH YO23 ....24 A2
Vyner St HEWTH YO31.....................18 B2

W

Waggoners Dr COP/BISH YO23.....26 D4
Waincroft HXB/STR YO32 ....5 F4
Wainers Cl COP/BISH YO23............26 D4
Wain's Gv ACOMB YO24...................22 D5
Wain's Rd ACOMB YO24...................22 D4
Walker Dr ACOMB YO24 ....22 B4
Walmer Carr HXB/STR YO32.............6 A2
Walmgate CYK YO1 ....3 H6
Walney Rd HEWTH YO31 ....19 F4
Walnut Cl FUL/HES YO10................25 E3
HXB/STR YO32.....................................6 D2
Walpole St HEWTH YO31.................18 C2
Walton Pl RYKW YO26 ....22 B2
Walworth St North
RYKW YO26.......................................17 G4
Walworth St South
RYKW YO26 *.....................................17 G4
Wandhill HXB/STR YO32....................6 C2
The Wandle RYKW YO26 ....22 A2
Wansbeck ACOMB YO24..................26 D1
Warwick St HEWTH YO31................18 C2
Wasdale Cl RAW/SKEL YO30 ....9 F5
Waterdale Pk HEWTH YO31............10 D5
Water End RYKW YO26....................17 G3
Waterings HXB/STR YO32..................6 B2
Water La RAW/SKEL YO30..................9 H4
RYKS YO19 ....21 H3
Waterman Ct ACOMB YO24 ....22 B3
Watson St ACOMB YO24....................2 A7
Watson Ter ACOMB YO24...................2 A6
Wattlers Cl COP/BISH YO23...........26 D4
Waveney Gv RAW/SKEL YO30.........18 A1
Waverley St HEWTH YO31 ....3 G2
Waynefleet Gv FUL/HES YO10......25 E1
Weavers Cl COP/BISH YO23............26 D4
Weavers Pk COP/BISH YO23...........26 D4
Weddall Cl ACOMB YO24.................23 F3
Welborn Cl FUL/HES YO10 ....19 F5
Welland Ri RYKW YO26...................17 E4
Wellesley Cl RAW/SKEL YO30...........9 H4
Wellington Rw CYK YO1 ....2 D4
Wellington St FUL/HES YO10 ....3 J7
Welton Av RYKW YO26 ....17 E4
Welwyn Dr FUL/HES YO10..............24 C4
Wenham Rd ACOMB YO24...............22 C4
Wenlock Ter FUL/HES YO10............24 B3
Wensleydale Dr FUL/HES YO10......20 A5
Wentworth Rd ACOMB YO24 ....23 H2
Wentworth Wy FUL/HES YO10........24 D2
The Werkdyke CYK YO1 *..................3 G3
West Bank ACOMB YO24..................23 E1
West End HXB/STR YO32 ....5 F2
West End Cl HXB/STR YO32 ....5 G2
Westerdale Ct RAW/SKEL YO30.....17 H3
Westfield Cl HXB/STR YO32 ....6 C2
Westfield Ct COP/BISH YO23..........26 C5
Westfield Crs TAD LS24...................30 C3
Westfield Dr FUL/HES YO10 ....24 B4
Westfield Gv HXB/STR YO32..............6 B2
Westfield La HXB/STR YO32 ....6 B2
Westfield Pl ACOMB YO24 ....22 B3
HXB/STR YO32.....................................6 C2
Westfield Rd HXB/STR YO32 ....6 C2
Westfield Sq TAD LS24....................30 C2

Westfield Ter TAD LS24 ....30 C2
Westgate TAD LS24..............................30 C3
Westholme Dr RAW/SKEL YO30......9 F5
Westlands Gv HEWTH YO31...........19 E2
Westminster Rd
RAW/SKEL YO30............................17 H3
West Moor La FUL/HES YO10........25 F4
West Mt TAD LS24...........................30 B4
West Nooks HXB/STR YO32.............7 F2
Westpit La HXB/STR YO32 ....5 F3
West Thorpe ACOMB YO24...............22 D4
Westview Cl RYKW YO26.................16 C2
Westwood Ms RYKS YO19 ....21 H3
Westwood Ter COP/BISH YO23.....23 H3
Wetherby Rd RYKW YO26..............22 A1
TAD LS24..30 B2
Wharfe Dr ACOMB YO24.................22 D4
Wharnscliffe Dr RAW/SKEL YO30....9 G4
Wharton Av RAW/SKEL YO30........18 A2
Wharton Cl STMFBR YO41..............15 G2
Wharton Rd STMFBR YO41.............15 G2
Wheatcroft HXB/STR YO32 ....5 F4
Wheatfield La HXB/STR YO32 ....6 D3
Wheatlands Gv RYKW YO26...........16 D3
Wheatley Dr HXB/STR YO32............6 C3
Wheeldale Dr HXB/STR YO32........12 B4
The Wheelhouse
RAW/SKEL YO30................................8 C1
Wheelwright Cl COP/BISH YO23...26 D4
Wheldrake La RYKS YO19..............29 H5
Whenby Gv HEWTH YO31...............11 E5
Whernside Av HEWTH YO31...........19 F4
Whin Cl ACOMB YO24.....................23 F5
HXB/STR YO32..................................5 G4
Whin Garth ACOMB YO24..............23 F5
Whin Rd ACOMB YO24....................27 H1
Whip-Ma-Whop-Ma-Ga CYK YO1....3 G4
Whistler Cl COP/BISH YO23...........27 E4
Whitby Av HEWTH YO31.................19 F2
Whitby Dr HEWTH YO31..................19 F2
Whitecross Gdns HEWTH YO31.....18 C2
White Cross Rd HEWTH YO31........18 C2
White Horse Cl HXB/STR YO32......11 E1
White House Dl ACOMB YO24........23 F2
White House Dr ACOMB YO24.......23 F2
White House Gdns
ACOMB YO24...................................23 F3
White House Ri ACOMB YO24........23 F3
Whitelands HXB/STR YO32..............7 F3
White Rose Av HXB/STR YO32.......10 C3
White Rose Cl RYKW YO26...............8 C5
Whiterose Dr STMFBR YO41..........15 G3
White Rose Gv HXB/STR YO32.......10 C3
White Rose Wy RYKW YO26..........16 C1
Whitestone Dr HEWTH YO31.........10 D4
Whitethorn Cl HEWTH YO31..........10 D4
Whitley Cl RAW/SKEL YO30..............9 H5
Whitton Pl FUL/HES YO10..............19 H5
Wigginton Rd HEWTH YO31...........18 B2
Wigginton Ter HEWTH YO31..........18 B2
Wighill Garth TAD LS24..................30 D2
Wighill La TAD LS24.......................30 D2
Wilberforce Av RAW/SKEL YO30...18 A2
Wilkinson Wy HXB/STR YO32..........5 F2
William Plows Av
FUL/HES YO10.................................24 C2
Willis St FUL/HES YO10.....................3 J7
Willoughby Wy ACOMB YO24........22 B4
Willow Bank HXB/STR YO32..........10 D3
Willow Ct STMFBR YO41................15 E3
Willow Gld HXB/STR YO32............11 E3
Willow Gv HEWTH YO31.................19 E2
HXB/STR YO32..................................7 G4
Willow Ri TAD LS24.........................30 B4
The Willows HXB/STR YO32.............5 G3
RAW/SKEL YO30 *...........................18 A2
Wilsthorpe Gv FUL/HES YO10.......24 D4
Wilstrop Farm Rd
COP/BISH YO23..............................26 C5
Wilton Ri ACOMB YO24...................23 F1
Wimpole Cl RAW/SKEL YO30............9 H5
Winchester Av RYKW YO26...........17 F5
Winchester Gv RYKW YO26...........17 F5
Windermere ACOMB YO24............22 D5
Windmill Gv TAD LS24....................30 B4
Windmill La FUL/HES YO10............25 F1
Windmill Ri RYKW YO26.................23 E1
TAD LS24..30 B5
Windmill Wy HXB/STR YO32............7 E2
Windsor Dr HXB/STR YO32..............6 A1
Windsor Garth ACOMB YO24.........22 D3
Windsor St COP/BISH YO23...........23 H3
Winscar Gv RAW/SKEL YO30............9 F4
Winterscale Ct FUL/HES YO10 *....24 B2
Winterscale St FUL/HES YO10.......24 B2
Witham Dr HXB/STR YO32...............7 G5
Woburn Cl HXB/STR YO32................5 H1
Wolfe Av HEWTH YO31....................19 E4
Wolsey Dr COP/BISH YO23............28 A4
Wolsley St FUL/HES YO10.................3 J7
Wolviston Av FUL/HES YO10..........25 G1
Wood Cl HXB/STR YO32...................5 F3
Woodcock Cl HXB/STR YO32............7 E2
Woodford Pl ACOMB YO24............22 D3
Woodhouse Gv HEWTH YO31........19 F4
Woodland Cha RAW/SKEL YO30...10 A5
Woodland Pl HXB/STR YO32..........10 D2
Woodlands Av HXB/STR YO32.........6 C3
TAD LS24..30 A4
Woodlands Gv HEWTH YO31.........19 F1
Woodlands Vw TAD LS24...............30 B4
Woodland Wy HXB/STR YO32........11 E2
Woodlea Av RYKW YO26................16 D5
Woodlea Bank RYKW YO26............16 D5
Woodlea Crs RYKW YO26...............16
Woodlea Gv RYKW YO26................16
Woodleigh Cl HXB/STR YO32...........5
Woodside Av HEWTH YO31............19
Wood St HEWTH YO31......................3
Wood Wy HXB/STR YO32................11
Woolnough Av FUL/HES YO10......25
Worcester Dr HEWTH YO31...........19
Wordsworth Crs ACOMB YO24.....22
Wray's Av HEWTH YO31..................10
Wycliffe Av FUL/HES YO10............19
Wydale Rd FUL/HES YO10..............20
Wykeham Rd RYKW YO26..............16
Wyre Ct HXB/STR YO32 *.................6

Y

Yarburgh Gv RYKW YO26...............17
Yarburgh Wy FUL/HES YO10..........25
Yearsley Crs HEWTH YO31.............18
Yearsley Gv HEWTH YO31..............10
Yew Tree Ms FUL/HES YO10..........19
York Rd ACOMB YO24......................22
HXB/STR YO32...................................6
RYKS YO19.......................................21
TAD LS24..31
York & Selby Pth
COP/BISH YO23...............................24
COP/BISH YO23...............................27
CYK YO1...2
RAW/SKEL YO30................................8
RYKW YO26..2
York & Selby Pth & Trans
Penine Trail
COP/BISH YO23...............................28
York St RYKS YO19..........................21

Index - featured places

1066 Battlesite
STMFBR YO41 ....15 H3
Aaron Rd Industrial Estate
HEWTH YO31 ....18 D1
Acomb Primary School
ACOMB YO24 ....23 E1
Acomb Wood Shopping Centre
ACOMB YO24 ....22 B5
Acorn Business Centre
FUL/HES YO10 ....3 J6
Alhambra Court Hotel
RAW/SKEL YO30 ....2 D2
Allied Leisure Megabowl
RAW/SKEL YO30 ....9 H2
All Saints RC Lower School
COP/BISH YO23 ....2 D6
All Saints RC Upper School
COP/BISH YO23 ....23 G2
Applefields School
HEWTH YO31 ....19 G4
Archbishop Holgates School
FUL/HES YO10 ....25 G1
Archbishop of York CE Junior
School
COP/BISH YO23 ....27 H3
The ARC
CYK YO1 ....3 G4
Askham Bryan College of
Agriculture & Horticulture
COP/BISH YO23 ....26 A4
Assembly Rooms
CYK YO1 ....2 E3
Badger Hill Primary School
FUL/HES YO10 ....25 F2
Barbican Leisure Centre
FUL/HES YO10 ....3 H7
The Bar Convent Museum
ACOMB YO24 ....2 D6
Barfield Estate
HXB/STR YO32 ....11 F5
Barley Hall
CYK YO1 ....3 F3
Bedern Hall
CYK YO1 ....3 G3
Beechwood Close Hotel
RAW/SKEL YO30 ....17 G2
Best Western Kilima Hotel
ACOMB YO24 ....23 F1
Best Western Monkbar Hotel
HEWTH YO31 ....3 G2
Best Western York
Pavilion Hotel
FUL/HES YO10 ....24 C5
Bishopthorpe Infant School
COP/BISH YO23 ....28 A3
Blue Bridge Hotel
FUL/HES YO10 ....3 G7
Bootham Bar
RAW/SKEL YO30 ....2 E2
Bootham School
RAW/SKEL YO30 ....2 D2
Burnholme Community College
HEWTH YO31 ....19 F4
Burton Green Primary School
RAW/SKEL YO30 ....18 A1
Canon Lee School
RAW/SKEL YO30 ....17 H1
Carr J & I School
RYKW YO26 ....16 D4
The Chien Clinic
ACOMB YO24 ....23 F3
City Screen
CYK YO1 ....2 E4
Clementhorpe Health Centre
COP/BISH YO23 ....24 A2
Clifford's Tower
CYK YO1 ....3 F6
Clifton Bridge Hotel
RAW/SKEL YO30 ....17 H3
Clifton Green Primary School
RAW/SKEL YO30 ....18 A2
Clifton Health Centre
RAW/SKEL YO30 ....17 H2
Clifton Moor Business Village
RAW/SKEL YO30 ....9 G4
Clifton Preparatory School
RAW/SKEL YO30 ....2 B1
Clifton Without Junior School
RAW/SKEL YO30 ....17 G1
Compass Drug
Dependency Clinic
ACOMB YO24 ....2 B7
Copmanthorpe Primary School
COP/BISH YO23 ....26 D4
Coppergate Walk
Shopping Centre
CYK YO1 ....3 G5
Dean Court Hotel
CYK YO1 ....2 E3
The Deanery
CYK YO1 ....3 F2
Derwent Junior School
FUL/HES YO10 ....19 G5
Derwent Valley
Industrial Estate
RYKS YO19 ....21 H5
Dick Turpin's Grave
CYK YO1 ....3 G6
DIG
CYK YO1 ....3 G4
Dringhouses Primary School
ACOMB YO24 ....23 E4
Dunnington Primary School
RYKS YO19 ....21 F3
Ebor Industrial Estate
HEWTH YO31 ....3 K3
Ebor School
RAW/SKEL YO30 ....17 H3
Edmund Wilson
Swimming Baths
ACOMB YO24 ....22 D3
English Martyrs RC
Primary School
ACOMB YO24 ....23 F1
Fairfax House
CYK YO1 ....3 F5
Fishergate Bar
CYK YO1 ....3 G6
Fishergate Postern
FUL/HES YO10 ....3 G6
Fishergate Primary School
FUL/HES YO10 ....3 H7
Forest Park Golf Club
HXB/STR YO32 ....12 D2
Fulford Golf Club
FUL/HES YO10 ....25 E4
Fulford Industrial Estate
FUL/HES YO10 ....24 A3
Fulford School
FUL/HES YO10 ....24 C5
Grand Opera House
CYK YO1 ....2 E5
The Grange Hotel
RAW/SKEL YO30 ....2 C1
Green Lane Trading Estate
RAW/SKEL YO30 ....9 H5
Haxby Road Primary School
HEWTH YO31 ....18 C2
Haxby Shopping Centre
HXB/STR YO32 ....6 D2
Haxby & Wigginton
Health Centre
HXB/STR YO32 ....6 C2
Headlands Primary School
HXB/STR YO32 ....6 C3
Hempland Primary School
HEWTH YO31 ....19 G3
Heworth CE Primary School
HEWTH YO31 ....19 E3
Heworth CC & York Hockey Club
HEWTH YO31 19
Hob Moor Primary School &
Hob Moor Oaks School
ACOMB YO24 22
The Hospitium
RAW/SKEL YO30 2
Hull & York Medical School
FUL/HES YO10 25
Huntington Primary School
HXB/STR YO32 11
Huntington School
HXB/STR YO32 10
ICT@Westfield
RYKW YO26 22
Imphal Barracks
FUL/HES YO10 24
Innkeeper's Lodge
FUL/HES YO10 25
Jorvik
CYK YO1 3
The Joseph Rowntree School
HXB/STR YO32 10
Julia Avenue Retail Park
HXB/STR YO32 11
The Kings Manor
CYK YO1 2
Knavesmire Manor Hotel
ACOMB YO24 23
Knavesmire Primary School
COP/BISH YO23 23
Lady Ann Middletons Hotel
CYK YO1 2
Lakeside CP School
RAW/SKEL YO30 9
Learning Resources Centre
ACOMB YO24 27
Lendal Tower
CYK YO1 2
Link Business Park
FUL/HES YO10 20
Lord Deramore's
Primary School
FUL/HES YO10 25
Magnet Sports Club
TAD LS24 30
Manor CE School
RYKW YO26 16
Mansion House
CYK YO1 2
McArthurglen Designer Outlet
Retail Park
RYKS YO19 28

rchant Adventurers' Hall
YK YO1 ....3 G4

rchant Taylors Hall
YK YO1 ....3 G3

klegate Bar & Museum
COMB YO24 ....2 C6

dlethorpe Hall Hotel
OP/BISH YO23 ....28 B1

field Business Centre
YKW YO26 ....16 C1

thorpe School
OP/BISH YO23 ....23 H2

ster Hotel
AW/SKEL YO30 ....2 D2

Minster School
YK YO1 ....3 F3

el Therapeutic Clinic
EWTH YO31 ....3 G2

k Bar Museum
YK YO1 ....3 G3

kgate Health Centre
EWTH YO31 ....3 G2

ks Cross Shopping Park
XB/STR YO32 ....11 H3

unt Royale Hotel
COMB YO24 ....23 G2

Mount School
COMB YO24 ....2 A7

caster House
eworth Golf Club)
YK YO1 ....3 H5

ional Centre for Early Music
EWTH YO31 ....18 D2

ional Railway Museum &
orkshire Wheel
YKW YO26 ....2 B4

w Earswick Primary School
XB/STR YO32 ....10 C3

wspaper Office
YK YO1 ....3 H5

thminster Business Park
COMB YO24 ....16 A3

th York Trading Estate
AW/SKEL YO30 ....9 G3
AW/SKEL YO30 ....10 A2

votel
UL/HES YO10 ....3 G7

klands Sports Centre
COMB YO24 ....22 C2

Observatory
YK YO1 ....2 D3

eon
COMB YO24 ....2 C6

Old School Medical Centre
OP/BISH YO23 ....26 C3

Starre Inn
YK YO1 ....2 E3

aldwick Industrial Estate
YKS YO19 ....20 A4

aldwick Primary School
UL/HES YO10 ....19 H5

Ladys RC Primary School
COMB YO24 ....23 E3

Palace
OP/BISH YO23 ....28 B3

k Grove Primary School
EWTH YO31 ....3 G1

The Physical Therapy Clinic
COP/BISH YO23 ....23 H3

Pike Hills Golf Club
COP/BISH YO23 ....26 C3

Pioneer Business Park
RAW/SKEL YO30 ....9 G3

Poppleton Road
Primary School
RYKW YO26 ....17 E4

Premier Travel Inn
ACOMB YO24 ....2 C6
RYKW YO26 ....8 C5

Purey Cust Nuffield Hospital
CYK YO1 ....2 E2

Ralph Butterfield
Primary School
HXB/STR YO32 ....7 E2

Ramada Hotel
RAW/SKEL YO30 ....8 C2

Rawcliffe Infant School
RAW/SKEL YO30 ....9 F5

Red Tower
HEWTH YO31 ....3 J5

Regimental Museum
CYK YO1 ....3 F5

Riding Lights Theatre Co
CYK YO1 ....2 E5

Riverside Caravan &
Camping Park
COP/BISH YO23 ....28 B3

Riverside Primary School
TAD LS24 ....30 C2

Robert Wilkinson
Primary School
HXB/STR YO32 ....5 F2

The Royal York Hotel
ACOMB YO24 ....2 C4

St Aelreds RC VA
Primary School
HEWTH YO31 ....19 G4

St Anthony's Hall
CYK YO1 ....3 G3

St Barnabas CE Primary School
RYKW YO26 ....17 G4

St Georges RC Primary School
FUL/HES YO10 ....24 B2

St Josephs RC Primary School
TAD LS24 ....30 C2

St Lawrence CE Primary School
FUL/HES YO10 ....3 K7

St Olave's School
ACOMB YO24 ....2 B2

St Oswalds CE Primary School
FUL/HES YO10 ....24 C5

St Pauls CE Primary School
ACOMB YO24 ....2 A6

St Peter's School
RAW/SKEL YO30 ....2 C1

St Wilfrids RC Primary School
HEWTH YO31 ....3 G2

St Williams College
CYK YO1 ....3 F3

Selby College
CYK YO1 ....3 F4
TAD LS24 ....30 D3

The Shopping Precinct
COP/BISH YO23 ....26 C5

Siwards How
FUL/HES YO10 ....25 E2

Skelton Park Trading Estate
RAW/SKEL YO30 ....8 C2

Skelton Primary School
RAW/SKEL YO30 ....8 D1

South Bank Medical Centre
COP/BISH YO23 ....24 A3

Stagecoach Youth Theatre
HEWTH YO31 ....3 G2

Stamford Bridge
Medical Centre
STMFBR YO41 ....15 F3

Stamford Bridge
Primary School
STMFBR YO41 ....15 F3

Station Business Park
RYKW YO26 ....17 G5

Stockton Hall Hospital
HXB/STR YO32 ....12 D2

Stockton on the Forest
Primary School
HXB/STR YO32 ....13 E1

Tadcaster Albion FC
TAD LS24 ....30 D3

Tadcaster CC
TAD LS24 ....30 C3

Tadcaster East Primary School
TAD LS24 ....31 E2

Tadcaster Sports &
Leisure Centre
TAD LS24 ....30 C3

Tang Hall Clinic
FUL/HES YO10 ....19 F5

Theatre Royal
CYK YO1 ....2 E3

Thornhill Industrial Estate
RYKS YO19 ....20 D5

Tower Court Business Centre
RAW/SKEL YO30 ....9 G4

Tower Court Health Centre
RAW/SKEL YO30 ....9 H4

Tower House Business Centre
FUL/HES YO10 ....24 B2

Travelodge
CYK YO1 ....3 G6

Treasurer's House
CYK YO1 ....3 F2

University College of
Ripon & York (Heworth Croft)
HEWTH YO31 ....3 J1

University of York
FUL/HES YO10 ....25 E2

University of York
Sports Centre
FUL/HES YO10 ....25 E3

Walmgate Bar
CYK YO1 ....3 J6

Warner Bros
RAW/SKEL YO30 ....9 H3

Warthill CE Primary School
RYKS YO19 ....13 H3

Westfield Primary
Community School
ACOMB YO24 ....22 B2

Whitby Drive Medical Centre
HEWTH YO31 ....19 F2

Wigginton Primary School
HXB/STR YO32 ....6 B2

Windmill House Industrial Estate
HXB/STR YO32 ....6 A1

Woodthorpe Primary School
ACOMB YO24 ....22 C5

Yearsley Grove Primary School
HEWTH YO31 ....11 E5

Yearsley Swimming Baths
HEWTH YO31 ....18 C1

York Castle Museum
CYK YO1 ....3 G6

York City Art Gallery
RAW/SKEL YO30 ....2 D2

York City Crematorium
COP/BISH YO23 ....28 B2

York City FC
(Bootham Crescent)
RAW/SKEL YO30 ....18 A3

York City Knights RLFC
(Huntingdon Stadium)
HXB/STR YO32 ....11 E4

York City Rowing Club
CYK YO1 ....2 D4

York College
ACOMB YO24 ....27 H1

York County Court
CYK YO1 ....3 G6

York Cricket & RUFC
RAW/SKEL YO30 ....17 G2

York Crown Court
CYK YO1 ....3 F6

York District Hospital
RAW/SKEL YO30 ....18 B2

The York Dungeon
CYK YO1 ....3 F5

York High School
ACOMB YO24 ....22 C2

York Marriott Hotel
ACOMB YO24 ....23 F4

York Minster
CYK YO1 ....3 F3

York Model Railway
RYKW YO26 ....2 B5

York Motor Boat Club House
FUL/HES YO10 ....24 A5

York Racecourse
COP/BISH YO23 ....23 G4

York St John University College
HEWTH YO31 ....3 F1

Yorkshire Museum
RAW/SKEL YO30 ....2 D3

Yorkshire Museum of Farming
RYKS YO19 ....20 C4

York Sixth Form College
COP/BISH YO23 ....27 G2

York Steiner School
FUL/HES YO10 ....24 B3

The York Story
CYK YO1 ....3 F5

Youth Theatre Yorkshire
ACOMB YO24 ....2 C7

Acknowledgements

ools address data provided by Education Direct.

ol station information supplied by Johnsons

-way street data provided by © Tele Atlas N.V. Tele Atlas

den centre information provided by

den Centre Association Britains best garden centres

evale Garden Centres

statement on the front cover of this atlas is sourced, selected and quoted
a reader comment and feedback form received in 2004

AA Street by Street   QUESTIONNAIRE

Dear Atlas User
Your comments, opinions and recommendations are very important to us. So please help us to improve our street atlases by taking a few minutes to complete this simple questionnaire.

You do not need a stamp (unless posted outside the UK). If you do not want to remove this page from your street atlas, then photocopy it or write your answers on a plain sheet of paper.

Send to: Marketing Assistant, AA Publishing, 14th Floor Fanum House, Freepost SCE 4598, Basingstoke RG21 4GY

ABOUT THE ATLAS...

Please state which city / town / county you bought:

Where did you buy the atlas? (City, Town, County)

For what purpose? (please tick all applicable)

To use in your local area ☐   **To use on business or at work** ☐

Visiting a strange place ☐   **In the car** ☐   **On foot** ☐

Other (please state)

Have you ever used any street atlases other than AA Street by Street?

Yes ☐   **No** ☐

If so, which ones?

Is there any aspect of our street atlases that could be improved?
(Please continue on a seperate sheet if necessary)

ML154z

continued overleaf

Please list the features you found most useful:

_____

_____

Please list the features you found least useful:

_____

_____

_____

LOCAL KNOWLEDGE...

Local knowledge is invaluable. Whilst every attempt has been made to make the information contained in this atlas as accurate as possible, should you notice any inaccuracies, please detail them below (if necessary, use a blank piece of paper) or e-mail us at _streetbystreet@theAA.com_

_____

_____

_____

ABOUT YOU...

Name (Mr/Mrs/Ms)

Address

                                      Postcode

Daytime tel no

E-mail address

Which age group are you in?

Under 25 ☐   **25-34** ☐   **35-44** ☐   **45-54** ☐   **55-64** ☐   **65+** ☐

Are you an AA member?   **YES** ☐   **NO** ☐

Do you have Internet access?   **YES** ☐   **NO** ☐

Thank you for taking the time to complete this questionnaire. Please send it to us as soon as possible, and remember, you do not need a stamp (unless posted outside the UK).

We may use information we hold about you to, telephone or email you about other products and services offered by the AA, we do NOT disclose this information to third parties.

Please tick here if you do not wish to hear about products and services from the AA. ☐